If I had r... her, she would still be alive.

I woke in the small hours with the shakes and had a drink. I sat in the dark and went over my memory of the last words Clair had spoken on the phone when I had called her from France. They had haunted my sleep. "I have to finish some things here first," she had said. "I'll be traveling for a few days. I'll be in New York on Monday." Uninflected words on a transatlantic telephone, three sentences that had contained her death.

I told myself I did not want another and mixed myself another, a little heavier on the vermouth. Not that drink nor the one after helped. I had been a fool not to have asked her what those things were in California she had had to finish first.

GOODBYE

W. H. Manville

SPHERE BOOKS LIMITED
30/32 Gray's Inn Road, London WC1X 8JL

First published in Great Britain by Hamish Hamilton Ltd 1977
Copyright © 1977 by W. H. Manville
Published by Sphere Books Ltd 1978
Reprinted 1979

Readers familiar with my wife's work on female identity and sexuality will recognize how much I am indebted to her. I know how much I have learned living with her. This book is dedicated to Nancy Friday.

W. H. M.

FACT

A Puerto Rican boy
And Puerto Rican girl
Kissed;

He plucked her a daffodil
Planted by an urban botanist.

She was dead before dark,
Killed in Central Park

—another illegal act.

Goodbyes
The unpublished poetry
of Anatole Fugelman

book one

RETURN

1

Saturday Night–Sunday Morning

My nose ached, my head hurt and there was someone sleeping naked in bed with me, a soft breast pressed up against my back, an arm falling over my shoulder, an open palm resting lightly on my stomach. I was naked myself. I didn't know what time it was, I didn't know what room this was, it was dark, only a silent blurred carrousel of colored lights playing across the ceiling above me. There was a strangely sweet, powerful smell over everything. Her arm felt cold and I was cold myself; I waited a minute and tried not to wake her until I could remember which of the rooms of my life this one was. Then the room came together in shapes I knew; when I looked over my shoulder I saw that the colored lights were coming through the stained-glass windows with the painted-out faces. My old apartment in New York.

I pulled the blanket up around us for a moment more, trying to remember who she might be. But I drew a familiar alcoholic blank, a blackout, another time out of my time I would never remember, a hole in my life memory would never fill. I couldn't remember her name, couldn't remember her undressing or how I got undressed myself. I couldn't remember going to bed. I couldn't even remember if we had made it or not, and then I had the angry feeling that I had not made it with anyone at all. It had not been on my mind. I turned to her.

I was going to explain to whoever she was that she must have had too much to drink too, that someone at the party must have played a stupid practical joke on us both. I was going to laugh if I could and ask without haste if we had been introduced. I was

3

going to get her the hell out of there as soon as possible. (What time was it? Was that a key at the door? Thank God it couldn't be Clair—she wasn't due till Monday.) (Also, there was no sound at the door.) The face I saw was vaguely familiar, but I had been away for two years and I had never won prizes for putting names and faces together even when sober. Then I recognized her in a rush. Blue-in-blue eyes, calmly watching me.

She looked different: I felt a stab of remorse. Had I been such a bastard? Two years away from me had smoothed the lines of tension around her mouth, erased the anxiety from her eyes, made her serenely beautiful as the first time I had seen her. She looked young. "Clair?" The naked arm that rested so lightly on my stomach rested so lightly because it did not rest on me at all: it was held in place by a rigor of its own. I realized why she looked different. I felt cold but I would warm up. My wife felt cold because she was dead.

book two

BEGINNINGS

The Panhandler

—but first the black man had come into it.

It had been a Wednesday when I got back to New York, five days before I was to meet Clair. Like April itself, second chances cruelly mix memory and desire. The month was April; Clair and I were going to have our second chance.

In the two years I'd been away, New York had suffered an enormous identity wipeout. Living in the heart of the unending publicity war of all against all for recognition and celebrity, the losers had begun to wear pop emblems and signs telling you who they were, or at least that they communed with entities greater than themselves—pictures of Mick Jagger, Robert Redford or Mickey Mouse on their breasts; "Harley-Davidson Motorcycles" said the name on a sweat shirt going by. "Campbell's Soup," "University of Montana," "Yves St. Laurent," "Property of Alcatraz" and "I Love You. If You Don't Love Me Back, Pass This Message to the Boy Behind You" were written on T-shirts in the crowd. As I came through JFK customs and into the chill spring night, big *Daily News* trucks were unloading tomorrow's bulldog editions:

The police had no new evidence in the Waldorf Astoria bombing. The son of an airlines executive had been stabbed to death in a disco on Second Avenue by an illegal alien from Panama in a fight over drugs; the previous morning the boy's father had announced that the profitable nonstop jet run from Panama City to New York was being stepped up two more flights a week. Four hundred schoolteachers had been laid off in the latest reduced city budget, six more firehouses shut down while the South Bronx continued to burn. Standard & Poor announced it might take twenty years before the city could hope to sell bonds again in the credit markets. The President said in a speech at the launching of an $800 million aircraft carrier in California that even if New York went under, America would still be strong. A lot of show-biz people were going to sing and tap-dance at a last-ditch protest rally in Times Square to save Our Town on the six-o'clock TV news.

"Jesus Is Coming!" said the graffito on the wall of the Pan Am Building. "How About Mary?" was written under it in lipstick. When the taxi pulled up in front of the apartment house I could see uncollected garbage up and down West Twentieth Street; April winds blew torn sheets of yesterday's *El Diario* and *The New York Times* into the air, and they flapped together in the bare-branched trees. The city was dying. I was coming back to life.

The next day had been Thursday.

The dark bruise marks around my eyes were fading. I paid off the unemployed actor sent by Temporarily Thine to vacuum up the debris of the two-year sublet and was going out to the Chelsea Flower Market; I wanted the apartment filled before Clair got back with the dwarf palms and green Boston ferns she loved. The panhandler was black and dressed in black. He nodded to himself when he saw me leave the building and came across West Twentieth Street in that swing-shouldered, dance-stepped black strut, slipping a paper-bagged bottle of wine into his hip pocket. He spoke in deadpan upper-class English, exaggerating the broad A of his West Indian accent without a smile—an irony he would let me share if I were hip enough to get it. He was wearing a faded and ragged tuxedo as another unexplained joke, the Homburg on his head almost green with age, the once-stiff white shirt torn and grimy, canvas sneakers on his feet but the black bow tie neatly done, not ready-made, the dinner jacket expensive and old-fashioned but tailored for someone

half a head shorter than his own skinny six foot four or
five. He came to attention before me, throwing an
open-palmed British salute so hard his hand quivered.
He stomped his soft-shod feet with military briskness.

"SAH!"

"We got time for a martini before the war?"

"Ec-tually, sah, I was hoping you could spare
ninety-eight eighty for a case of brandy for a fellow
member of the regiment?"

He made me laugh. After a moment he joined in,
but his smile was remote. The joke had a further, fun-
nier punch line, too complicated to explain to me at
the moment, a larger, more humorous connotation he
preferred to savor by himself. I told him about my
own hangover, and we went into the little neighborhood bar across Ninth Avenue, on the corner of
Twenty-first Street, opposite the theological seminary.
I wondered how much English blood he might have to
go with the accent: startlingly soft gray eyes in a light
chocolate face. As we walked through Skelly & Kennedy's door he was taken by a spasm of hard dry
coughing. He waited for it to pass.

It wasn't the flu, he said, nothing as "boring" as
that. He was coming down from this two-week trip on
speed, "parachuting down on wine and brandy, you
see. Thank you very much. Ec-tually, I would like another. Most kind of you." He said he'd had a "shock-
ing" morning that made drinking "imperative." He
asked who I was.

"Nicholas Blake."

"I am called Sam," he said formally, and repeated
my name aloud. "Ec-tually, sah," he said, "it's a little
trick I've learned. Repeat a chap's name once or
twice and you've got it for good. Wouldn't care to
confuse one damn fellow with another. You've hurt
your nose."

"Yes."

"Cheers."

"Right."

He asked for some money for the juke. I gave him
a quarter. He took another quarter from his pocket

and a dime. He left to make a phone call. On his way back he put a half-dollar into the music machine. A falsetto tenor began to sing about the hills of Limerick. I asked Sam if he hadn't wasted his money.

"Sah," he said, "when you're broke, whatever action you get cheap is never wasted. No money, it's *Goodbye, Sam!* You might as well reckon to use the little you've got for noise. I mean, there's something about loud music, isn't there? I can get high on noise."

"Whereas a fool and his money are soon in a ranch house?"

"Precisely, sah."

He asked if I were married. "Most of the best fellows *I* meet are," he said. "Perhaps it was unfortunate I did not marry a certain girl I knew back in Trinidad."

"You asked her?"

"She married someone else before I got around to it."

"Were you sorry?"

"Life often resembles a giant, busted subway candy machine, sah. You can't even get what you don't want." He asked again if I were married. I said I was. "She's a painter."

"She home now, working?"

"California. She'll be here in a couple of days."

"An out-of-town gallery?"

"No."

"Been traveling yourself?"

"Yes."

"Ah," he said. I thought he was going to cough again, but he closed his eyes against it and it went away. I gave him a glass of cold water and asked if maybe he shouldn't go easy on the booze.

The question offended him. *"Sah!"* he said, drawing himself up to almost military attention. "The question of ephemeral pleasure is the great question of life itself. I was a ballet student once. I used to ask myself, Why do dancers leap? Where's the profit in that? What goes up must come down, why leap? A dancer spends his years, his youth and hope, his life, training. What does he get for his pains? Just a second or two. Two instants at the top of his leap, wrung from gravity, death, the end of hope, Gresham's Law, the Big Mac. Two seconds that feed our hunger for esthetic, two seconds of style and order imposed on the meaningless chaos into which we are born." He asked why I was smiling.

"My father used to talk like that."

"He black?"

"He's dead."

"Same thing."

"I've often wondered."

The black man was not listening.

He was wiping his lips with a paper napkin. "You must excuse me, sah," he said. "This coughing is a dreary thing, it goes on, I go on, it's never too painful, but we are always together like a profession you don't like but must stay with because you need the money. It's only a loud reminder—if we put our hands on our left breast, we feel a clock ticking us away. Our lives are like the dancer's leap, I think—two seconds of foolish exuberance, a leap out of blackness into blackness, sah, nothing left to show for it when it is over. But if it is just two seconds wrung from eternity, how can I bear *not* to leap?" There was a broad-bladed electric fan in the middle of the ceiling. April was just beginning, the weather cool, but they had it going slowly around and around. "A Sydney Greenstreet palm tree fan," the panhandler said and put his hand up through the blades, stopping the motion with a shriek of torn metal.

He continued to hold his hand up in the air. Blood began to trickle down his black wrist as he calmly watched. The other people in the bar were startled, someone was yelling for a cop or an ambulance, the bartender began cursing angrily about his busted fan. The panhandler was unconcerned. The rusty black sleeve of his tuxedo was turning a muddy wet brownred.

"What the hell you do that for?"

"The only thing you got to work with is fifty cents of noise from a cheap Irish jukebox, I mean, *Goodbye*,

Sam—why the hell shouldn't you put your hand in an electric fan? *Make something happen!* Perhaps we'd better leave, sah. Avoid the hassle." He smiled in his distant manner, bowing me out in front of him, taking his arm down at last to wrap a handkerchief around his wrist. It no longer interested him. He stood aside to salute with his wounded hand as I went through the door.

A taxi screamed to a halt in front of us. The back door was flung open before the car was fully braked. A little guy came skidding across the sidewalk, leaving the door open behind him, the motor of the taxi still running. The man had something cradled to his belly under a raincoat. He was wearing bright-green rubber dishwashing gloves. The thing in his hands was angular, ugly and metallic. He pointed it at us as he charged. His breath pumped deep in his chest, whistling like a blown horse. Sam dropped behind me; I began to run too, to one side, out of the man's path. Sam's arms were under my armpits, his hands locked up behind my neck in a full nelson. I was forced into a strangled half crouch, unable to move. Into my ear: "Tell yo' wife hello, moth'fuckah"—the words soft, black, slurred, laughing, the trick English accent gone. Sam was lifting me off my feet, slewing me around to point my belly into the gun. One of the kicks connected, the heel of my French boot spiking down into his canvas-covered instep.

His grip broke. I dropped down into the street. The gun exploded just above my head. Sam took it full in the face, the *whomp* of the double gauge lifting him off his feet and tossing him ten feet across the sidewalk through the plate-glass window of the bar, red and black gobbets of meat splattering the surrounding glass and brick, one sneaker off and lying empty on its side on the pavement. A car door slammed and the taxi slewed around a corner and was away.

The detective's name was Jim Wright. We watched the ambulance men put Sam into a dark-blue canvas bag and close the zipper up over his ruined face before taking him away. Wright had come up to the apartment with me. "I know it's a shock," he was saying, "but try to think. You any idea why the black guy said that business about say hello to your wife?"

At the end of the first summer Clair and I were married, the city lay panting with heat like a dying animal. A woman we knew had taken off for Europe to chase a frightened lover and lent us her house in Martha's Vineyard. I'd had one of the series of dumb TV newswriting jobs left over from the years before I knew her. I quit it over a weekend, we took the few hundred dollars we had in the bank and thumbed up to spend early autumn in New England.

Each day the sun came up white from behind the pine trees in back of the house and the sumac in front burned red and gold in the cold air. The ocean down the hill behind us gradually turned ice-blue and the cloudless sky mirrored the sea.

We dragged a big featherbed down from the second floor and slept in the kitchen beside the black, crackling wood stove. In the morning I put on a flannel shirt and a sweater and brought in logs from the corded pile out back to keep us going through the day; Clair fried ham and eggs for breakfast in a black cast-iron pan. Labor Day had come and the summer people had gone; when I bicycled into town for supplies and groceries every two or three days, the streets of Edgartown were empty and quiet.

Clair spent the mornings walking the shoreline collecting salt-smoothed shards of glass thrown up by the sea; her gallery was giving her a one-man show in November for the stained-glass windows she had begun to make the previous spring. Or else she was in a room upstairs behind a closed door, with a kerosene heater, brushes and an easel: she had become interested in formal figure painting too. She would never let me see these beginning efforts, carefully brushing them out with flat white paint after she finished each canvas. In the kitchen I was writing my first TV Movie of the Week on spec. We saw no one. In the beautiful afternoons we bicycled to Oak Bluffs or Vineyard Haven, bought lobsters from the fishermen in Lowry's

or Poole's in Menemsha, made love or walked for
hours across Gay Head or white South Beach, autum-
nally silent now except for the surf and the cries of
gulls that swooped and circled in the air above us,
begging for the bits of white bread Clair threw out behind us like a wake in the sea. Evenings I read and
she silently figured out the wiring for the illuminated
shadow boxes she would use to hang her windows. I
woke once at dawn to find she had never come to bed,
working at the kitchen table under the overhead lamp,
the fire in the cast-iron stove gone out, blowing on her
fingers to keep them supple against the night chill, too
intent on her soldering iron to see the bulb above her
head had paled in the low-angled pink light coming
in through the window from the east. She looked up
at me uncomprehendingly, gray with fatigue, face
smeared, hair matted. She said something, she took
a step toward me. Her speech was incoherent, her legs
giving way beneath, numb from being in one position
too long. "Time to go to bed," I said. She stood still a
moment more, still not recognizing time or me, rousing
herself then, holding on to my shoulder as she stamped
her foot to drive the sleep from her leg, coming alive
at last with a slow smile of comprehension and a sigh
of pleasure for the work she had done and now running before me toward the big double bed, unbutton-
ing her clothes as she went and letting them drop in a
straight path on the floor, throwing herself naked between the sheets in the spot I had warmed like a swim-
mer who dashes out of the sea to fall on the hot sands,
laughing and tired, sated. She was asleep.

More often I played second chef to her Julia Child,
peeling carrots for the boeuf Bourguignon, whipping
cream for a chocolate mousse, washing up after the
lovely dinners she would make us. We kept a little
white wine in the house, but only she had an occa-
sional glass. It was the first time in my life I had gone
on the wagon and in my memory it seems that Clair
was always smiling.

There was a new automatic washing machine and
dryer in a back room which Clair used with all the
zest that only a girl who's lived in tiny one-room New

York apartments could understand. One day she sent me into town on a hunt for duck and some oranges. When I came back she was out in the yard behind the house and there was a wicker basket of new wash on the grass at her feet. The salt breeze that snapped the white sheets on the line blew her heavy black hair around her face and made her long, gypsy-red skirt balloon out as if hooped. Suntanned skin, blue-in-blue eyes. The sun glinted on the sea, and the breath I drew carried the smell of pine trees and a cherry pie baking.

Clair had come running to me as I propped the bike up against the house. She hung on my neck as I carried the groceries in, nuzzling her face in the hollow between my jawbone and shoulder. Inside, she dropped her arms around me and put her hands into my hip pockets. She pulled herself closer to me, I cupped her face in my hands to tilt her up for a kiss. "Don't take me back, Blake. Don't ever take me back to the city. Let me live here with you," she said against my lips. I kissed her with my mouth closed. I had had a vodka in town. I wonder what there is in a man that frightens him at the happiest moments of his life and makes him ask, "Yes—but is this all? Is there nothing left now but the long, slow, peaceful walk, hand in hand, to the grave?"—and the procession already begun. Love is not enough.

The next time I bicycled into Edgartown I stopped in the Navigator bar, and the time after that I brought a bottle of gin back with me, and we didn't stay on the island much longer after that.

I told the detective again: I had returned to the U.S. only the day before. I had been living in France. My wife was in California, not due in New York till Monday. Neither one of us had lived here for two years. We had been separated. We were going to try again. Why would anyone want to kill me? How could there be a connection between a random act of violence on a New York street and Clair, who was three thousand miles away? The detective listened politely.

"You know what your wife's been up to out there?"
he asked. It was as if I had not spoken. "I mean, can
we phone her?"

"She's finishing off some business, I don't know
where. She'll be here in four day."

He was on the phone, talking to me and listening to
someone at the other end. He held his hand up for me
to shut up while he made a note of something just
said in his ear.

"You know any of her friends out there?" he asked.

"No."

"She have anything to do with dope?"

"What!"

But once again he wasn't listening. He was writing
down something more that had just been said on the
phone. He hung up. "What it adds up," he said, "is a
bungled amateur job. The way he did it, even if it
had gone right, he still could have caught some of
the buckshot himself. The M.E.'s preliminary report
says he was up to the eyes in smack. So he was brave
as six Pittsburgh Steelers. And just as dumb." Wright
said they had found almost nine hundred dollars in the
black man's wallet. The police did not consider it a
case of attempted robbery or mugging.

"Let's look again," Wright said. "First, about you.
We can check you only came back to New York yesterday?"

"I still have the Air France ticket stub."

"Your statement is you never saw the black guy
before?"

"Right."

"OK. Now, about your wife. You haven't seen her
for two years, you've had a reconciliation, and she's
coming back to you on Monday. As far as you know,
Sam is unknown to her too. We got to ask why's he
interested in her? He asks if you're married. Then he
asks is she home waiting for you. Is he asking has
she arrived from California yet? Does he want to know
has she spoken to you, have you seen her, maybe he
wants to know has she given you something? Who else
knew she was coming from California?"

"I haven't told anyone yet." I said again I didn't

see how the black man could have any connection with Clair. "Maybe he was just making conversation."

The detective was writing in his notebook. "We know who he is," he said. "They call him Goodbye Sam. A retail pusher. His business, nine hundred in the poke isn't a lot, but they usually don't carry heavy money on them long. For obvious reasons. Usually he works Times Square. So why's he in this neighborhood? Maybe the money was a payoff in front to do the job on you. You weren't buying from him, trying to rip him off for the cash?"

"I'm not a buyer. I'm not a user."

"Read it the way we have to see it. He's waiting for you across the street from your house. He asks your name and repeats it out loud so he's sure he's fingered the right guy. He giggles you up so you take him somewhere to buy him a drink. Then he makes a phone call and gives you some hocus-pocus about the sweet mystery of life until¹ the sawed-off has time to arrive in a stolen taxi. He holds you down for the slam. You were targeted."

He read me a list of names from his notebook. They were the black man's known associates. "Any of these people mean anything to you?"

"No."

"Any of them known to your wife?"

"Ask her when she gets here."

"When will that be again?"

"Monday."

"And you don't know what she's been up to the past two years?"

"It wouldn't be anything to do with dope."

He shrugged. "It's your life," he said. "Your statement is that you are not a user, not a seller. Is that true? Lie, and you're on your own for the next gun they hire on you. Tell the truth, we can protect you. You bring any shit back with you from France?"

"No."

He made some last notes and got ready to leave. I told him again I could not believe the black panhandler had been after me. "He must have gotten me confused with somebody else with a name like mine."

"You're the one confused," Wright said, "turning down our help. Sam didn't get it wrong."

"Suppose they didn't either?"

"How's that?"

"Maybe they didn't miss. Maybe it wasn't an amateur job. Sam was in the dope business, not me. Maybe he was the target all along. He saw the gun coming and tried to use me for a shield, but he was the one they wanted to take out."

Wright opened the door. He wrote a phone number down on a piece of paper. "This is the number the chief of detectives the precinct house. When your wife gets to town Monday, have her give him a call."

"Why not you?"

"I got caught in the mayor's budget. This is my last day on the force. The chief'll give her the name the guy taking over my case load."

"Clair had nothing to do with this."

"Midnight tonight, it doesn't matter to me either."

He went to the door. "Do yourself a favor, buddy. She comes back, ask what she was up to in California."

I didn't want to think about that.

"Somebody hates you," he said and was gone.

3

The Fountain

The next day had been Friday.

Violence so outrages reality that it carries its own anodyne: the mind forgets to believe. The panhandler's death had receded, the details no longer carried emotion. I was not sure which events had really happened, which I had already begun to invent and embellish to make into a cops-and-robbers TV script I might sell. Like getting your apartment burgled or being stuck in a subway breakdown, the black man's death had dwindled to its true proportions, become only a reminder of New York's other face; random, stupidly violent and ugly events were part of the urban rent. The city had been home now for years. It was known, familiar, but alien and exciting too—like living in Hong Kong or Paris, an electric foreign place where you didn't really belong and there was something exotic about the customs and people, but you shared a world with them, a perception and attitude more familiar than that of those among whom you'd been born. The producer wanted to give a celebration, and at my suggestion he had rented a place I knew, a Puerto Rican dance hall over an artificial-flower factory on Eighth Avenue. The picture had started in France—it was from Tom's suite at the Grand Hotel de Nice that I had phoned Clair—but had returned to New York to finish now with a last two days of second-unit shooting in the East Village. The party was for the cast and crew; the entire company was back. The second leading lady had had a heart attack in Monte Carlo in the middle of production and had had to be written out of the rest of the picture in a hurry. I had done the emergency patch-work and had come back on their charter flight.

Two bands played, a good one that had a Cuban singer I remembered from the old days, and another, which had an accordion. A large sculptured fountain dominated the center of the dance floor, and from a corner of the ceiling Tom's set designer had dressed the party with a 1937 Dick Powell, million-mirrored, million-prismed crystal ball, one of the trite but obligatory props from the film. A baby spot played steadily upon it through a slowly turning wheel of colored gels while the ball itself spun through the night. Red, blue, yellow, green and gold bars of light whirled across the walls, changing the drifting clouds of cigarette smoke into meretricious dreams: incandescent coins of color flashed across the laughing faces of the dancers and the flushed musicians, the people in the cast who had come to the party, and the drunks; they chased themselves across the face of the blonde reflected beside mine in the Byrrh vermouth mirror hung behind the

bar—another prop from the film. Movie effects, movie
emotions, no less effective on me than on anybody else
though I had been the one who had written them into
the script.

Tom and I were at the bar talking to two actresses,
a brunette who had been in the picture, the blonde
who wanted to be in his next.

He smiled and patted the brunette on the ass. "How
the hell do you get into cute tight pants like that?"

"You can start by ordering me a Teacher's Scotch
Mist on the rocks."

. . preguntas, nada mas . . .

La Cubana sang from her little podium in front of the
fountain as Tom and the brunette passed her to dance.

I was left with the blonde.

"Poor baby," she said. She was looking at the bandage. "What happened to your nose? A fight?"

"Yes."

"Over a woman? Maybe another drink will make
it feel better."

I told myself I didn't want another and told the bartender we'd have another—a little heavier on the vermouth in mine. From the dance floor Tom sent the
blonde beside me a flashing smile. The girl in his arms
immediately stepped up her own smile to full Gale-
Force-Ten-Star Animation, but when the music ended
he left her and came back to stand beside the blonde
and me. He and I had worked together in the past
when he had been a producer at CBS, but this was his
first real movie. "Lucky we ran into you over there
when we got jammed up," he said. "Great news about
your wife. When's she coming back?" He was smiling
at the blonde.

"Monday."

"What she doing in San Diego?"

"Once she told me the only way to leave a man is
you call a taxi. Maybe she forgot the meter was running." I asked him about the money.

The smile came off his face, an unsatisfactory cigarette butt thrown away. "Nick, come *on*," he said.

"You did a job—once we threw out the heavy message you were trying to write in on us. This picture is as hot as I think it is, maybe we can do something else together. We finish shooting here, I'll phone you from L.A. Maybe you'll come out to the Beverly Hills a few days, I'd like to hear what you feel about the rough cut, we can talk about another project. Listen, maybe you should move out to California? I know a dozen successful writers, Oscar winners, your age, more successful than you, and they're less talented. Bill E. Barnes came out to California only two years ago from NBC. Twenty-nine, he's already a writer-director."

"Do me a favor."

"Anything."

"Don't tell me about success in my own generation."

He laughed and turned away to the bartender.

"A night for serious drinking," he said. "One more ought to do it. *Let's get there, Nick!*"

"So high not even dogs will hear us?"

"Right on!"

He told Julio to make them doubles to celebrate our marvelous future together.

"You're giving me the Hollywood Yes," I said.

"Which means?"

"Which means No, you didn't get the money for me yet."

His smile grew more brilliant. "I was just on the phone to the studio. I told them to put a rush on it, so help me God. But the only credit we can give you is 'Additional dialogue.' "

"Shit."

"The other son of a bitch, he had a contract."

"Unlike this son of a bitch, who only had your promise."

"Don't get sore. You're taking it too hard. You haven't even touched your drink."

"I was thinking about something else."

"Think about tomorrow," he said. "Yesterday don't pay the rent." He was drinking champagne and poured me a glass from the bottle he carried with him. He pointed at my untouched martini. "What's the matter?

You sick? Have some of this. The carbonation will help your stomach."

"I had enough to drink."

"You don't drink too much," Tom said. "You get the work done, right?" He turned to the bartender again. "Julius? Get some Fernet Branca for my friend here to settle his stomach."

He tossed off his third glass of champagne and went off to dance with Raquel Welch. I had told him again I needed the money and he promised again he had a rush on it. "What more can I do for you?" he said. "Give you hot and cold Beaujolais enemas?" He shifted emotional gears. "Listen," he said, "I got a joke for you. Put this in your next screenplay and you won't have to go around hondling for a lousy credit. For a healthy guy, movie biz is a lot like golf."

He paused to set up the punch: "Nine holes a day."

Funny enough—and why not? It was a joke Tom had forgotten he had first heard from me only two weeks before in the Café des Singes in Cagnes-sur-Mer, but it was also a reminder of all the saloon jokes I had ever made, the kind over which Clair and I had had our last quarrel. A week ago I had phoned her from halfway around the world and told her I had changed, but now in Julio's uneasy eye I recognized the familiar, troubled look I used to catch in my own when sneaking a glance at my drinking father in barroom mirrors; we used to drink together while I still lived at home. Looking past Julio into the Byrrh glass itself, I caught a glimpse of me beside the blonde. An unexpected moment like the first sight of yourself in a hospital window pane, after the operation, before the anesthetic has worn off. Behind the white bandage of my nose, and the black, green and yellow bruises around my eyes, the face I wore was my father's. Ugly and half drunk.

. . . sombras, nada mas . . .

I had first been brought to La Perla by Felix Sar, perhaps my oldest friend in New York. It had been in

the days right after my father had died and I had come
East to live. Felix and I would come here to dance
with the various girls we knew. I had heard my first
live Latin music here, here I had first been set afire
by black Caribbean dancing; here I used to take Clair
to dance those nights, three or four years later, when
I had begun to fall in love with her.

Poignance of confused time: this was the same heavily rouged and henna-haired Cuban singer, hers the
voice, piercingly sweet, this was the melody, immediately thrilling, as if tonight were that first New Year's
Eve when Clair and I had danced here together and
she had sung the words La Cubana was singing now
into my ear. A night as brilliant then as diamonds,
diamond-hard in memory now, a night begun in silent
debate: since our affair inevitably had to end, should
I end it now or later?

... perdida ...

Watching the gin trickle down through a shaker of
ice, I wondered how different I might be, how different
Clair might be, but the life of inanimate objects has a
mystery superior to our own: La Perla had a new
name now, and the lines in La Cubana's face spoke of
time passed but the fountain in the center of the dance
floor was unchanged: the old, familiar gray and green
brass merman perpetually sounded his sea trumpet
there still, forever calling surrounding mermaids to a
wilder dance. No cold water flowed from that fountain; something better: the great ocean basin was
filled with all the bottled wines of the world. That
New Year's Eve when I had brought Clair here, I had
thought the fountain would preside over the end of our
affair. I had proposed it instead, at the end of the
night, as an image of the way we would live: generous,
naked, overabundant and noisy. As we danced, I had
kissed the question into the palm of her hand. Above
the blue silk scarf that enigmatically veiled her face,
Clair's blue-in-blue eyes had smiled into mine. *Yes*.

Why had that night been not the end, but our beginning?

To please her, and because I thought it was going to be the last thing I would ever do for her, I had persuaded Julio to make it a Heads Only costume party; Clair had spoken wistfully about a midnight masked ball she had once attended. Around us the other New Year's dancers had worn their usual Hispanic finery, but their faces were hidden like Clair's: black dominoes, Spanish lace mantillas, green Halloween witches, gorilla heads, faces painted into abstract geometric shapes, sprinkled with pink sequins; my own whitened like Pierrot's. Yes, Clair had said. The yes that says *yes, yes,* right now, but does not promise tomorrow.

... mi vida ...

In Tom's film we had used the spinning mirrored ball and the Byrrh mirror for the same reasons we had used the empty beauty of the women all around me: to evoke envy in the audience and a swoon of nostalgia, an unearned bath of warm emotions, feelings of desire and sweet loss for a time and place, music and love they had never known. But memory is not nostalgia, and I felt the hair lift on the back of my arms as I remembered again the sharpness of desire with which Clair had changed my mind that New Year's Eve. Dancing, afloat in each other's arms while La Cubana sang this same tango she was singing now, Clair's face hidden by blue silk to her blue eyes, neither of us sure where we were going but me thinking we were going to end. *"Affair,"* Clair had whispered into my ear as if she could read my thoughts, "a game for two players in which each withholds that which the other does not wish to receive." The music had stopped. Clair took off her mask and kissed me.

"Goodbye," she had said.

Her heart against my breast, wholly within my grasp, hip to hip, belly to belly, she had never been more distant. As we had danced together that New Year's Eve and I had pompously and silently mused about leaving her, she had sung to me, words that said *alma,* my soul, *vida,* my life, *corazón,* my heart, but behind her veil she had already left me. She had smiled at my sad clown face. The moment in which everything changed.

Clair's ability to end without tears, without guilt or blame, but with a kiss and a smile and no regrets had pitted her will against mine, changing a bland and affectionate no-contest into something like war. At the beginning of the evening I had thought of her with melancholy affection, someone I had once loved. I looked at her now as at an enemy I must possess.

It was new: to feel that double thrill of fear and greed that comes when, as if the light has shifted, someone reveals herself to have a life perhaps larger, an essence more thrilling than our own; that passage of power from the self to the other in which those emotions we imagined had only been play harden into iron. I had to keep her, touch her, focus her elusive eyes on me and make them see me alone; hold her, quicksilver, in my hand. The fever for possession came upon me that night as much through fear of loss as through love. I did not think of it as love at all. I wanted Clair as much through antagonism and enmity as desire. I wanted to punish her because she had made me need her. I had to impose my will upon someone who had become more important to me than myself. She lived in psychic and inviolate space, an ambiguity and ambivalence, an enigma greater than my own, and if the angry wanting of her for these reasons was not love, well, then, wasn't I tired of love? What Clair offered—if I could take it—was as contradictory and heady as anything I had ever had to drink. She was fire. Words in my mind: *This is a woman to be won*. She had cut through the puzzle of love. I didn't know if I loved her. I didn't have to. I knew I must have her. She was all the impossibilities of my own desire.

My emotions had not been very pretty. Is any event touched by need, paradox and the beauty of women wholly ugly? Does it matter what brought Clair and me together? That night took me out of the onanistic room of the self—the self that is, after all, too narrow and contingent to be a serious life's work, the self I drank to escape. It had happened, that was the fact, these were the events, what had gone on between Clair and

me that New Year's Eve was real. It had heat, heat
enough to melt the selves and fuse the pair. We had
begun. And if time and booze and my own dumb,
numbed heart had made me forget Clair, the iron need
to mesh her life so strongly that never again would I
fear she could again become someone separate and
aloof from me, an unattainable and secret life of her
own that she could close against mine as irrevocably
as the door of the plane on which you will never fly,
going to a faraway country you will never see—the
desire was on me once more now: I wanted her.

A few days before I had told Clair in a telephone
call that had spanned six thousand miles that I had
stopped drinking. Couldn't I stay sober I few days
more?

... en tus brazos ...

sang La Cubana on the bandstand behind me I left a
double martini, an untouched glass of champagne and
a full shot of Fernet Branca on the bar and went home.

4
Breakfast Dance

My first clue that friends knew I was back in
town was a pair of women's naked legs on the breakfast table and my old friend Felix himself pouring
champagne over frozen Birds Eye in a coffee cup the
next morning. "Let's just skip the How's-your-mother?
department, and the full, frontal, manly handshake
too," he yelled, pouring more Clicquot over orange ice.
His pleasure in seeing me again embarrassed him
("Notice that my usually relentless cool remains unbroken, Nick?"); he was making a lot of noise to keep
himself in countenance. He sang little high-energy

snatches of songs from what he called his "Worker's Anarchist Alliance Days" under his breath:

> We're starving, almost dead,
> The poor folks said.
> Rockefeller gave them a word written
> on paper.
> The word said "Bread."
> Oh, will you eat that, boys, can you beat that?
> Can you eat that, boys? . . .

The naked legs were part of a hosiery dummy, the lower half of a woman's plastic torso, cut off at the waist and used in store windows to display panty hose. "Dress the place up," Felix said. He propped it up. "Some guys use cars, Borzoi dogs, a lot of money, another girl. Attention-getting devices. You get a little *nervous* about the dead-cold approach like me, you need something to bring them over." He hadn't changed at all.

Slim and medium height, with a blaze of premature white zigzagging a narrow streak through the left side of his tobacco-yellow hair. The eyes his own, hidden behind a constant pair of silver-framed, sky-blue sunglasses; Felix was half merry Groucho Marx, half poised and demonically bearded trapeze artist. Pan's knowing half smile. And never still. "I don't have the love-at-first-sight looks, man," he'd once said to me. "I'm no long-distance killer across the crowded room. I *need* five minutes up close. Just give me a chance to talk to her alone *five* minutes. . . . *Energy,* man!"

He was doing a lope around the room. "I brung along some crazy rum for later too," he was shouting. "Some of that 168-proof, black Jamaica, go-to-the-moon rum you like. Cigars too. Havanas. Smoke, smoke, *smoke!* No, goddamn it, *don't* open the windows." It was ten A.M. "Felix barely manages to live on twenty-four hours a day," Clair had once said of him. They had never gotten on.

"People got a conditioned reflex a lot of cigarette smoke," Felix was saying. "Enough smoke in the air, they don't tell you it's too early in the day for a drink."

"You bring anything more than cigars?"

He looked surprised but had some well-rolled shit in emptied-out Marlboro Filter King 100 skins. He himself drank wine from the neck of the bottle. "I don't slip out on grass much any more," he said. "I don't usually like to carry, these days. All that hassle." He looked at me admiringly. "You knew something cool all along, right? *Booze is legal, man!* You get busted for something, the cops find you're drunk, they love you for it. You're drunk they don't figure you for a speed freak going to pull a knife on them. Drunk is law-and-order, man. They bring you *coffee,* they call the *lawyer* for you, they *drive* you home. You can't be Irish from Queens, the best thing you're busted is drunk."

He ran to the phone. "Hello, Kitty, it's me, Felix. Yeah, yeah . . . the one I told you about. He's back. In his old place, West Twentieth Street. Yeah. Listen, Kitty, you bring that thing over here now, we're turning this place on. *Don't* tell me 'early in the morning.' It's *supposed* to be early. THIS IS A BREAKFAST DANCE! We'll pull the window shades, we'll wear dark glasses. It'll be night. Break the candles in half, burn all *four* ends! Yeah, bring her too, but forget her boyfriend. That enema specialist, I can't *stand* him. He falls into pig shit, he comes out Vice-President of the Hogs. *Don't* let him near me. What? HE'S A LOUSY DEALER, THAT'S WHAT! This is a welcome-home party, not a dumb-out. I don't want him here. No, no, *Miss Jennifer* is not coming. No. Yeah, yeah. OK, so put some aspirin in your wine. Start on that till you feel better."

He hung up.

> *Oh, we'll bomb the bourgeoisie, boys,*
> *Let's bomb the dirty bourgeoisie . . .*

he sang. But he caught my eye on him.

"*Jennifer,*" he said. He smiled shyly. "Remember I was always looking for the perfect girl?"

"Yes."

"Jennifer was looking for the perfect man."

He turned back to the telephone. "Not going to fall in love any more, Nick. I can't bear to tell my *story* again." He called twenty or thirty other people. "The shampoo is going to give out you don't bring that silky thing over here *in a hurry!*" he screamed at them. "Listen, it's only Saturday morning, we got time to run a hell of a party!"

He turned to me. "You live over there—what? Three years?"

"Two."

"What's it like, Villefranche?"

"Disorderly times."

"The French are pigs," he said. "Nobody lives in France any more." He had learned his own taste for Veuve Clicquot during a six-month hegira he had once spent somewhere outside of Marseilles. He smiled, dislike for the French forgotten. "You haven't had any this new bottle yet."

"In a minute."

"What happened to the nose, Nick? Falling-down drunk?"

In the mirror the bruises around my eyes were purple and black. I touched the bandage at the bridge. "Yes."

"Listen," Felix said, "you are not drinking enough. Your best friends are worried about you. You have to try. Have a drink and *be* somebody. Start now!"

"In a minute."

His smile stopped. "Clair?"

"You can't live how-high-the-moon forever."

"She send you a carrier pigeon on the Riviera, she definitely's coming?"

"We finished shooting in Nice last week, I phoned her in California. She thought I was drunk. When she believed I wasn't, she said OK. She'll be here Monday."

"But you came early? Can't wait?" He stubbed out his cigarette. "Just like that, one phone call and it's all *on* again?" He lit another cigarette. "She surprised to hear from you all this time? What's wrong she can't be here the same time as you?"

"She said she had some things to end in San Diego first."

Immediate: "What things?"

"I didn't ask."

"And you want to be married to her again? Shit, New York's full of beautiful women."

"Miss America selling you dog food on television."

"What does that mean?"

"The beauty of other women isn't serious to me. I used to feel even the way Clair combed her hair was important."

"And what the hell does *that* mean?"

"I'm not sure I can get off the booze without her."

Felix was staring at me. "You can't get off the booze *because* of her. You don't know how lucky you are she left, man. You better run quick to your psychoanalyst and get *all* your money back. Listen, what you need is a genuine, one-hundred-dollar—no, a *two*-hundred-dollar Ph.D. A two-hundred-dollar Per-Hour-Doctor." He smiled ruefully, amused for a moment by his invention. "What she doing in California two years? She change her name and start all over again a virgin? You never drank too much. She only told you you did. Women try to reform a guy, it's not for his own good. *It's for hers!* What they want is feel their power over him. Only *she* can hold him. That's one iron maiden you were married to."

"Don't say that."

"Whatever you did for her was not enough. You never knew what she wanted. Where you stood with her."

"I knew."

"You knew so much she walked out on you, no warning," Felix said. Clair's lack of small talk had always made him nervous. "Turn off all that beauty and *say* something," Felix would half joke with her when we'd run into him on the street. "How many words today?" he'd wink, turning to me.

"You know the manifestos painters write for their catalogs?"

"Yeah."

"Explaining their art?"

"So what?"

"The best ones shut up."

"Very romantic, man. She's silent, doesn't tell you she's planning to skip, doesn't let you know where you are, and that's got something to do with art. SHE WANTED TO CUT YOUR BALLS OFF AND RUN YOU! *THAT* WAS HER ART! WHEN SHE SAW SHE COULDN'T, THAT'S WHEN SHE LEFT YOU!"

"YOU'RE TALKING ABOUT YOUR WIFE— NOT MINE!"

Felix drew breath but stopped himself before he yelled again. He smiled.

"Ex-wife," he said. "There's no Tamara."

"I'm sorry."

"In the cards even before you went away."

"Yes."

"It's no secret I never liked Clair. I'll be honest."

"Don't be honest. Like her."

"New times?" Felix asked. "A goddamned new era? *Marriage? Love?* You know what Freud said? The *necessary* overevaluation of the sexual object, man." He put out a hand, palm open and turned flat toward the ceiling: what the hell. He smiled again; it was one of his constants and made me remember how much I liked him. "Jesus," he said, half surprised, half remembering, "you always were just an old-fashioned kind of guy, weren't you?"

The doorbell and the phone both rang at the same time. I picked up the phone and asked them to wait and went to the door. It was the delivery boy from the speed shop around the corner. "Case of vodka for Mr. Sar?" the kid read Felix's name off a piece of paper. On the phone the operator read me a telegram from Clair confirming she would arrive Monday noon.

Felix came in from arranging the lighting in the other room so that it looked like Dusk in the Club de Paris on the Island of Samoa in the Spring of 1928. "Oh, look, look," he said, enraptured by the sight of all the alcohol being delivered. "Yeah, yeah," he said, "I ordered it." He paid the kid and wrestled the case away from him. "Oh, baby," he said to the twelve jugs as he unloaded them. "If only I could dehydrate you and take you all at once in one total, wild, screaming *go-to-the-sun* pill!"

He sat down to rest among the champagne and took a deck of postcards out of his pocket. They were printed. YOU LOOK VERY INTERESTING AND I LIKE YOU, they said in capital letters. BUT I CAN'T AFFORD TO MEET ANY NEW PEOPLE. I AM IN PSYCHOANALYSIS. He gave me a half dozen. "You see a raver turns you *on*," Felix said, "slip her one." He opened more wine. "And she's yours!"

He turned to me. "And to think you never even *wanted* her in the first place!"

"Felix, what the hell do you need psychoanalysis for?"

"I fell in love with myself at first sight but I was rejected."

He ran around the room dropping ashes and torn bits of paper into the clean ashtrays so that people would not be timid about using them. "The common mistake," he said, "people believe a good psychoanalysis makes you a guaranteed winner. What it does, it only makes you a competent player. But maybe you weren't dealt the right cards no matter how you play." He spun an ashtray around so it whirred like a top but stopped it with a laugh before it died. "No, no," he said. "The real reason, some people go into analysis to become more loving, mature, decent human beings. I go to become a more efficient rat. Let's get organized before the people get here."

He began to count the liquor bottles. "We'll put two jugs vodka in the can, some wine in the bedroom, and I got some on a little table the hall outside while they're ringing the doorbell. Enter laughing. We'll scatter the rest around the whole ranch. Keep the ice cubes in a big box as far away from the main liquor supply as possible—that keeps traffic moving, people crossing the room, *break* up the clutching couples, nobody crouched against the walls. No food, goddamn it! *Don't* let Kraft Cheese fool you—it's not clever little hostess-toasted-cheese-and-olive sandwiches make

your party, it's *movement*. See, once they come in and
sit down facing each other in a circle, your party's
dead. No, no, you *can't* let that circle form. 'Oh,
Janet' "—he mimicked a woman's voice—" 'do you
like the steaks at D'Agostino's? You ought to try
Gristedes. And Junior just began eating solids yesterday, isn't that *heaven?*' " Felix stood a moment in
despair. *"That's* the noose, man," he said. *"Don't* let
them start that. Don't let couples bunch up in a frightened corner with the people they came with. *Crowd*
the room, *force* the bashful bastards to talk to new
people, but give them an excuse to get away from each
other also if they want. Put the sick poets in one room,
the politicals in another, make *sure* some girl locks
herself in the can to have hysterics, keep pouring the
booze, keep everyone smoking, tell lies, stop the
clocks, pull the shades, *make* them be happy!"

Felix opened another nebuchadnezzar of Clicquot.
"Listen," he said, "wait'll you *see* this Kitty. I knew I
would love her the first minute I sneaked a look in
her medicine cabinet. That's the new thirty-second psychoanalysis. *She has no downers in her medicine chest,*
man, not a single Valium. You hip how rare she is?
No three A.M. crying phone calls from *that* woman,
man. Listen, you know how some guys, these super
he-men, studs, they describe themselves as leg men,
breast men, ass guys? Doesn't that total you out?
Imagine coming on so jaded, so epicure, so *butch,
chauv and barbed wire?* But I tell you, this Kitty, she's
got a different thing—hips. *Hips!* She's going to burn
down *Vogue* Magazine and bring hips back into style.
You know that little line that women got, that line
where the hip swells, that little dimple *in* when the
weight is on one foot and that full-moon curve of the
other hip is the roundest and most convex? When I
see that sweet little curve, that inshoot that brings you
face to face with the shape of her woman's *bone* beneath the flesh—that's fire in the ice, man. I melt. I
turn to farina. Oh, Kitty, Kitty!" Felix bayed at the
ceiling. "Where are you? I'm dying, Egypt, dying,
man. Hurry, *hurry!*" He turned to me. "New York's

better now. While you were away they turned off the
death ray. The fags are helping. They sent out word
even *fat* women are in this year."

Felix cocked his head suspiciously. "I don't hear
no music."

"I only have a little French transistor."

"You want to buy some sounds?"

"You still in the business?"

"Things change. But you're a friend."

"Got something lo-fi?"

"You broke?"

"A guy I used to know at CBS came through Villefranche on location. I did a little rewrite for him . . ."

"On spec?"

"It was just script-doctoring."

"You're past that."

"You go away, you get out of touch. People forget."

"He paid you yet?"

"A little up front."

Felix looked around the apartment. "Who subleased
the pad you were away? Addicts? They sell your TV
on you too? You want to place an order?"

"How much?"

"Same as ever," he said. "Thirty percent list." He
took a little notebook out of his pocket and wrote a
few words. Neither "TV" nor "hi-fi" was one of them.
"Your order's taken," he said. "A tape setup, no
Mickey Mouse. Maybe a sixteen, maybe nineteen-
inch TV, color. OK? Delivery as soon as. You pay
me when your serious script money comes in. Turn the
French radio louder. WRVR."

I asked if it was OK to invite an old friend.

"He's gone on the cops, you know," Felix said.

"Even before I went away."

"Sure, ask him. Why not?"

"You used to like Lou."

"He's made detective now."

"So?"

"It's different from directing traffic."

"Then we won't ask him?"

"Sure, sure. I told you. I'm not taking orders any more."

"The real estate hustle?"

"Nick, don't ask."

"But it's OK?"

Felix shrugged. "Lou?" He smiled. "Let him come. It'll be cool. It's a *party*, Nick." He raised his glass. "Three martinis closer to the moon, Nick. *Let's go!*"

The doorbell went again. Another kid with three or four huge bouquets of tulips, daisies, roses and all kinds of other flowers. They were wired into horse-shoe shapes and said "Good Luck" and "Welcome Home" on blue-and-gold satin ribbons. Felix tipped the kid but he was bugged. "The guys I put in the order," he said, "shit, they didn't get me. This is a party. What kind of flowers they think I want? For a funeral?" He pulled the wire off the flowers so they were loose and threw the ribbons away. He put most of the roses into vases around the apartment and the rest in a pitcher in the refrigerator. He poured some champagne into the water. "High pH," he said. "It feeds them." He sighed. "In case a girl has to wear the same clothes again tomorrow, she puts fresh flowers in her belt or shoves them down her V and it's not so much of a drag for her to wear the same clothes two days a row. When I'm with a girl I don't make that I've-got-to-go-home-to-change-now shit. You're together, *you're together!* The time comes *soon enough* you got to get away from each other, right? Change your clothes then."

The guests arrived like bursts of laughter. Judy Esfox, Henry Klayman and Bob Carringson. Lou the Cop (detective now) in an off-duty disguise as a mo-torcycle rider, the poet A. E. Fugelman and Matti Cosworth, Mel Parigi and Big Mary; intellectuals, horn-rimmed men, organic restaurant Queens, thrift-shop adventuresses, Greenwich Avenue corn god-desses, women intelligent as the night, pretty girls like showers of confetti and some from *Ms.* Magazine too; heartbroken Socialist Workers, bright young urine-analysts, West Coast fly-throughs, gong players, Cedar

Bar painters and their rent-paying, big-breasted Earth Women, the beautiful Miss Colbert and her white French poodle, Lavish. A Brazilian movie star with an aerosol spray can of ether for giggles. Editors, acrobats, sexual engineers, tenors, Bulgarians, Hungarians, Spanish waiters from the Jai Alai restaurant, bust-ups, tap dancers and busted skulls, but Felix would not let any serious dope people in or any singles-bar people either. We kept the party alive, we were alive ourselves, old friends turned up and some new ones too; we kept moving, we told lies, we wore dark glasses, he danced and flirted and no toasted-cheese sandwiches were eaten at all; we crowded against each other but could leave in search of ice cubes when we were bored; no supermarket circles formed. The poets went into the bedroom to read aloud, the politicals formed splinter socialist parties in the hall, the *Ms.* women compared speculum stories, three love affairs began and one was consummated, the booze poured like sunshine, the cigar, cigarette and other smoke was thick as dreams, one amorous couple locked themselves in the can, the poet A. E. Fugelman ate the flowers in the refridge, the clocks were smashed and stopped, someone had scotch-taped a rose in the crotch of Felix's hosiery dummy, the window shades were drawn, the apartment dark, people were breakfast-dancing to my radio WRVR, it was only Saturday morning, the best time in the world to have a party, I was sober, Clair was coming back to me, and Felix, tutelary to us all, Felix, vision shielded by blue shades against a midnight sun only he could see, crazy lock of white hair running a stream of riot down his forehead, Felix, quick eyes darting from right to left to see that everybody was drinking, everybody was smoking, everybody was dancing or in the arms of a beautiful stranger, Felix shouting "Nothing succeeds like excess!" as he got on the phone to invite more people to the party and then more again, Felix, true to his name, Felix, good as his word, Felix had made us happy.

Was it an hour later—was it five or ten?—that I waked with Clair murdered beside me? Three or four half-empty liquor bottles on the bedside table said I would never know. The powerful sweet smell in the room was shit.

5

Clair

"A Spoken History," begin Tape 4B revised.

That hot Sunday night I was going to one of the Upper West Side rerun movie houses with a man I'd first met when I came to New York and he was just divorced and new to the city too—bewildered by how much the rules had changed during his eight-year married idyll in the suburbs. We had held on to each other like beginning swimmers, and I occasionally saw him still, half grateful we had been friends so long, half annoyed he aroused no greater emotion in me. He smiled from the corner of his eyes, half wise, half sly:

"Whenever you phone I always know. Another one of your enchanted episodes is over, right?"

"It was Circe's fate to live among swine."

He had been telling me about how discouraged he was becoming with New York and that he was thinking of moving out to California. Behind his words, I remember wondering if his feeling for me was enough to begin an affair upon after all; he had always wanted to. He fitted my mother's prescription. "Don't get involved with a man who doesn't love you," she had nerved herself to whisper shyly the night before I left De Haviland, West Virginia, for New York. "With any couple, the rules are made by the person who loves least." It was the opposite of what she had done herself in either of her marriages, and represented the sum total of all the sex education she had ever been able to give me. I would tell my mother now that her own had been the wiser choice. One-sided love is flattering at first, but feeds and rots on power alone, and finishes by driving you into unfair fury, loved for the wrong reasons, stifled in cotton candy, controlled and blackmailed. His very adoration gives him power. You must remain what he needs to dream or lose his love. But I was at the paralyzed end of another kind of love affair when it seems the quickest way to get over one man is to start with another—an alcoholic promising himself one more martini is all he needs to get sober. Wasn't his wistful talk about California a disguised plea for me to ask him not to go? I decided our trip to the movies would end that night in my bed.

In the darkness when we were seated, the head in the row just in front of me looked familiar. It was Blake. The girl with him was one I'd heard he was half living with that year. (But he was a famous solitary and in the end always lived alone.) At one point in the picture—*Black Orpheus,* the third time I had seen it but had loved it always—she leaned toward Blake. Arching his neck to receive her, he half turned in his seat.

He saw me.

Neither he nor I gave any further sign of recognition, and unconscious of what had just happened, the girl continued to move her head the last inches to take the place Blake had just made for her—that tender space of skin between the line drawn where a man's whiskers end and his ear begins. A glance, one silent exchange—but enormous. I could not understand the obscure, weighted, lunatic outrage that welled up in me. There in the darkness of the ratty-tatty Paradise, I was gripped by sudden words—letters of fire—writing themselves in my brain: *I should be that girl.* That place was mine.

I had never been alone with Blake, but as simply as that I loved him. I had not even been aware I wanted him. I had often been in love before, but this was the first time falling in love was involuntary and against my better judgment. To this day I cannot understand how it happened when I had already begun to think of an affair with another man. (But that, after all, is merely Dr. Joyce Brothers wisdom. I do know why.)

I believe now you fall in love against your will only once in your life, but it means you have never been in love before. Up till then I had only thought of Blake as an amusing man I would run into now and then at parties in the Village or loft showings in SoHo, someone to whom I'd nod when he'd be sitting over a drink with some painter or writer friends on nights when, after finishing work at the Waverly, I might wander into McGruddy's, Raoul's on Prince Street, or any of the three or four West Village bars where people I knew went. Clean-shaven and shorn, often wearing a suit as if in ironic disguise among the masculine-protest beards and heavy Viva Zapata mustaches of the usual customers in these places, he had a certain quality about him, a distance that always put me off. We all drank too much but he drank even more. He'd written an episode for *Police Story* I'd liked more than most things on TV, but when I tried to talk to him about it I could not connect my feelings about what he had written with *him*, the man speaking to me who had done it—there was something remote and unavailable behind the alcohol and all the jokes. A man who made his own hours, often appearing late at night and alone, just as often with a new girl he would introduce to people at Ira's Glue or the 55, and she would be around with him for a season or two, six months, and then once more there'd be a new one. He had never come on with me, and one of the things I had noted and liked about him was that I had never seen him eye any woman except the one he was with at the moment. And yet in the way a woman will automatically appraise every man she meets, no matter how remote the possibility, I had long ago placed him in the category of men my mother had warned against. More interested in power than emotion. I knew those men well enough. My father had been one. Bored by small-town life, perhaps bored with her, he had left without a word, without a note, when I was six, never to be heard from again. What I had not known when I had secretly smiled at my mother's naive injunctions against men like him was that her warning was not necessary. In my three A.M. moments I am afraid I may be the female version of that kind of man myself. How can I not be?—determined *not* to be whatever my fond and foolish mother was? Almost from the first moment I'd met Blake I had carefully and yet almost without thinking decided he would have nothing to do with my life at all.

What happened that night? Was it because I had never before seen him so *with* a woman? Was I wrong in my first idea that he did not have the quality in men for which I have always looked? Masculine tenderness is what I need but I've been taken in instead too often by its male counterfeit—passivity, the revenge of the "nice guy." Was tenderness being presented to me right here, wearing an unexpected face? Why do women never "see" the right men? Why do we unerringly fall in love with the same lousy kind of guy over and over? We think we fall in love because we are physically attracted. What if we fall in love with the psychological type first—and camouflage the reasons from ourselves by deciding, but only after the fact, that he is physically magnetic? We think we are responding to the color of his hair, the slope of his shoulders and his smile, but what is attractive is the unattainable look in the eye, the faint, subliminal message of avoidance, noncommitment, inability to love. These are his names: the rapist who cries, the smiler with a knife, the charming Mr. Rat. We have picked up the signal that he will satisfy the part of our heart that is not whole and does not wish us well. I have recognized this division in myself—wanting a man to love me but afraid of being tied down. Fidelity the puzzle. The *dailiness* of marriage choked me; it had never been the nice little house in the suburbs I wanted but the fever of emotion without end. Is danger necessary to intensity? I had long known that permanence is its enemy.

"Change your luck, baby?" goes the black invitation

that every girl in New York gets sooner or later. We are annoyed, accept, laugh or blush, but the persistence of the idea that changing one's physical type might open new vistas of feeling has dread persuasiveness. If he is an unfamiliar physical type, mightn't he arouse new and unpredictable emotions in us too? Is this a way out of the dead-end maze the enemy within remorselessly constructs for us, ever enticing us to run through gardens of delight only to wind up once again in the arms of the minotaur? Blake did not have the looks I had always gone for. My men had always been fair, the opposite of me, but Blake's looks were dark, his eyes the color of my own. He was not my type. He was strange. My feelings about him were new, bewildering. I felt excited and out of control, a tinge of apprehension too. *I will not be able to make him do what I want.*

I had had enough of nice guys—phallic but frightened, shrinking from the necessary murder of their father's memory, afraid to take his place because the next death would be their own. They bring out a bitchiness in me I hate, drive me to any excess to find the hard reality hidden in the mush between us. My efforts to reach the man behind his conditioned-reflex jerk to please at any price make me ugly in my own eyes.

"What would you like to do tonight?" the nice guy says.

"Let's drive to City Island in a big rented red convertible and find a place where we can dance and eat lobster and drink white wine until four A.M."

"Why not?" he automatically replies, even though he can't afford it and must go to work early the next morning. "As long as you're happy."

Guilty in advance because he knows he will soon leave her, the nice guy thinks he wants only to appease and placate the outrageous woman beside him. Hiding his anger, constructing treachery out of his seemingly sweet nature, always leaving the choice and responsibility to her, he gives himself one more mark on his secret list of grievances to justify his final rejection every time she rages against the vacuum with which he presents her.

New York had taught me secrets I would rather not know: what men want from women is not love but release from their Oedipal claustrophobia. Obsessively they yearn to repeat and reenact their childhood. "Love me," he says at first. "I'm suffocating," he says later. It is their double message, red and green lights both flashing at the same time. I have learned the iron rule: leave first.

I have learned to say no when I meant yes, announced the affair was over when it was just being born, kept my own secrecy and privacy throughout, guarding it even when I wanted more than anything in life for him not to accept my limits, to invade the ground I kept from him. And invading it, to find me. I hide the sinking feeling in my stomach from the time of the first phone call he does not make. I know what his silence is saying before he finds the courage to put it into words for himself. I used to tell myself his lies for him, to ease my hurt. I face them today. When he does phone at last, expecting me to be reproachful or angry, he gets my smile instead. Men say they want freedom. They want rejection. They call it oxygen. "Ah, Bob, I'm so sorry, but I can't make it tonight. No, tomorrow I'll be busy too. Call me when you like. I'll miss you. Goodbye. I love you."

Goodbye. I love you. It is the double-edged message with which I have learned to respond, my own red-and-green reciprocal to the stop-and-go they send out. It works but cuts my own life too, diminishing my hope for men. As if by magic, his love revives, stronger than before, fascinated by the puzzle I have posed him, renewed by the distance I have put between us. But my own feelings are dead. He has become all too familiar to me, his glamor gone, just another nice guy beyond his depth. Strategies for defeat. Tactical victories I need. I cannot bear rejection, the numbed black weeks and months; I grew into my looks too late to believe in them even today. My hold on sex and self-confidence can be crushed by a simple put-down, a word, an unthinking comparison. *If he leaves me I will die.*

"You look marvelous tonight. What a terrific dress!"

"This old thing?"

I have learned to bite back that automatic response, but it is what I feel. I live for compliments but never ask for them, even indirectly; I am too disappointed when they don't come. I defeat myself by expecting the man magically to know what is on my mind when I go out of my way to deny or hide it, and then take it as a test he has failed. I need compliments to live but am unable to believe them when they come. The nice words must be insincere, a momentary whim or piece of kindness from someone who has not correctly perceived me. The thirsty skeptic does not drink from the lake because she knows it must be salt.

I cannot bear it when men tell me admiringly: "You can really take care of yourself. You're so together. You don't need anyone. You're the great survivor!" They are telling me why they are afraid to ask me out. I have succeeded too well in showing them my false face, constructed my own despair. *I am not strong.* Most of the painful conflicts in my life have not been conflicts at all: I always knew what I should do but lacked the courage: the deliberate turning away from knowledge that the difficult choice is better in the long run. Instead I get hung up by the easier, rationalized path of least resistance. When I first came to New York I knew I would be cheating myself out of a special time in my life if I did not live alone. I moved in with two other girls. It would be better for me not to have a roommate now, but I have never been able to walk into an empty apartment late at night and feel at ease by myself. I hate it that I am one of those women who cannot live alone. Somewhere in me that stringy, too tall, lonely adolescent girl lives on still, the one who sang "The Battle Hymn of the Republic" to herself all during her teens to gain courage against the unrelenting beauty of the *in* group of girls at school, and their pity (contempt too—it had always been taken for granted I was too funny-looking ever to hope to be a member), who swore to herself before her

first Christmas hop that it would not matter if not one
single boy asked her to dance that night, and who
believed it did not when not one did—even while she
carried lists of their glorious names close to her heart
in the cup of the brassiere she wore only because she
was so afraid that if she waited she would never need
to wear one at all.

The affair with the too-nice man beside me in the
movie house had not yet begun, but I could already
see the end, feel the guilt and remorse—but the disgust
and anger for us both too—that I would know when I
would have to tell him it was over, I had met someone
else, and he would plead for us to have one more
chance. I dislike that in myself which has learned to
fight these wars so well—*but men are the ones who
set the rules*. (The revolution will not have been won
until women who dine in restaurants alone learn to
stop calling waiters "sir.")

Why did I suddenly feel I would not have to use
these absurd femme-fatale ploys on Blake? I was sick
of them. In some eerie moment of identification I felt
he must be too. Something in him matched me. He was
the kind of man I would be if I had been born male.
Whatever else I thought about him, I had never
thought him absurd. What had kept me off was the
coolness of emotion I had always felt in him—the
ironic detachment, the jokes, the ease with which he
shed one girl and took on another. But now I saw this
meant that he was always looking for something more,
that if he could be won, his love would be real, the
victory measured by the toughness of the resistance. In
the darkness of that movie house I felt a surprising,
answering resistance in myself. The real question was:
Why had I until then—with only one exception—
chosen only men whom I too could not love?

I had never understood faithful girls. Marriage
frightened me. To swear to see life, the world and all
of sex itself in just one man until death . . . ? But something in me wanted to be faithful. With Blake the un-
answerable question seemed to have a solution. I felt I
could be faithful to him.

I left not because I did not love him but because I

had made him need me, and his need was turning my love into contempt. It was I who answered the phone calls from his agents in California and New York when he was drinking and had not finished a script, and told them the work was in the mail. I would pick him up from the floor in the middle of the night when drinking had felled him and put him to bed. I handled his money, his clothes, his hangovers and remorse, the angry people who threatened to sue. I cajoled friends and story editors who never wanted to speak to him again. We think that if a man needs us it is better than love. Need is unchanging. Liking and loving is fickle. He will never leave us, because he cannot. I did not realize that from the first, in the name of protecting him, I was constructing a prison for us both, chaining myself to him through a kind of angry pity just as much as I was chaining him to me through need. He was gin's prisoner. I was his. I left to break the unending cycle of drinking and regret. Promises made, promises broken. *If I were a better wife he would not be drinking like this. It is his way of punishing me because I won his love under false pretenses. It is my fault.* Two people, each a prisoner, each a jailor, a Beefeater on guard at the door. With me to love him, his drinking did not slow down; with me to protect him, it began to speed up. Together, neither of us stood a chance. Alone, he might face his life. I believe in his unknown strength. It is my hope for any future for us, if there is ever to be one. But if he puts away the bottle only to please me—if he wants me back only because he can't have me—*if he turns out to be just another nice guy*—he would drink again when he had me back. I wait for him to stop drinking, not to win me but to win himself.

But what if the Blake I fell in love with, the difficult, intransigent part of him I could not control but wanted to win, is not Blake himself but my enemy—the angry man behind the curtain? Blake is as afraid of him as I am. He walks out of quarrels so that no one else should see him, he drinks to keep him hidden from himself. If the price he must pay to stop drinking is for that man to come out for good—if the Blake I married is the false face and the angry man within is the real one—a copy of the father who killed Blake's mother with his drinking—what will I have gained? When I was little I thought love was many things but I had never thought it could be dangerous. Blake's mother found it was. I need men important enough to match my emotions. One of my nightmares is that I have overestimated Nick.

My painting has gone to hell, stained glass is forgotten. I wait but I do not wait. Blake may never stop drinking. If he stops he may not want me. And every day I feel my love for him dying.

The life I have made here in California is an adventure for a different kind of woman than I ever thought I would be. (At times I wonder—Is this how it also is for Blake in France? Exhilarating and charged, but uneasy and impermanent too? Not at home?) Sometimes it seems like a funny little life. Other times, caught up in it, the work grows big and exciting, I go here, meet that stranger there, catch a plane, make a phone call, do the other thing, the surface gleams; I know what I am carrying underneath. But with the careless and elegant indifference with which a bottle of gin waits for the alcoholic who has hidden it from himself in a suitcase at the back of the closet, loss waits for me.

For hours and days it sleeps at the back of my mind, I'm too busy, I forget it, I wonder why I am so suddenly happy, feel so free, a weight lifted, and then it is here again. His absence hits me with the aroma of a cigar from the next table or the breakfast coffee in the morning. Hallucinations of seeing him on the street, turning a corner or getting into a taxi. Every ring of the telephone is his until I answer it. A month ago I saw a tall dark man walking toward the bar of the Hotel de la Playa in Quito. He carried his head at the same tilt as Blake, but when I ran to get ahead of him and turned, it was a stranger. I wake up every morning in love with him and wonder why I am here. The times of the Pan Am and TWA polar flights to France are on a pad beside my bed. A plane leaves every morning and every evening from Los Angeles—

why am I here? Last week I was in Paris. Why didn't I phone him in the south of France? I know his Ville-franche phone number by heart. It is a daily effort of will, a problem I cannot solve, only get used to the way a diabetic learns to live with his needles and his disease. Figures of keening sorrow, something missing, something gone, haunt my dreams. Half asleep, I grope in my mind: what disaster happened yesterday, what danger awaits me tomorrow? And then I remember he is gone. I fight the feeling of being a woman without a man, floating somewhere in space, functionless, valueless, not really a woman at all. I left him, but he had already gone away from me. We were in love for a while, but there is no symmetry in the love of women and men. Women know they need men, but men do not think they need women. They take their ignorance to be invulnerability. It is the strength of a maniac swinging a double-bladed axe in a crowded room. They are proud of their weapon and suspect your motives if you tell them they can cripple themselves first of all. All they know is you are trying to disarm them. A woman in love is already half victim. Love is not enough, say men, but women know it is all there is.

And yet love brought me here.

When I'm not in love I'm free. I feel adventuresome and daring, I get a kick out of moving around alone. I'd rather go to a party without a man than with one I'm not crazy about. Because I grew into my looks so late and need to test them still, the feeling of going into a bar or dinner party—flying to a Caribbean island—alone, without a man encumbering me, is still a thrill. I know the night will end well. I am totally different—less—when I am in love. I lose courage.

When I am in love, if I even go to the movies without him, I hate it. The evening has no meaning. I am thinking about him, wondering what he is doing. Without love I am my own woman. When love is offered I become tied to it, unable to do without for an hour. I live from phone call to phone call, dominated by my own awakened need, neglecting everything else—an addict who cannot rest until she's living with her pusher.

I would go through it all again tomorrow if Blake came for me tonight.

He grew used to my love, never doubted it, discounted my unhappiness and anger. What man can think of a woman sick with love as anything but a burden? When I learned to ski I had to learn to fight fear, the beginner's natural craving to lean back into the hill, away from the frightening drop below. In time I overcame it, learned to resist the body's treacherous instinct for safety, taught myself to face down into the drop, accept the danger, and accepting it, find exhilaration, speed and control. The night I left Blake, I decided if I could not build a life on love, I would rather have him admire me. Love is like a muscle, admiration is the bone underneath. Muscles tire. The bone does not. Everything in me wanted to lean back into the hill, to wait for Blake, stay at home, be safe. I fought my fear. I went.

After he had walked out in the middle of our last quarrel I veered ineffectually between going back to the poster I was preparing for my new one-man show at Mrs. Korne's gallery, and fantasies of revenge—a new, faceless stranger that very night!—or running weeping after him. But I have never let him see my tears.

I had gotten used to the idea that Blake finds a kind of excitement in drinking that I find in bed with a man—that subjective, healing rush of mind and body no longer divided. I had even got used to the fact that I was more sexual than Blake and must not ask him for more than he could give. Booze made him impotent at times, preoccupied with sex at others. That was how he was. But as I waited through the midnight hours and knew at last he would once more not be coming home, I changed in sorrow and in hate, angry and laughing, suffused by impulse, broken in heart, liberated by rage: I would not sleep one more night alone.

My first show at Mrs. Korne's gallery had been four years ago—right after we got back from Martha's Vineyard. It had been small, there'd been a certain amount of success. I had needed a second, bigger show now to nail down my niche in the art world. I had let it all go.

Blake's drinking slowed me down, but marriage had confused me more. I had decided my first work must be him. That was a mistake. But even while we were married, I had slowly begun to separate in a way he never knew, not from him, but from his drinking. I began to work again.

The windows for my second show were finished by the night I left. All that had to be done were the posters, the publicity and the rest, and I was working on the details with Mrs. Korne. I left it all unfinished. Mrs. Korne, the gallery, my second show—they would all have to do without me.

Leaving is pain, but it is demonic energy too—energy that has been tied up in unresolved angers, remembered resentments, the effort of love; that energy becomes available again. I did not want to be in New York to be faced with the overt sympathy and hidden questions of pitying friends, to feel their avoidance when I was not with them. Marriage was the disease for which I would take a geographical cure. I would go away.

And the conflict resolved, the mind healed by action, the somnambulistic feeling of living in a dream in which you cannot move broken by a decision made at last to go right or wrong but to go!—energy was mine, exhilaration too. The nag, nag, nag worry about money had never left my mind, but it seemed less important. I felt light. Everything was simple, all was possible. Singing "The Battle Hymn of the Republic" under my breath to give me courage (it was still my song), I wrote the words down with pencil and paper to get them right, carefully rehearsing the amused and amusing cadences of my tape-recorded goodbye, speaking them over and over into the machine—all the while hoping for his step at the door—erasing my mistakes and beginning again until I had spoken it all without break or hesitation. I did not want him to know how much it cost me to go. There would be no tears, no slammed doors or impotent threats, none of the self-defeating armament of the forlorn woman. He would have to deal, not with my emotion, of which I was weary myself, but with my fact: I was gone. I will live with him, but I will not die with him—his mother's death not for me. I live resigned never to see Blake again and ready for him to come for me tomorrow. He haunts me like music. But I resent it.

All my life, unstructured time has brought anxiety. I use work to bind time, to give it form I can grasp and so be free of the gnawing, loose rush, rush, rush of it. But I cannot work now. I do this instead. As I try to remember—as you must at these times—how it was with Blake and me, I feel my love for him as a kind of humiliation. I grow angry that I cannot put him into perspective, close the door on him at last. Our mouths say "Goodbye." How long before we mean it? Memories, old emotions rule my mind. I resent seeing myself transfixed before my past like a bird before a snake, unable to rule my feelings, not in control of my life. The love I feel for him is mixed with fury because he can command it without trying. Even as I welcome the hold he still has on me, I hate him. I cannot learn to live with how much the past dominates the present. Because a young woman went to see a revival of *Black Orpheus* one day a few years ago, and there exchanged a glance with a man in the dark, am I today to be a captive, never again my own woman? I will not bear it. I will not be limited by love. Recently I have begun to catch myself in the midst of vivid fantasies, coming to with images in my mind of him dead, guiltlessly killed in a sudden, painless auto accident, disappeared silently at sea. I want him dead so that I can mourn him, and mourning him, be rid of him. He is more of a ghost to me alive than dead. The release I find in these fantasies of his death horrifies me. They are voluptuous too.

Loving Blake was a disaster, but it has given me an understanding of why ex-soldiers who would never have volunteered for combat often say when it is over they were glad they did not miss the battle. Blake gave me some of the blackest moments of my life but also its most piercing joys. Without him life is calmer. The tenor is flat. He was my war.

Even while I wish him dead I cannot find it in me to wish I had never met him. If we lose the man's love we are destroyed as women, but if we do not ourselves love, we are dead. I go over my past for the reason that I am at once too bored and too keyed up to do more serious work. When the Sunday-evening despair and fear of death we will not name—calling it free-floating anxiety instead—used to grip me, I would arm myself against it by creating something permanent, rearing up glass and stone monuments to immortality. It no longer works.

Blake used to say his father drank because he wanted more than life could give, but I believe now Blake drank for reasons more than just morbid identification with his failed father. Barbara Walters gets up on television every morning and says that Americans are afraid of sex, but it is death we fear. The evidence is in the amount of repression. Everybody talks about sex. Nobody mentions death. What the alcoholic wants is not more intense life but the experience of dying. Why else does he continue to drink after he is already high? Why the relentless progression, glass after glass, through and beyond the euphoria he says he wants—a drive that stops only when oblivion is reached? Blake does not want physical death but its psychic form—unconsciousness. Nirvana. The alcoholic is half right. He, at least, is facing the problem —he wants to conquer death. He enters it again and again, descending into the blackness on his own terms, kills himself nightly and yet lives to rise again the next morning. The phoenix. It is an effort of mastery through repetition of the primal fear. I used to hate it. I hate it still. But I would be more sympathetic to Blake now. I think I understand it. Without my work to believe in, I have begun to make these experiments myself.

I talk into this machine to comfort myself with visions of a future time when the mourning will be over, I will have gotten used to it, over him, when I can read these tapes on a typed page or even just listen to them on my machine, all pain gone and only a smile left for my scattered past. It helps, but the deeper reason is I don't want my love for Blake to die. Speaking about him makes him real to me again, closer, as if he were merely in the next room or had just run out to the grocery to buy something I forgot for dinner tonight. In the way I used to write those boys' names in my schoolbooks when I was a kid, writing "Robert," "Willie" and "James Junior" over and over again in secret lists that brought them closer to me, I say his name aloud in this empty room, into this machine. Blake. I am Mrs. Nick Blake.

Or am I?

Is he alone? Is he drinking, are there other women? I am haunted by visions of other, laughing girls, women with whom he has no long, boring history of quarrels about drinking. "Sure, I'd like another. Let's tell him to make them doubles, right, Nick?" I have lost the certainty of that first night in the Paradise movie house when I had no doubt that if this anonymous girl beside him could have him—if it were possible for anyone—why couldn't it be me to whom he offered a place to rest my restless head? The affair with my old friend did not begin that night, nor did it ever.

Why and how was I so suddenly taken, an unwise Minerva in the grip of desire, born (I am sometimes afraid) not of him but sprung full-blown from my own mind? For all my dislike of power games with men, hadn't I unerringly chosen only those, one after another, with whom I could fall into old, familiar and dominant roles as easily and safely as kiss-an-old-friend? Determined to change my pattern but afraid because this man represented that change and I could not predict how it would be with him, resolved not to lose my nerve, I ran forward into the danger to commit myself before I could change my mind and have to call myself coward. *It will be different with him* something in me half promised, half warned. *So soon?* said something else, awed by the rush with which, decision made, my real life had begun.

As for the rest, all I can remember when I try to resummon that evening are my feelings of an immense, almost illicit excitement. A screen of lovely but mad-

deningly irrelevant memories of that summer night
and of the film itself get in the way—a movie that
four people had without arrangement come together
to that place that night to see but from which two
left changed forever. Behind the flickering images of
Black Orpheus I cannot see Blake or myself, cannot
remember what he said or did when at the end of the
picture the house lights came on and the four of us
recognized each other (two pretending we had not yet
done so) and said our hellos. Blake did not speak to
me. I did not try to speak to him. We stood, a silence
between us, beside two already irrelevant people as
the rest of the audience—Central Park West psychoanalysts and each other's patients to a man—pushed
past on the way to their Sunday-night dinners at
Szechuan Chinese restaurants. The four of us talked
idly about the picture as we walked together to the
Seventh Avenue subway through the steaming Ninety-
sixth Street crowd of black night people listening to
Puerto Rican music on loud transistors held to their
ears, past little old Jewish grandmothers sitting on the
folding wooden chairs and park benches, their own
Miami Beach on the corroded, green-and-black center-
island strip down the middle of Broadway. That four-
block walk was our courtship, my wooing and
winning, the girl with him, the man with me, both un-
knowing of what was happening, making it all the
sweeter, unconscious witnesses at a drama being
played before their eyes and of which they were unaware. I felt my nipples point and grow hard, warmth
—the palm of an invisible hand—covered my stomach
and moisture felt like silk between my legs. A heavy,
heated and solemn beat began to pulse in the weight
of my breasts. Once or twice I tried to catch Blake's
glance to read there some confirmation that I knew
what I was doing, but he would not look back—and
the last step was taken. His veiled eye, that immovable
silence gave him my central mystery—of those un-
earthed, noble and headless ancient Greek and Ro-
man statues, emblematic to our hearts because they
will never show us their faces. The mute indifference
with which they deny our longings to know them has

always given them an unnameable poignance to me, an inconsolate beauty for which I haunted the Metropolitan from the time I first came to New York. I used to enter their rooms at the museum half excited and leave them half afraid. I began with Blake the same way.

We nodded our goodbyes at the subway stop and went our separate ways, Blake and the girl getting into a taxi. I had understood by then that I could leave it to him. I tried for no further acknowledgment; what had been was enough. We had begun. I can remember no more. I can only go over again that moment in the film when Blake first saw me. It was the scene in which Death, the murderer at the Carnival, enters. Death—unmotivated and unfair, masked, anonymous and relentless. "A man wants to kill me!" the beautiful young girl cries to the other people dancing in the streets. And no reason is given. But is it ever?

Typist, this tape ends here. Please do not run into the next segment which follows on this same tape. LeClair Pottinger.

"You finished yet?" Eddie Johnson yelled from the bathroom.

"Just putting the cover on the machine."

"We don't want to be late."

"Ready in five minutes."

Eddie came into the dining alcove where his wife did her typing. He was wearing a red-and-blue satin jacket. On the back it said "West L.A. Bowling League Champs" in gold letters.

"What is it?" he said. "A script?"

"A couple more of those tapes from that nice girl in San Diego. They came in the mail two, three days ago."

"She pay you yet?"

"She sent a hundred and fifty dollars and said to work against that. She doesn't like to keep the manuscript at her own place. She's got a nosy roommate."

"Hot stuff?"

"So far, mostly boy meets girl. Some kind of diary. She'll never sell to the movies."

"Well, come on, come on. Everybody'll be there by now." Eddie picked up his bowling bag and fumed until his wife joined him.

He leafed through a pile of manuscript pages.

"How many tapes she send you in all?"

"Eight or nine. We're still ahead on the money."

"A lot of papers cluttering up the place."

"Oh, she'll pick it up one of these days."

book three

MASKS

6

Blackout

Two cops arrived. As they came up the stairs I could hear the police dispatcher droning out orders to the late-Sunday-afternoon silence through the open windows of their radio car downstairs. They walked quickly into the apartment behind me, not seeming to pay any attention to my explanations but writing down what I said, carefully neutral in their suspension of disbelief. "In here?" said one, and I nodded and took them into the bedroom. They barely looked in before they entered, quickly stepping over the broken glass, Felix's overturned hosiery dummy, the empty bottles, flooded ashtrays and clothes strewn across the floor. The first cop put his arms firmly behind his back. He would not touch anything; bending from the waist in an exaggerated dancer's pose, he put his ear close to Clair's slightly open mouth. He listened. I held my breath. He put a finger to the pulse point on her throat. He straightened up. His partner looked at him.

"She dead?"

"Everybody's dying."

"Let's get Homicide here."

I began to shiver and sat down.

The hands on the clock in front of me said twenty-five past.

The hands on the clock in front of me said twenty-nine past.

The two policemen were staring at me. The shaking had stopped.

I was on the sofa. One cop stood with his back to the door, watching me. The other declined my invitation to use the phone in the apartment. He did not want to touch it. He went downstairs to the radio in their car.

"Where are you going?" the cop at the door said when I stood up.

"To pee."

He wanted to say something. He was embarrassed. He wanted to go easy on me but was trained to be careful too. He didn't know how to say it. "Could you sort of hold it in a while?" he asked at last. "The detectives won't like it."

"Come in with me."

"What I mean, even the water in the bowl right now is maybe evidence. You never know. They don't like it even the toilet is flushed until they have a look."

"Why?"

"One case last week, the alleged perp said he had to crap, they found heroin dissolved in the water along with the turds."

Two plainclothesmen from Homicide came in wearing gold-and-blue-enameled detective badges on leather holders outside their clothes. The older one had it on his sports coat breast pocket, the other had it hung on the zipper of his leather jacket. The man in the sports coat was bulky and pink-faced; he never smiled and he never blinked. He said he was Detective Sergeant Frank Toomis. He asked questions in a rhythmic code. A couple hard, then two or three soft until he felt he had misdirected my attention, then—very fast—another hard one. The banality of this chilled me. They were acting as if this were a TV drama. *Déjà vu;* I had written too many of them myself. The younger detective was a surprise. It was Lou. "Frank was answering the calls. I'm his partner," he said to me when he could. He shrugged, half embarrassed, half business, an old friend but a detective first. One of those bachelors who liked to attach himself to married couples. More often than not, when Clair and I had seen him for dinner or to go to a movie, he would come alone. Of our friends, Clair had liked him most.

"You called the medical examiner yet?" Toomis asked him.

"No."

"What are you waiting for? Tell him to bring that lamp of his."

Lou looked surprised.

"That's right," Toomis said.

Lou left the apartment to use the radio in the cop car downstairs. Toomis turned to me.

"What time was it you woke up?" he said. "Tell me again why you said first you didn't recognize your own wife in bed with you. You were banging some other broad, you expected to wake up with her? You buy your clothes in New York? You don't look like a hippie. Your clothes have an Italian look. You like Italian food? Lou says he was at your party last night, he left with your friend"—Toomis looked at a page in his notebook—"named Felix Sar. He didn't see your wife. What time she come in? The parties you give, your friends always crash the furniture around? Who painted the apartment? It's a co-op, right? What was the name the tenant subleased it from you while you were away? What the hell's wrong with your nose? If your wife said she wasn't coming until tomorrow, why did she come yesterday? She came in here before you expected her, you were shacked up with this other broad, and you had a fight, right?"

I could not address my numbed attention to these questions, I could not understand that Lou—who had come back to the apartment—was somehow here not as a friend but as partner to this stupid Toomis. Above all, the central fact was Clair's death. The triviality of answering questions in the face of that. Even Toomis himself did not seem to think they were important. He threw them out at me from under his lowered gaze as if they were only afterthoughts to keep me distracted while he was thinking about something more real, more important, unnecessary or too early for me to know. I was not even in the room from which he was speaking. Toomis had me sit in the living room, a uni- formed cop's eye unobtrusively on me as he shot his questions out through the wide arch of the bedroom. Usually a painted screen shielded it from the rest of the apartment, but someone at the party had knocked it over. The cops would not let me touch it to put it back up. I watched the detectives in the large gilt mirror that hung over the dresser in the bedroom.

They had clamps in their pockets that looked like sugar tongs and used them to pick up everything that caught their eye. When they put something down, it was always in the same position. They did not touch anything with their hands. Toomis did not start with the bed and what was in it but with the space around it, walking with his head down, picking a shoe up with his tongs, putting a piece of underwear down, rattling off questions at me. His path was systematic but convoluted and off-center, like a snail shell or a child's pinwheel toy, circles that spiraled out in ever-increasing patterns to touch the outer edge of the room. But the pattern was not off-center at all: at the heart of Toomis's searches was the bed and the death it held, temporarily covered by a sheet. He was saving Clair for last. I wanted to protest. But to whom? About what?

Lou looked like he always did, a guy with a handlebar mustache and an old fringed suede jacket, like a dozen others you might meet in the Glue or McGruddy's any night of the week, a paperback copy of R. D. Laing sticking out of his pants his pocket. He looked the way I had last seen him—when?—only twenty-four hours or so before, when he had come to the party. But as he examined the bedroom he looked different too. I was used to the familiar bulge beneath the fringed jacket over his right hip where he wore his off-duty gun even when he was still a uniformed cop; the sight of a pair of handcuffs dangling from his civilian belt down the center of his ass, revealed when he knelt down to look at something on the floor, was new, but the difference wasn't there: fear touched me when he did not answer my glance.

There had been no discussion between the two detectives, but Lou's system of search was different from his partner's. He divided up the bedroom into squares of a graph whose invisible lines he could see in his head. He walked from square to square, like a kid playing hopscotch, up one line and carefully down the other, starting from the left wall of the room and end-ing up hugging the right. He quartered every square with his eyes and his metal tongs as he stepped into it, never speaking to me or his partner at all.

Like maniacs in the grip of a repetition compulsion, the two of them ignored Clair while they performed their cop rituals over and over, avoiding each other wordlessly and expertly in their practiced movements. Round and round, circle after circle went Toomis, the pinwheel growing out to take in the entire room. Linear box after linear box went Lou, one at a time. He too took in the whole room. Like the abstract, vertiginous qualities of the De Chirico paint-ings Clair loved, where deserted piazzas and black-shadowed towers loom over vistas devoid of life but menaced by unnamed emotions inherent in the emp-tiness of space itself, the detectives and I seemed unreal, doing things I could not understand, speaking words that made my life unrecognizable to myself. "Clair is dead!" I wanted to shout at them. "What about *her?*" But "You sure you drank so much you can't remember what went on last night? My partner here says you were laying back on the booze when he saw you." It was Toomis speaking. He did not wait for my reply. "And what have we here?" he was say-ing. He had stopped at the table beside the head of the bed. The steel tongs rang different chimes as he counted off some liquor bottles. "A fifth of gin," he said. "Empty." He read the label on the second bot-tle. "Calvados," he said. "Maybe one-third gone. A couple dead vodka bottles."

He turned to me. "A fancy fellow like you, you'd go for a fancy drink like Calvados, right?"

"I usually drink gin."

Toomis stood still, his back to Lou; waiting.

"That's right," Lou said from behind him, not look-ing at me. "He drinks martinis mostly."

"We'll check the prints, Lou," Toomis said. "Just for the record."

"What'll it prove?" I said. "What if my prints are on all the bottles? I was pouring for people all night.

People were in and out of the bedroom all night on their way to the can."

"OK," Toomis said, smiling patiently. He liked it when I spoke, and he made a note in his little book. And then he ignored what I had said. "Tell me— this empty bottle of gin here, you and Clair finish it off together?"

"I can't remember; I didn't see her last night."

He shook his head in mock despair. "You always drink so much?" he asked. "Or was last night an exception? Maybe you blacked out because you had no dinner. Did you have something to eat before you took Clair to bed to welcome her home?"

Maddening questions, irrelevant, and they had these clumsy traps built into them. But an alcoholic black-out of memory is not an alcoholic passout from consciousness or action. I've driven a car skillfully enough through city traffic not even to scratch it and yet so drunk that I could not remember the next morning where I had left it parked or even having taken it out of the garage. In a dizzying rush of blood from my brain fear suddenly told me what my numbed mind would not realize. The questions the detectives were asking were not silly, they were not irrelevant, and the fact of Clair's death was at the heart of them all.

When the detectives finished with the room they approached the bed at last. Lou took out a small metal nail file from his pocket, wiped it clean on a handkerchief, and very carefully began scraping whatever he could find from beneath Clair's fingernails, one dead finger at a time. He did it like a surgeon, slowly. He did not miss one, and he put what he found into ten little glassine envelopes, labeling each one. He looked at me. I held out my own hands to him. My body began to shake and I needed a drink. But I was not shaking because I needed a drink. The final question they would get to in time should have been obvious to me all along, but I was suddenly not sure I could answer it even in my own astonished heart. In those hours last night that alcohol had masked from my memory forever—Lou's nail file was asking as he scraped under my fingernails one at a time—had I killed Clair?

When he was finished I motioned with my head for him to come with me. He watched while I threw up in the kitchen sink.

He gave me a glass of water. "Take it easy," Lou muttered too low for Toomis to hear. "I know how you felt about her."

When they finished, Toomis took a police sign out of a briefcase Lou had brought with him and put it on the door. Nobody came past the sign after that without Toomis saying OK. Not the medical examiner, who showed up after a while carrying a little battery-operated lamp, not the police photographers and fingerprint men, not the ambulance guys, who were waiting outside for Toomis to let them take Clair away.

Toomis had been talking in an undertone to the white-coated intern who had ridden the ambulance. The intern seemed eager to get going. Toomis seemed to want him to stay. From the corner of my eye I could see flashes of violet-tinged light in the bedroom as the medical examiner turned his lamp on and off in short bursts. The intern nodded at last to what Toomis was saying. He sat down.

Toomis grunted at Lou, "You give him Miranda yet?"

"No."

"You're his friend, all right. Maybe you should take yourself off the case."

"No reason," said Lou.

"No?" said Toomis. He turned to me and asked if I knew anyone who might have a motive for killing Clair. I said no.

"Maybe they have a motive against you," Toomis said. He looked around the place while I tried to understand what he had just said. "Jesus, what a mess," he said. "What does it cost you don't invite me to your next party? The place been tumbled?"

I looked at him.

"Turned over. Robbed. Where's your wallet?"

I felt in my pocket. "Here. Nobody took it. No money gone."

"Revenge killing?" Toomis said to Lou.

"Revenge for what?" I said. "She didn't hang around

with the Mafia. It must have been a maniac. Nobody expected Clair to be at the party. She wasn't even going to arrive from California until tomorrow."

"Someone at your party," Toomis said, "when she came in early, he knew she wasn't coming no tomorrow." He turned to Lou. "We'll get a list who was here. What time you leave yourself?"

"Maybe midnight, maybe one."

"She hadn't showed yet?"

"No," said Lou. "Nobody expected her until Monday. Like he said."

"So there wasn't any point anybody waiting around for her?"

"No."

Toomis looked at Lou. "She have any enemies in New York?"

"Not that I know," Lou said.

Toomis turned to me. "You know any?"

"Why would she have enemies? She hasn't lived here in two years."

Toomis rattled his pencil on his teeth. "You ever do something to somebody before you went away? Something a creep wouldn't forget?"

"Like what?"

"Banged somebody else's wife, dummy," said Toomis. "Like that. Maybe some tourist's wife, while you were in France?"

I stared at Toomis. "Why does there have to be a motive? I didn't know all the people here. One of them must have been a nut."

Toomis's smile was relaxed and amiable. He liked my stupidity. "It's too careful," Lou said in a quiet voice, letting me off the hook. "If the story happened the way you tell it, somebody did the job, stole nothing; he undressed you, he undressed her, put you both together in bed naked and closed the door as he left. It sounds like a plan, not some impulsive maniac. Whoever did it, he enjoyed imagining how his joke would go over with his audience."

"What audience? There was nobody here."

"You were here," Toomis said.

They looked at me. "You better think," Toomis said. "You got any enemies?"

"Maybe it was a grudge against her, Frank," Lou said. He didn't like to say it. "Hell, she's the one dead. Maybe some hard-partyer followed her from California. Or came with her."

"A grudge against Clair?" I was always one step behind.

Toomis said: "Burglars sometimes shit on your living room rug or your bed they don't find enough to steal. They're mad at you. They want you to know it. 'Shit on you.' Some player maybe wanted you to know what he thought of her. What was she up to in San Diego? You know?"

"Know what?"

"What she was up to in San Diego?"

"I never asked."

"What kind of work she do?"

"She's an artist." I pointed to the stained-glass windows.

"Why are the faces painted white?"

"She wasn't satisfied with how they turned out."

"There's a poster in the shithouse that says she's a saloon singer," Toomis said. "A picture of her at the piano."

"She used to do a little cocktail singing at the Waverly." I took him to the kitchen. The stained-glass windows were reproduced on a different poster, faded and old, framed above the sink. It announced her last show at the Korne Gallery.

"You two were married?"

"Yes."

"I mean, legally. Both posters say 'Pottinger.' "

"She used her own name when she worked."

"What she doing in San Diego? Singing or making windows?"

"I don't know. She never wrote me."

"When you phoned her last week and said let's kiss and make up, you ask her her personal life out there?"

"No."

"You got back to New York last Wednesday. She

told you she couldn't get here until Monday. You ask her why?"

"No."

"Afraid to know?"

"I always thought one day I'd stop drinking. We'd get back together. It's better you don't ask each other too much what went on the time between."

"You have any heavy romances yourself these two years?"

"Nothing serious."

"That the kind of marriage you had?" Toomis said. "An arrangement?"

"When we were married we were married. There's no rule for being separated."

"Two sophisticated people," Toomis said. "You lived in France, she lived in California, and you still considered yourself married. What the two of you do? Telephone it to each other?"

Lou said, "Come on, Frank. His wife's dead."

Toomis went on as if Lou had never spoken. "You the jealous type?"

"I don't want to be."

"Clair ever give you reason to be jealous?"

"No."

"You ever feel jealous about any other woman? Like before you were married?"

"How do you mean?"

"You ever sock a guy in the jaw because of a woman?"

"I try to handle my feelings."

"So the way you handle it, you don't know anything, not her job, not her friends, not men, not women, nobody, nothing in San Diego, male or female?"

"No."

"You're the jealous type, all right," said Toomis. "While you were married, Clair ever cheat on you?"

"I never asked."

"Do you think she did?"

"No."

"Was she a virgin when she married you?"

"I wouldn't have married her if she had been a virgin."

"OK, so you shacked up with her before you give her the ring. What I mean, she a virgin when you met her?"

"Do you live in Queens?"

"How do you know?"

"I met Clair in New York."

"What the hell does that mean?" said Toomis. I walked away from him. Behind me, Lou spoke to him, too low for me to hear.

"Lah, di, dah," said Toomis. "Excuse me for moving in the wrong circles."

When Toomis asked for Clair's address in San Diego I told him about the telegram she had sent saying she would arrive on Monday.

"What flight number?" Toomis asked.

"She didn't say. Only she would be in around noon."

"She'd be at the apartment around noon or her flight would arrive around noon?"

"It wasn't clear."

Toomis grunted. "So she didn't want you to meet her. A very private type." He looked at Lou. "Who do we know in the San Diego P.D.?"

"Joe Dolan?"

"Major Crime," said Toomis. "Yeah. We want to know what flight did she take."

"You also want me to call Western Union?"

"Yeah, check the exact wording. And was it a day letter or sent the night before."

Lou went to the phone. I could hear him in a long conversation with Western Union. Just before the ambulance men went out with Clair's body strapped on a stretcher beneath a blanket the medical examiner came over to whisper in Toomis's ear. Toomis never took his eyes off me while the medical examiner spoke. He just stood there a moment longer. The intern, seated uneasily behind Toomis, waited for him to say something. Toomis sighed. He came over to stand right in front of me. Something had changed. The medical examiner went out without looking at me.

"You have the right to remain silent," Toomis

abruptly said to me, "and to refuse to answer questions. Do you understand? Anything you do say may be used against you in a court of law. Do you understand? You have the right to consult an attorney before speaking to the police and to have an attorney present during any questioning now or in the future. Do you understand? If you cannot afford an attorney, one will be provided for you without cost. Do you understand? If you do not have an attorney available, you have the right to remain silent until you have had an opportunity to consult with one. Do you understand? Now that I have advised you of your rights, are you willing to answer questions without an attorney present?"

He had read the whole thing to me in a fast, formal, sing-song voice from a little printed card he had taken out of his wallet. When he finished he held out a pen. "Are you willing to initial this card?"

I wrote my name on it. Toomis nodded. He had been holding his breath. "OK," he said, putting the card back carefully in his wallet. "When your lawyer asks, you were given Miranda. I got your signature on it. Now, you mind giving us a blood sample for testing?" It was the first time he had waited for me to answer.

"What the hell blood test?" More and more unreal. "I don't understand. . . . There's no blood here. For Christ's sake, she wasn't stabbed or shot—"

"Yes or no?" said Toomis, weary, and I saw he had taken out a little notebook and was going to write down my reply.

"Sergeant Toomis?" said a fingerprint man near the bed. He motioned with his head. Toomis shot a glance at me and walked over. They had a conversation I did not hear.

Lou was bent over near me as if examining a broken wineglass on the floor. He shifted position and spoke without raising his voice or turning his head, looking away. "Give him the goddamn blood."

"But Lou—"

"Give him the goddamn blood. *You don't, he'll get a court order you'll have to jerk off in a test tube.*"

The ambulance man stuck a needle into my forearm.

I looked at him. He looked different too.

I asked Toomis again, but he would not tell me why my blood type was so important when there was no cut or wound on Clair, no blood shed anywhere in the apartment. I looked at Lou, but Toomis had his eye on him and he shut up too. They made me tell them a few more times about my life in Villefranche, about my phone call from Tom's hotel in France to Clair in San Diego. I wrote down a list of all the people I remembered at the party and an hour-by-hour timetable of exactly what I had done, what I had said, and to whom, from the moment Felix had first mixed the champagne and frozen orange concentrate for my breakfast in the morning, to my last memories of the party.

"I remember talking to a guy at the door about how expensive it was in France, and thinking I was sober. Then I don't remember anything at all."

"The lights went out?"

"I was fully dressed, talking, and then—blank."

"Retroactive amnesia," Toomis said. The phenomenon seemed familiar enough to him. "Something in you doesn't want to remember. Let me tell you something. The more you remember, the better it will be for you. Now think again."

"The last thing I can remember is thinking I was sober."

Toomis exchanged a glance with Lou.

Their other questions were about my life with Clair before we had separated. Photographers came and went. Once the phone in the kitchen had been dusted for fingerprints, Toomis kept going in there to use it— avoiding the one in the living room, which was close enough for me to overhear. The hours dragged by, numbed, static periods I remember as empty of content as time spent in the waiting rooms of dentists. It was dark when they led me out of the apartment to a police car downstairs. I had held myself against the

anxiety that hollowed my stomach, talked to them
calmly and did not run out of the room. My body had
to do something with the unexpressed, unrelieved energy endlessly and insanely chasing itself around within me: I began to sweat. I had had two drinks to kill
my shaking hands, but the sweat was cold. Death is
the unending crisis.

7

Kover Kote

"You never made me jealous of another woman,
and I have learned to accept your need to drink with
your father's ghost until you close the saloons at 4
A.M. half the nights of the world, but you use alcohol
to put a distance between yourself and the man I know,
pulling down a curtain behind which lives another man
who does not love me, and who I am powerless to
reach," said Clair on a tape she had left in her machine for me to find on the morning, two years before,
when I had come home to find her gone. We had been
quarreling about what she called the male anger hidden in some dumb joke I had made while drinking,
and I had walked out and spent the night in a hotel.
"If you are going to live with anyone, I know it would
be with me," her voice went on in the silent bedroom
of our apartment, the noon sun streaming in blue and
gold bars of light through the stained-glass windows
she made herself, "but when I am afraid, I think you
would prefer to live alone, and I will not live with fear.
There have only been two times in my life when, for
reasons I did not then understand, I didn't allow myself to be chosen by men who really wanted me. You
were one. I don't blame you. That you don't love me
is not an accusation. We all make our choices and you
were mine. I would only blame myself if, realizing this

now, I stayed with you. I want to change my life. I
want to meet men who are beautiful and unscrupulous.
I want to live to be a grand old lady on the Riviera,
wearing a Significant Hat with an eagle on top wrapped
in yards of tulle, playing chemin de fer over a glass of
dry vermouth before lunch every day and wearing a
monocle. I hope I wake up every morning for the rest
of my life with someone I love in a first-class cabin of
a ship sailing south. I want to travel mysteriously and
erratically around the world and let there be careful
men everywhere who keep themselves informed of my
movements. When you hear this, I will be three thousand miles away. Goodbye."

Aspects of Clair I had never fathomed: a silence in
the recesses, a life of her own which continued whether
I was present or not, an ability and need to work that
sped so deep that—unlike any other woman I had ever
known—and unlike myself, for that matter—it could
not be stayed or stemmed by any turbulence of emotion. No matter how she may have felt when, for a
day or two, sometimes longer toward the end, I might
go off drinking, she painted still. When I returned, the
walls of the apartment would present me without com-
ment or reproach with a handful of new sketches and
drawings, sometimes an oil or two, casually hung,
breathtakingly beautiful: but with an air of unreality
for me, begun and finished as if by magic while I had
been away. At her easel Clair had the imperiousness
of will of those photographers who demand of reality
itself that, through their lens, it will conform to the
image they have already seen in their minds. Sometimes in the abstract set of a nose, the stare of a disembodied eye, I would think I could recognize some of
her figures, people I knew, friends like Felix or Lou;
but in the end, no matter what the men were like whom
she painted while I was away, no matter the size, shape
or self of her models, clothed or nude, I always found
in their features the shadow of mine.

Or do I flatter myself?

When we had bought the co-op with my first serious
television money, Clair had removed the brick between the two windows in the bedroom and crowbarred

out some of the building wall to enlarge the space she had to work with; the stained-glass windows she had put up instead were full-length portraits, the best work she had ever done: side by side, life-sized and serene as angels, she and I stood naked and glorious, hand in hand against a field of blue and gold, looking back at ourselves when we were in bed, the only natural light in the room. She had not liked my jokes, but in her absence she had spoken to me with a joke of her own: when I returned after our drunken last quarrel two years before to find her gone, all the paintings in the apartment had been blanked out with flat-white Dutch Boy Kover Kote, and the two faces in the stained-glass windows had been painted out too.

Memories of Clair in the police car as the detectives took me to the station house.

8

A Third Party

I was sitting in a small windowless room. Three or four hard wooden chairs, an out-of-place large mirror on the wall. The graffiti of the black and sexual revolutions had reached into the police station itself. "RAS TAFARI 124," said one slogan scratched into the green paint with a key or a ballpoint pen; "Be Fruitful. Don't Multiply," said another. Toomis sipped a mug of tea and offered me one as he and Lou took turns sitting with me, repeating their questions and listening to my answers. Occasionally one or the other left the room for a few minutes. They took turns, but one of them was always with me. They were getting ready to let me go.

"Three little things," Toomis said as I stood up. "*One,* don't leave town without you tell us."

"OK."

"Two. She was just off an airplane, right? We looked all over your apartment and the basement. You been here, our guys have checked all the baggage left over flights from California the last forty-eight hours. Where'd you put her suitcase?"

"I didn't put it anywhere. I never saw it. I tell you—"

Toomis was hurtling his big, bulky gray body through the space between us. He had me by the collar of my shirt, cutting off my words. He pulled me up out of my chair and across the room. He brought something out from behind his back in a big fist. I thought he was going to hit me. I put up a hand to ward him off. He was pulling something down over my head, blinding me and making me trip over my feet as he shoved me across the floor. Only his grip on my shirt kept me from falling. When he stopped I was standing in front of the large mirror on the wall. *"Three,"* Toomis said, his voice hard, "the other thing we did you were here, we stripped the bed back at the apartment. We found this underneath the blanket, tangled up the sheets the foot of the sack. You going to tell us it was some kind of lampshade some faggot put on his head to sing dirty songs?" I looked into the mirror. I was wearing a scarred and tortured mask.

Covering the entire head from skull down below the jaw, it was made of the same gleaming heavy leather as a motorcycle jacket. Shiny and smooth, domed and powerful, the face I saw in the mirror had a serene and iron rage, biding its time, keeping its counsel, waiting its revenge. The mask spoke of hideous, latent strength and the cruel force necessary to keep the strength reined in: three heavy yellow welted belts were strapped across the naked face, bolted shut with black cast iron on the opposite cheekbone; an oppressive brass chain was gashed tight against the eye slits, rendering the image pleading and half blind; a steel industrial zipper, each tooth as big as a knuckle, punished and silenced the mouth. The heaviest belt of all crushed the ebony forehead in its grip as if against an imminent, inner explosion; the same belt crossed in back and came forward and around to cinch in the lower half of the face, forcing the chin back upon the throat. Anonymous and awesome, the masked face I saw spoke of insane suffering and titanic power; it was gagged but accepting too, wise, unfeeling and emotionless as a giant stone robot waiting to come to life. Despite myself, I took a step closer to the mirror. Active and passive at the same time—*but only as long as I acquiesced to my own confinement, like the somnambulist subject in hypnosis who obscurely knows he can break the trance any time he wants but somehow agrees not to want!*—I was controlled and held not only by the rawhide strength of leather, the hardness of steel, the weight of brass chain, but by the latent power the mask itself conferred on me. A movement of blood was coming to flood beneath my belt—separate, untouched by the mind or will, sleeping its own sleep and coming awake with its own needs and with no regard or shame for me. I felt frightened, obscurely guilty. I wanted it to stop, but it would not stop. I grew hard. I grew enlarged, larger than life, larger than myself. Beneath the mask my face was hot.

"Sexy, ain't it?" Toomis said. He was holding me by a leather draw strap that pursed the bottom of the mask tightly around the neck, choking me. "She comes back. She's got this little sex game she thought up to keep your mind off the booze. She gets undressed. She puts on the mask. She's naked, different, exciting. Close your eyes, you bastard, and imagine yourself. You're facing a woman's naked body, only her face is masked. She's someone you don't know. Who knows what emotions are going on in her? How can you hurt her? You can get it all off, all the little sexy tricks at the back of your mind you always wanted to try but never did because she's your wife. She's not human, you don't love her, you just want to fuck her, and she wants it. You give it to her, you get wilder, hotter—you give it to her all the way, you can't see what she is feeling, all you can see is the mask, you want to make her scream behind the mask, you want to get some response from the woman in the mask, and she screams behind the mask, and you want to make her scream again, and again, and again . . ."

He let the strap go. I almost fell. He didn't let me catch my breath, his bulk coming at me once again with unexpected speed. He seized my head in his hands from behind so I could not look away from the hideously powerful, brutally suffering, anonymous face in the mirror. "You recognize it, don't you, you degenerate?"

"No."

"You played bedroom games with her."

"No."

"You were mad because she left you. When she put on the mask you got jealous. Is that what she was doing in California? Who taught her to wear the mask? You ever play this game before she went to California?"

"No."

"So she learned it from somebody else. It got you mad."

"No."

"She put on the mask. You imagined her doing it with this other guy."

"No."

"So you killed her."

"No."

I started to take the mask off.

"YOU LOVE IT SO MUCH, LEAVE IT ON!" Toomis's face was beside mine in the mirror, his eyes bulging with dislike. He pushed my face closer to the glass.

"Is it your wife's?"

"I never saw it before."

"How do you know what you see when you're drunk? You don't remember!"

"I never saw it."

"But you like to wear it!"

"No."

"*You love it!*"

"No."

"Look at your pants. It's giving you a hard-on!"

"No."

"Was your wife kinky?"

"No."

"Are you?"

"No."

"Did she wear the mask or did you?"

"Whoever wore the mask, it wasn't her!" Lou's voice was too loud.

Toomis's arm was around my shoulder, pushing my face toward the mirror. His body went still as a beast in ambush. In the silence of the room his eyes shifted in the glass. He looked at Lou, letting me go. I almost fell.

I was breathing hard. Lou was avoiding Toomis's eyes. The hangover had settled down behind my forehead. I could not think. I could not read the expression on Toomis's face, but "While you were dictating your statement," Lou was suddenly saying in my ear, leaning forward on my blind side over the chair so I could feel his warm breath on the back of my neck, "we put your name through the Information Unit. Why didn't you tell us about the black pusher tried to kill you two nights ago?"

Toomis was smiling at me. He was a reasonable man. Clair was dead. He didn't need this new evidence. I had killed her. He was certain.

The absoluteness of his conviction changed my perspective, set up an unreality I did not understand, bringing something cold to sit in my stomach. For a strange moment he reminded me of Clair herself. He had her implacability of purpose. But his purpose was my destruction. "Why?" I wanted to cry to him like a child. "Why me?" But I wasn't a child. I took off the mask and stepped away from the mirror.

Toomis was a big, fat man, but his fat was cold, congealed and hard. It had been accumulated over the years in layer upon layer, solid and dense, weighted with power like his cop muscles beneath. His animosity had the same quality of coldness and hardness and self-contained weight as the accumulation of years of chill cop dislike that he was focusing on me. I had been in quarrels, had had one or two fist fights in my life, run across people who didn't like me. I had never before faced hatred. "We'll talk again," Toomis said. Without looking at Lou, he left the room.

Lou was watching. He looked concerned. He had some papers in his hand. "The detective went out on the call, Jim Wright. I got his report here. Why didn't you mention it to me? Even at your party, the next night, you didn't mention a guy tried to kill you."

"I didn't want it to be the first news Clair got when she came to New York. She worries more than you think."

"She never looked worried."

"I'm married to her."

"You were," Lou said.

It was hard for me to listen to what he was saying. I was staring at the mask. I could not concentrate on Lou. My eyes wouldn't move. I had to turn my whole body away.

"Why'd you keep the business about the black guy secret from me and Toomis?" Lou was saying.

"WHAT DID THAT BLACK MANIAC HAVE TO DO WITH CLAIR?" Like a cry onstage from an actor for whom it was not written in the script, the unexpected force of my own words stopped me. I could not give a name to my confusion.

"Take it easy," Lou said.

I summed it up as much for myself as for Lou. "That black guy was a pusher. Maybe he was holding out money he owed. The money they found on him, maybe he was keeping some of his dope money back. He was afraid to work his usual beat in Times Square. Maybe he knew they had a number on him. So he was hiding out in my neighborhood. They found him anyway. The guy who killed him was a pro. If you use a shotgun, you don't miss who you're aiming at. The black guy grabbed me, tried to hide behind me, but they got him anyway. I just happened to be passing by."

Lou walked across the room and drank some of Toomis's cold tea. "We got to think there's a connection," he said. He was standing at the window, a foot up on the ledge, looking away from me. "Some guy tries to kill you, reasons unknown. Some guy's killed Clair, also reasons unknown. We got to think the same guy maybe had a hand in both deals. First, an attempted murder. Second, a successful one. Both in one family, both within two days of each other? You don't get coincidences like that a murder case. Not when drugs are in it too. You protecting someone?" He seemed to be pleading with me. He seemed to know more than I did.

"Who would I protect? Me? Clair? I don't know anyone in the dope business."

"You sure?"

"Is that what you think?"

"That's what I was trained to think. That's what the book says. You got to help me convince Toomis to see it like that. That you and Clair both have somebody out there who didn't want either one of you alive. Maybe for reasons you know. Maybe for reasons you don't know. So far Toomis doesn't buy it."

"Why not?"

"That mask got him. For once he isn't going by the book. You held out on him about the pusher trying to kill you. So he doesn't believe you. But he believes, whatever the angle is, the black guy was about dope. The mask makes him think whoever killed Clair, that was some kind of sex kink. Nothing to do with dope. Toomis is a family man. He can't handle the idea of kinky sex. It puts him away. He can't be objective there's sex in it."

"And he connects me with the mask, and the mask with Clair?"

"Think a second," Lou said. "What third party could want both you and Clair out of the way?"

"Nobody."

"Think again."

"Toomis's got sex on the brain."

"You're not helping yourself."

"If I'd killed her, why would I leave her there in my own bed and call the cops?"

"Your own testimony is you were so drunk you didn't know what you did."

I lit a cigarette.

Lou said:

"Just give it to me, Nick. Don't dress it up. There's more here than you know. By any stretch of the imagination, is there any link in your mind? Why should someone try to kill you or Clair? Did she know that black guy Sam?"

"How could she?"

"She ever talk about dope?"

"No."

"She need money?"

"I don't know."

"She did."

"You saw her?"

"Maybe three, four months after you split for France. She came through New York for a few days on a quick trip up and back from California. We had dinner." He paused. It was hard for him to say it. "You know I always liked her."

"Yes."

"I asked her. She told me she was broke. You know what she's been living on these two years?"

"No."

"You ever send her money?"

"She never asked. You give her any?"

"She said she didn't like to borrow." He stared at me for a moment. "The two of you ever use any hard stuff?"

"You saw me smoking some pot at the party. When I don't want to drink too much. It doesn't do much for me."

"You ever sell any of this pot, beside smoke it?"

"Sure. You were my best customer."

"Did you?"

He was standing in front of me, leaning forward, one arm on the chair rest, the other cradled around me, his weight on the back.

"No."

"Did Clair?"

"What the hell kind of question is that? You knew her, Lou. I never saw that black guy before in my life. Clair never did any kind of dealing. Neither did

I." He stood looking into my face for a silent second or two more.

His weight began to move back but his eyes held mine. He did a funny thing: he came forward and put a hand to my face, the way a blind man might to know you better. He was my friend but he thought I had killed Clair. I had more to fear from him than from Toomis.

I asked him, "Is that a trick mirror?"

"What trick?"

"Is it a two-way? Is Toomis listening on the other side?"

"No."

"Were you in love with Clair?"

"Yes."

"And she?"

"No."

Toomis came back into the room, some papers in his hand. Lou walked away to stand somewhere. I could not see him. "Hell, Lou," Toomis was saying, "the lying son of a bitch wants to hold out on us, let him get killed for it."

"If I knew anything more I'd tell you."

"With your mask on or off?"

Toomis laughed. "OK," he said angrily. "Something like this happens, a lot of cockroaches come out of the woodwork, they say they did it. Psychopaths. Glory grabbers. We got to check their stories." He pushed the leather mask under my nose. "We don't want anybody else to know about this. We don't give it to the papers. You shut up about it. A guy comes in, he says he killed your wife, if he knows about the mask, either he did it or you told him about it. We don't want it to be you told him. Got it?"

"Yes."

"Yes," he mimicked. Contempt.

"If it's a test whether a confession is true or not," I said, "why tell me about it?"

Toomis's answer was flat: "Because I believe you. There's no tie-up between that black bastard tried to

kill you and your wife's murder. One's about dope,
and that was done to you. The other's about some sex
act, and that was done to her. I don't have to hold
out on you about the mask. You already know about
it, baby. I don't want you for dealing some lousy shit.
I think you killed her. I'm going to hang you for it."

Lou gave me a glass of water.

"You and me," Toomis said into my eyes, "we
understand each other." He put out his cigarette. "What
we got to find out is why she comes to New York
maybe forty-eight hours before she tells you to expect her. Where does she stay? Who does she meet?
What happens to her suitcase, what is she doing in your
bed, with what man? And what the hell does the hard-
on mask mean to her? In other words, we got to find
out what kind of woman your wife was. What was her
life in California? You can't help us. You said it yourself, you didn't want to know. Get the hell out of
here."

I was on my feet when he called me back. On his
face I could see that whatever was coming, he enjoyed the thought of giving it to me. He had a sheet
of paper a uniformed cop had just brought in. "The
preliminary autopsy report," Toomis said, a bitter
smile. "The lab report says positive. Sperm in the
vagina. There was a guy. Whoever it was, she knew
him. She didn't fight. She was willing. No blood or
foreign skin scrapings under her fingernails. See you
around."

A yellow cab came rolling around the corner and
stopped at a run-down apartment house down the
street. When the door opened, two sadly beautiful
girls came out, stumbling into the empty, early dawn
street. They were dressed in feathers and long, bil-
lowing chiffon dresses, lovely and elegant, but their
makeup had begun to run during their long night,
their once elaborately dressed hair falling in steamy
tendrils down still-luminous faces. The brunette had
a bloody nose, and she stood beside the cab as her
friend paid the driver, her head thrown back to slow

the streaming blood, a wet and bloody red handkerchief clutched in front of her face. The street was quiet; I could hear her sobbing, straining for breath behind the tears.

"Hey!"

Toomis had come out the street door of the police station. He flicked his cigar at me.

"Something else?"

"Come on back a minute."

I had flagged the girls' taxi driver to pick me up. I closed the door and waved him on. The driver cursed and put the car into gear. Down the street, the blonde had put her arm tenderly around the brunette's narrow, naked shoulders, supporting her wounded friend, fumbling in her purse for the keys with her other hand. A dog came out from around a garbage can and began to sniff at them. I climbed halfway back up the steps of the station house and looked at Toomis. He flicked his cigar again, ignoring the two girls, the light river-smelling early breeze, blowing his ashes into my face in a fine, gritty mist. "I been thinking," he said.

"Yes?"

"People like you, maybe murder is what you call 'a form of communication.' The perp wants to communicate something to the other person. I like to call it, he's sending a message. This murder happens the way you say it happens, the message is meant for two people. One of them is dead. She received her part of the message. The other one is you. Your statement is, you don't know why they undressed you, why they killed her, why they left her in bed like that with you?"

"How the hell can I?"

"How the hell can't you?" He threw the cigar away angrily. "I got a nine-year-old kid. What I find out about kids, they know all sorts of things without they know how they know them. Especially about sex. Whatever corner your head you keep these things hidden from yourself, you better figure it out. Next time, the message will be plain as the one they send your wife."

"I don't follow you."

"What I'm telling you, you don't want to face it. Maybe you can't believe it. But somewhere, you know who set all this up. You know who the guy is."

Down the street, the brunette was pushing her friend away. She staggered a few steps and then turned to face the wall of the apartment house. Toomis, the blonde and I watched as she hoisted up her dress. Her hands were under her skirt. Fresh blood began to flow down her cheek and dripped onto the street as she shot us a fierce and defiant look; she began to piss into a garbage can.

"The other one's a drag queen too," Toomis said, and spit on the sidewalk. "Think about what I said," he told me. "Let it grow on you."

9

France

They had taken the cop off the door by the time I got home. I pulled the Crime Scene sign down and went in. The apartment still showed all the evidence of the party, and of the police invasion that followed: as if a giant bulldozer had plowed through, upsetting chairs, scattering ashtrays and drinks over the floor, breaking glasses and bottles, hurtling pieces of furniture into corners where they did not belong. I had no heart to clean up.

I made myself a cup of instant coffee, put a lot of milk and sugar into it for the body, hit it hard with Scotch for myself. The first fast, the second slow. It was enough. I took a can of beer into the shower and then lay down under the stained-glass windows in the bedroom. I had to put together the different pictures I had of my wife.

How to reconcile memories of the Clair I had met

and married and known on Martha's Vineyard with the woman who had painted out the faces in the stained-glass windows and left me with a tape-recorded joke? A third Clair had looked at her killer and known him. It was not an idea I could handle.

When I had heard Clair's voice on her Sony the morning I returned to the apartment to find her gone, my first feelings had been confusion and bewilderment but bitter anger too. I was shaking with that combination of fear and rage that so often go hand in hand, stunned that she had left me but hurrying myself as if—if I could do it quickly enough—I would be the one leaving her, outracing the disorientation of her loss, running as fast as possible to get away from her—or was it toward her? Half of me saw this as my chance to journey unencumbered to Rome and London, to meet new women in Barcelona, to see Paris; half of me wanted to fly to California, to find her, to fight or spite-fuck her, to reach some final, satisfyingly violent resolution to the unanswering void in which she had left me. Two different directions at the same time. A week of mindless motion, of muttering curses and threats to myself, of denunciatory speeches composed as if in sleep but maybe while drinking. In the darkness and silence of the bedroom I'd find myself rehearsing arguments aloud—all the more angrily because they were so right and Clair would never hear them. Days of bewilderment and more drinking. Nights of retaliation: an ugly and stupid forty-eight-hour SoHo affair. And obsessively singing a mindless little song to myself over and over in a voice too low to hear:

You've had the best . . .

How long could a marriage last? I'd had the good years.

Why stay for the rest?

Within the week I had gotten permission from the co-op management board to sublet our apartment, found a tenant and succeeded in getting Universal Tal-

ent to hurry some money David Susskind owed me for
a completed TV pilot. Clair had made an early-
morning withdrawal of two thousand from our bank
before she left New York. She had also used, I later
learned from the monthly statement, our Master
Charge card to buy a one-way ticket to Los Angeles,
but she must have burned the card after that—she
never used it again. I also told my agent that I would,
after all, take on the quick little script rewrite I had
turned down a couple of days before, and was on a
plane—fueling the whole rush to escape my divided
emotions with enough gin not to remember how I did
the script fix—in five days flat. I remember phoning
my friend Felix and explaining why I must go; I remember his insisting that he and whoever his girl
friend was at the moment must come around and help
me pack. I remember drinking with them in the taxi
on the way to Kennedy and the airport bar and Felix
playing "Definitions" as we drank one toast after another—*"Today:* too soon," *"Now:* too late"—and
even his making one to *la belle France.* But I don't
remember when they left me or why I chose to go to
Paris after all instead of Los Angeles, do not remember the seven-hour flight or arriving in France, going
through customs, or anything else. When I next
clicked in, I was in a little rented Fiat, driving south,
the Alps Maritimes behind me, one hand on the wheel,
the whitewashed tree trunks that lined the road on
both sides rushing past in long, parallel swoops, singing along with Yves Montand on Radio Monte Carlo
at the top of my voice, the Mediterranean ahead—and
the sudden violet, green, blue and gold of the littoral,
palm trees and a road sign pointing to Nice. Too used
to these blackouts to do more than just dismiss this
one too from my mind and go on from there.

A bottle of *marc* in the hand not on the wheel.

The only other communication I had received from
Clair was a card sent not to our New York address
but directly to my furnished two-room apartment in
Villefranche. The front showed a sunset and some
sailboats anchored in a marina at La Jolla, California;
on the back in Clair's handwriting it merely said, "I

am OK." She did not say how she knew my address, it had not been signed *love,* it had not been signed at all, nor had she given me her address. Goodbye, three words on a picture postcard, one bill from Master Charge, silence. That was all I had to remind me of her through two years of drinking and rage so Caligulan I would wake in the middle of a dream eaten by despair that all the women in the world did not have but one pair of legs so I could get between them and, in one mighty night's revenge, fuck and forget the entire female race forever. Periods of couldn't-care-less followed by spasms of jealousy and humiliation. Slow, sunny days and fast nights. Months gone by like a drunken party and as soon forgotten. Unable, unwilling, to connect with anyone, drowning in loneliness but prizing nonattachment more, back in the life I'd known before Clair. I made no friends. The transient, face-value, nothing-counts-on-a-holiday life of the Riviera was what I wanted. I would go out to meet strangers when I felt like it, talk to tourists in bars, have conversations with swimmers on the beach, fall in with yacht people and travel with them for a week or two to St.-Tropez or San Remo; locals, foreigners, gamblers in the casinos of Nice, Monte Carlo and Cannes. And women: above all, the sun, blue water, pine-and-orange perfume and honey smell of money of the Mediterranean coast brought women through my life. Drinking my way past uncounted days, noncalendared months, sex became the one tenuous hold on reality I had, the only part of myself I did not find fake or wearing or an effort of the will. When I could feel nothing else, the erotic was a reprieve from torpor and passivity; looking forward to seeing a new woman in the evening the only reason not to begin drinking before breakfast that day. I was grateful to each woman. They made me feel real while it lasted.

One at a time I was faithful, one at a time desire would come to an end and I would go back to drinking. I'd be left restless and angry, not at her but at myself. From the beginning of each affair—three or four weeks, a month or two—I would be able to pre-

dict the end. Most would leave me. A few would stay.
Beautiful girls bitter, lovely women weeping: "What's
wrong? *Qu'ai-je te fait?*" The ever unexplainable and
sour knowledge that she had done nothing wrong and
therefore could do nothing right; the fault and insuf-
ficiency was in me. Perhaps for believers in the sexual
apocalypse, lay mystics come of age in the time of
Eisenhower or Pat Nixon, the erotic gleams with infinite and forbidden promise, but is it after all anything
more now than the pastime of an evening, like an
hour or two of roulette at Le Sporting de Cannes?
Very nice, even exciting, but naive if thought to be
of any serious transcendence. As Don Juan knew, in
the erotic life it becomes quickly apparent that only
novelty is inexhaustible, change for its own sake the
only never-fail aphrodisiac. But was desire so artifi-
cially induced and boring worth the effort of its satisfaction, these anonymous orgasms worth the candle?
All too soon I would want to be alone again, subject
to change, open to chance, knowing nothing different
would happen but wanting it anyway. Imminence.

The more a woman makes love with a man, the
closer they grow, the more she wants to make love
again. I was the opposite. How could I say, "All you
did wrong was to say yes when I asked?" She could
be as beautiful as the moon, voluptuous as Venus, it
made no difference. The song would begin again:

. . . Why stay for the rest?

Futility, depression, anger—there is no guiltless way
to say goodbye, nothing worse than to stay. In the
end I would go out only during the week, spending
Friday and Saturday nights alone, unable to be. with
anyone with whom I had slept for a day afterward,
let alone the entire weekend. The stupid and ugly
trivialization of a disconnected life.

—but against that, the bleak exaltation of being
alone again, living alone; of being high, high without
limit or care. I spent two years alone drinking and
manic about the renewed possibilities of tomorrow
while memories of yesterday with Clair knotted my

stomach too tight for even gin to reach. The first year
I had dreaded the arrival of each morning's mail, not
wanting to hear, not wanting to think about her and
the pain it would bring: a letter saying she was sorry
and wanted me, a half-humorous request for some
money, a legal letter from her lawyer about a divorce,
a note saying "Let's try again." She answered my
expectations with silence. Indecisive and unresolved—
but furious too—I had been unable either to throw
away her one picture postcard or keep it visible, in-
serted under the molding of the mirror, where I kept
letters to be answered or bills to be thought about
tomorrow; shoving it down at last under a pile of
books I intended to read but would never get around
to. In the second year I came across the card again
and pinned it above my bed. I am OK. But I had kept
her tape recording too, and obsessively I began to listen
to her voice, trying to hear what she had wanted to
say to me behind her goodbye, playing her last spoken
message over and over to myself until in the end I had
come out on the other side: released. The curse of
Don Juan lifted.

Our emotions ebb and flow in the brief seconds it
takes to say "I love you," and we are no more certain
we mean it than is the masked woman in our arms. If
Clair had been happiness, the blue-in-blue thread of
continuity that gave pattern to my memories, gin
held imminence for me, an unknown life opposed to
one with her, the promise of the as-yet-unhappened.
Before Clair, how often had the most voluptuous moments with even the most beautiful and willing of
women been the long, slow, anticipatory taxi ride to
her apartment after my last-minute phone call but before I picked her up? ("Let's go the long way round
through the park, please, driver." The lights of the
GM Building and the Essex House on Central Park
South mirrored in the shining black lagoon off Seventy-
second Street. Legs stretched out, feet up on the jump
seat, me alone in the back. The invulnerable certainty

that the game was fixed in advance: I had never become attached in the past; I would not tonight.)

The drinking life gave me the feeling for which as a kid I would stay to see Westerns twice and still watched *Shane* as often as I could on the three A.M. Late Movie: the potentiality latent in the stranger riding into town on his black horse—into what? We don't know, but we see Fay Spain is secretly watching him from behind a drawn lace curtain in a room upstairs over the saloon. And while the gambling boss and the rich corrupt rancher will fight him with any means at hand, he holds our respect because he rides by certain unspoken rules he has brought with him from that unknown country from which he came, and to which he will return alone. My father, too, had lived by rules of his own, and I often wonder how much, how little, in this was I still his son. The year before I moved to New York I had flown there for a job interview and had come back on the 5 A.M. TWA Chicago Red Eye, not to miss my day's work at WCHI-TV. I found an empty fifth of Jim Beam sitting on the open piano when I went home to shower and change clothes, gooseneck lamp over the music stand still lit, my father not there. It was not new. He had begun to start his days this way often enough since my mother's religiously resigned and disappointed death, my sister's early marriage and removal to Tulsa, loss of his belief in the certainty of sleep.

I walked over to Temby's, a twenty-four hour auto-towing-and-wrecking service, where old man Temby whiled away his empty nights and made a little no-tax cash on the side by running the only after-hours bar in town, in the spare-parts room over his garage on Railroad Avenue, near the Chicago & Northwestern station.

> Camptown races,
> Doo Dah, Doo Dah . . .
> Camptown races,
> Doo Dah, Doo Dah . . .

a sleepy young trucker monotonously sang to himself in a corner, keeping time with a bottle of beer until

Temby told him to shut up. It was a little after eight in the morning. My father was there.

"Stay here long enough," he said, "you run into everyone you've ever known. Why go to Paris? Good morning, Nick."

He looked gray, his eyes red from drinking and lack of sleep, but carefully dressed, debonair enough.

"Hello, Pop."

"You're not here to be a good influence?"

"I thought I'd have a drink with you."

"But home it is, sooner or later?"

"You look like shit."

"You want me to live forever?"

"Longer than me is good enough."

We stood together, with our backs to the spare-parts counter that served as Temby's bar, and watched a large silver semi-trailer truck begin making a three-point backup to the loading platform below. Coveys of cars driven by chauffeur-wives in curlers were nervously dodging around the truck, hooting horns to get their Elmhurst husbands to the station parking lot in time for the ride to the office. Most got on board, but one or two would be taking later trains: pinstripe blue suits and attaché cases, averting their eyes from one another as they got their morning start at Temby's. One vodka fast, the second slow. I asked for two more.

My father picked his up, but before he could get it to his lips, his arms lurched, endowed with a sudden life of its own. The whiskey splashed, the glass hitting his teeth with a click. He swallowed the rest of the bourbon with a shudder, but the drink straightened his shoulders and he turned to me with a smile. "If you can get through the day," he said, "you can get through the night." He gestured at the commuters down below running for their trains. He had once wanted to be a songwriter but had retired as assistant credit manager at Illinois-American Pneumatic Brake Shoe.

"You call that life?"

I told him it was almost nine o'clock; we could stop at a package store for a bottle and finish our drinking

at home. "What?" My father proffered formal disbelief. "The day just begun?" He raised his glass toward
Temby's oil-and-grease-smudged back door. "Strangers
are on their way right now," he said. "Glorious men
and women about to walk through that door, stepping
out of the dawn to change our lives forever. Desert
them? Miss our chance? *Give up on hope?* We'll greet
them with a round of Orange Fancy."

"Fancy?"

"Or Strawberry Surprise."

The silver truck backing into the garage below us
had big red letters stenciled on the side of the twenty-
four-foot trailer:

JOHN MUHN & SONS, INC.
CARRIERS

"People who drink," my father said, "want more than
life can give."

"What do you want?"

"I want to carry the moon in my arms."

And he had, though the weight had killed him. Here
at the end of his life, he was my son, I was his father,
but I would not treat him as a child. "Common sense,"
my father used to say to me, "is the kind of intelligence
that tells you the earth is flat." It had been one of
our secret jokes against the world when I was growing up, but it was his reasoned decision now, and I
would not diminish him by pretending it was still only
a joke. I drank with him until he was ready to let me
take him home, and I had lifted his frail body in my
arms and put him to bed. I had been offered a job by
NBC-TV while in New York, but I wrote that I would
not be taking it after all. We lived this way for the last
year of his life, sons and fathers, fathers and sons,
a family of two in all. He had spent the time trying to
write his songs at last, but I had buried them with
him—he had more music in him than the world cared
to know. I could no longer be his son but drinking
made me forget that. And yet my time in France had
not been all riots, routs and revelry without end.
Booze enables you to hide for a while, and then it

presents a bill so staggering you have to face up or die. Knowledge had been born in me: I must become a father to myself, a son no more. It was late but I had hoped it was not too late to become a husband to my wife.

If I had never finished the television screenplay I'd given myself as rationalization for taking flight, something better had written itself in me: it had not been the tie to Clair I had resented. I'd used marriage as a last stage on which to rehearse and keep bitterly burning the double-faced love I had had for my father: old, suffocated resentments of his dependence on me; and of mine on him. There had been some secret, inadmissible and dirty little gain in nurturing these furies in my breast: as long as I felt them, my father had not died, I did not have to face his death: he lived as the object of my anger. Some radical if gradual and quiet realignment had taken place during my two years abroad, some unconscious knitting and raveling had gone on behind the drunken noise. Between a sleeping and a waking, and with no thought at all, I had buried my childhood need for him to live on within me, putting the old man away as I had his body and his songs. It left me with an emotional vacuum I did not have to resolve to fill with Clair. She was already there.

Somehow she knew my address, but I did not know hers. La Jolla was a town outside of San Diego. A week before, I had been sitting in Tom's white-and-gold suite overlooking the Promenade des Anglais. I had picked up the phone to order a drink, but as if it had been my intention all along, when the hotel operator came on, I asked her to get me U.S.A. (714) 555-1212, Information (I had known for over a month) for both La Jolla and San Diego. When I found Clair listed, I had talked to her from France. I said I admired her, admired her instinct always to leave the party early, to get out before the breakage began. I admired her for going, even more for the way she had gone. I admired her silence. I said I missed her and wanted to be married to her again. I asked her to come back. I said I was sick of drinking and wanted to stop. Clair's absence had said something her presence never could: I loved her all the more because she could live without me. I told her I had loved my father but taken my anger with him out on her because I loved her too. The words made her cry. When she believed I was sober she said she would come back. If I had not called her, she would still be alive.

I woke in the small hours with the shakes and had a drink. I sat in the dark and went over my memory of the last words Clair had spoken on the phone when I had called her from France. They had haunted my sleep. "I have to finish some things here first," she had said. "I'll be traveling for a few days. I'll be in New York on Monday." Uninflected words on a transatlantic telephone, three sentences that had contained her death.

I told myself I did not want another and mixed myself another, a little heavier on the vermouth. Not that drink nor the one after helped. I had been a fool not to have asked her what those things were in California she had had to finish first.

10
Young

"A spoken History," Tape 19, LeClair Pottinger. Begin.

Memories of New York: I remember my first sight of the city when the train began to cross the Jersey flatlands, the rails ahead curving in a wide sweeping arc and pointing toward a tunnel far away that seemed to bore into a funny little humpbacked mountain. Behind that tunnel I knew was "Grand Central Station, crossroads of a million lives," as the radio announcer used to cry from an echo chamber when I would listen as a kid every Thursday evening, growing up in De Haviland. It was the kind of town where you were born in the same house in which your grandparents died, and nobody left to go north even to Washington, but I already knew Grand Central Station was the name of the place through which I would walk one day. De Haviland had not been enough for my father. It was not enough for me.

I carry a picture of him still, a blurred wedding snapshot of him and my mother, found in one of my insatiable childhood rummagings in the attic, his features indistinct, the Polaroid chemicals fading both their faces to mere white-on-white blurs. I had tried to talk to my mother about the photo, asking her what my father looked like, but she had been unable to speak. I had turned my back on her tears. That night I cut the picture in half, throwing her out, keeping him to myself—a photo of a man I would not recognize if he stopped me in the street, a face I will never know. All my mother had been able to tell me between tears was that he was not from De Haviland. He was from Baltimore, and somehow I knew it was to Baltimore he had returned alone.

For years I hated him too, but even as I had divorced him from my mother with my scissors, it had been clear which parent I wanted to keep, which one I wanted to throw away. From the day I knew my own name I knew I had been born in the wrong place; I can't remember a time when I wasn't already planning to run away. When I was a child I had dreamed of going to Baltimore to find him. As I grew older I knew it was to New York to which I must go, and Grand Central Station was the way you arrived. I wouldn't have come by plane even if I could have afforded the fare.

The skyline came up slowly over the marshes and old auto graveyards as we got nearer the railway tunnel, and far away in the gray smoke and clouds I could see the looming shapes of the tall buildings—so enormous I could not understand the scale. There seemed no proportion I could take in between them and me. I had left De Haviland but lived in its two-

and three-story landscape still, unconsciously measuring all things by the trees, the church and houses I had moved among all my life. The city, even low down on the flat horizon, seemed remote and impersonal, as infinite and hostile to my existence as the universe itself. In the Late Late Movies on TV, when Dick Powell comes to New York to write the Tenement Symphony and become famous and win the love of Alexis Smith, he has an early setback but shakes his fist defiantly at the billion glittering lights and shouts against the rain, "New York, I'll beat you yet!" Then he puts his hands in his coat pockets and walks away, his back hunched against the wind, but it is a thrilling moment, because even though he has to quit writing music for a while and take a job driving a taxi with Frank McHugh, you know he will succeed. But when I had my own first sight of that towering skyline I had always dreamed of, something happened: I lost touch with the victorious certainty that I had always shared with Dick—that promise New York had always held out to me of coming into my own at last. My first sight of New York frightened me. I suddenly felt the immensity of the distance I had come. There is a story I once read about a racehorse that always won because he was fed on roses, and when they made him eat grass, he lost. I had always believed I would beat New York, but realized now I would only do so if I did not let it beat me first. We arrived, not at Grand Central but at Pennsylvania Station—and I had had my first defeat.

The buildings were too overwhelming, shoulder-to-shoulder giants packed too tight, too tall and crushing, too preoccupied with their own interior events even to notice my presumption at wanting their attention. There didn't seem to be any room for me—a sense that the world was already there, New Yorkers who had been discussing politics and Proust since they were six, so glib and articulate they made me shy and unable to speak when I was around them, hip people who would be amused when they found out I was still a virgin, jet-set people laughing that I would think New York would have only one railroad station, glamorous women with expensive new clothes and sophisticated about sex, knowing how to tip taxi drivers—an entrenched, hip community already started, ensconced, dug in, calling each other up to come to penthouse parties, *their names already listed in the Manhattan telephone book*—and I the only one out of place.

That's why I liked the Village right away. As soon as I arrived downtown I stayed. A lot of rinky-dink shops, the funny, crooked streets, the buildings shabby and all different heights. Village people, most of them my own age. There seemed a way for me to get into it there, an alley, a window, an entrance. My first day looking I found a job as a hatcheck girl at the Waverly Club. Joe, the owner, was a nice fat Italian man who liked me because I said I had come to New York to go to Cooper Union and learn to paint. He said I was serious, like his grandfather who had painted a fresco in a church in Castellodelmare, and when this or that happened—I fell in love or just got tired of working and took off for a couple of days, a week or a month, a winter working with stained glass in Provincetown— old Joe would always take me back again as soon as the current hatcheck quit. Falling in love is an occupational disease with hatchecks; they never last. So there never was a great wait for the job to open again when I would need to work. Later when the Waverly began its supper club policy, Joe heard me practicing at the piano one afternoon before the customers had come in, and asked me to sing. I knew the Gino Paoli and Sergio Endrigo records and so I became the pianist for the cocktail hour, with a few songs later to warm up the audience over their drinks and reading the menu before the real show began. My first day in New York and I had found one of the goals I had set myself: a way to make money that would not eat up too much of my days and would leave me enough light to paint. A job that would not get in the way of my life. So perhaps I had begun with a victory after all.

I shared my first apartment, on Jane Street, with two girls who had advertised in the *Village Voice* when their roommate had left to get married and they needed someone to help carry the rent. One had been living in New York for three years, the other two. The first thing they said was that if I was going to live in the Village I'd have to learn how to do the bar life. They had little hip ways to go into places like the 55 or the Glue alone. We kept a large brown-paper A&P bag packed with Kellogg's Cornflakes boxes—empty, to cut down the weight. If you had nothing to do and wanted to go somewhere for a drink to see who you might meet, you took the A&P bag with you, bought a bunch of inexpensive celery or carrots at the Midnight Shop across the street to drape over the top of the bag and give it a fresh look. This way it's clear you are not cruising, not a woman alone and desperate in a bar waiting to be picked up. You're a neighborhood girl, *together,* someone who goes in for wholesome home cooking, and you've only stopped off on your way home from the grocery because you're thirsty for a beer. It was a way to inoffensively brush any creeps who might bother you—your excuse for leaving established in advance. And if the guy was nice, it was all the more flattering that you would change your mind about a quiet evening at home by yourself (a serious girl) and have dinner with him instead.

My roommates also had ways to save money, like using Brut after-shave instead of cologne. We blew the extra on wine-and-cheese parties. It was a way to meet new people and was all we could afford. "Bring a bottle of Almadén and a handsome stranger." I used to think that life in New York was like a lottery. Parties, parties, drinking beer in Ira's Glue with a painter tonight, the 55 alone tomorrow, more people arriving on the scene every day from Nebraska, Gary, Indiana, and California, new faces, the years swinging along and everything like a lottery with a new drawing every week. I used to buy a fifty-cent ticket every week on the New York State Lottery, but that wasn't the real one. In the important lottery, every once in a while the wheel spun, a new ticket was pulled from the barrel, you looked up, the girl next to you at a party, maybe she had a book published, she was a winner. Tomorrow someone else you knew made a hit singing at the Bitter End or the Bottom Line. Another winner. Or someone became an important connection. A different kind of success. But all the time it didn't matter that they hadn't drawn your ticket yet. You'd go back to the Waverly, the wheel would start to spin again, spinning, spinning, the months, the people, the men you'd meet, the parties, time went, winter, summer, all spinning. As long as you stayed down in the Village—that was my feeling then—as long as you stayed down there, it didn't matter that you weren't a winner yet. You still had a chance tomorrow. My paintings were going to electrify the world. New York made me so happy I could not believe I was alive. I was young.

I remember one night no one wanted to go home when McGruddy threw us out of his place because he wanted to leave town early the next day to go fishing in Key West. Felix suggested the 55, and we got into two if not three taxis and made it to Sheridan Square.

It was quiet there, late, dark, just a few hip people, all cool. We put a lot of money in the jukebox, and Lou began to talk to two redheads at the end of the bar. "Let's smoke a lot," said Lou and threw a bunch of cigarette packs on the table. "Let's do everything a lot," said Felix. He had come to New York on impulse, leaving his parents' formal anniversary party in New Jersey ten years before at the moment the lights went down and a spotlight picked up the cake being brought in. He was wearing his tuxedo and no overcoat in the middle of December, dancing pumps. He was drunk when he got on the train, no money, and only a paper bag of caviar canapés with him, but he never went back. *"Mother?"* he once said to me. "You mean the well known, overrated cook who used to work, apparently, for your family and mine?"

Felix brought the redheads over. The live one's name was Margo and the other had a patch that said "I am a FUCKING GENIUS" sewn in red on the ass of her blue jeans. "No entry" said the patch sewn on the front. Lou pulled a blue pencil out of a pocket and wrote something on a paper napkin. He showed it to the girl. It said: "We must live dazed, dazzled, sun-drenched with delight." While Margo watched, Lou took the napkin back, popped it into his mouth and solemnly ate it. She said, "I can tell we'll have a long, tragic love affair together. But if I ever ask you to marry me, you must promise to say no." Lou began to hum the Pleasure Song.

Matti Cosworth was calling for Felix: "Speech! Speech!"

"No dancing allowed," said Malcolm from behind the bar, and Felix ordered a fleet of stingers, one for everyone in the world. Ronnie the waiter stopped by to tell us the new graffito in the men's room: "Cancer Cures Smoking." The other redhead suddenly woke up and did a funny Balinese dance step or two in time to the jukebox. Lou took a new napkin and wrote to Margo: "I am too shy to tell you I love you." Margo took a napkin and wrote him a message of her own: "Illegal to Read This Sign." Mel Parigi for some reason was wearing a papier-mâché nose.

"Speech, speech!" Matti said. "Felix, Felix, Felix!"

Felix finished his drink and got up on a chair. "Now that summer is here and all our psychoanalysts are away, everyone's got a few extra bucks in his pocket. And we got to get up some material for next winter's analysis, right?"

"I wish you wouldn't talk so much about psychoanalysis, Felix," said Matti Cosworth. "You make the not-yet-couched feel only half-civilized "

"I'll tell you something for when you *do* start," Felix said to Matti. "The best way to bug your analyst is to turn over on your stomach and stare back at him. It will cost five hundred dollars just to get that idea out of your head when you *do* start. Don't interrupt any more."

Felix went on. "Here's the plan. First, we'll open a free employment agency for summer replacements. If Matti or Mary or Lou or whoever, if they make it up to Provincetown for the summer, we'll get someone to keep his place at the bar at the 55, free of charge. No Jersey people allowed. In fact, next we'll buy New Jersey and close it.

"Next, we'll open a Village chapter of Divorced

People Anonymous—a fellowship of sufferers: One marriage is too much, and a dozen divorces not enough. If a member feels the uncontrollable desire to fall in love and get married again, all he has to do is call Divorce Anonymous headquarters, and all the members will call up all the good-looking people we know of the opposite sex and go over to the poor addict's house and dance and hold parties day and night until the urge to marry again passes."

"No dancing," Malcolm said.

"And finally, Help Keep New York Clean: Eat a Pigeon Today. Thank you, thank you. We will march to victory under the banner 'Total Loss of Control for Everyone.' "

"Get out of here. Don't you people ever have to get up in the morning?" Malcolm said.

"It's the early worm gets caught," Felix said.

He led us out. We went over to the Shanty for coffee. "You know, I made a sad discovery," Felix said to me. "I was having breakfast yesterday, absentmindedly I put four spoons of sugar into my coffee instead of two like I always do. It wasn't just a matter of different quantity. The extra sugar made a *qualitative* change. It flipped me out with pleasure. It turns out I love coffee that's extra too sweet, like old Italian guys, and I never knew it."

"What's sad about that?"

"I had to *stumble* on it, man. I might never have found out. I might still be drinking it with only two spoons of sugar if I hadn't goofed. I'm thinking of all the cups of coffee I've had with only two spoons of sugar in the past, all those years I was like cheating myself. It's sad to realize there are other pleasures, so many other sensations, experiences, moments, emotions, all, *all around us,* waiting for us to discover them. And we may never know about them, don't even know we're missing them. That's unlived time, man. Nothing sadder than unlived time."

It was still dark when we left the Shanty. In the night silence of the city we could hear the whine of air conditioners in bedrooms where everybody was asleep but us, the lonely clicking of a policeman's heels, a late taxi cruising by. The wind shifted and Felix said he could smell salt; we drove out to the beach and lay on the sands, bone-tired, bleary-eyed, muddled with alcohol and stunned by the heat, dazed, dazzled, sun-drenched and delighted by dawn.

One Sunday afternoon I took Lou along to do some new SoHo gallery openings on Spring and Mercer streets, and we stopped off at the Glue for a beer. Felix came running in, his blue sunglasses glinting, the strange white streak in his hair blown by the wind. "Lou, Clair, come on, *come on!* Hurry, we're going to have an adventure!" he yells and grabs me by the arm and we go. There's a car parked at the curb. The big paper sign pasted in the rear window says "YOU ARE PARKED HERE ILLEGALLY." Felix says he's rented it. It must have been one of his good periods at home, because his wife Tamara is with him. He's got a couple of bottles of black Jamaica rum in the glove compartment, and we're off to New Jersey. "Jersey! Jersey!" we yell when Felix tells us. "What's New Jersey? Wait a minute, *wait a minute!*" But Felix won't stop. "We'll find one of the really great *and* charming country saloons somewhere down there," he says. "Cherry-wood fires and cheddar cheese, mulled wine, we'll drink and dance, eat New Jersey *food,* we'll be happy," Felix yells. By this time Tamara has decided that she can live no longer if she does not trade blouses with me. We swap. I don't know why.

But the way Felix drove! "It's like you're insured!" Lou says. We almost hit a truck, so we make Felix stop, and Lou takes the wheel. Felix insisted that Tamara and I both sit in the back seat with him, and he got the rum out of the glove compartment. We passed the bottle back and forth, bombing it. "Give me some," says Lou over his shoulder. *"Drive faster!"* Felix tells him and passes him a stick of grass.

We had come to the Garden State Parkway. There is a toll booth. "STOP. GET YOUR TICKET HERE" says the sign. "Busted," says Felix, "and we ain't even had our accident yet." "What's going on in there?" says the Meter Maid they got collecting money in the toll booth. Felix takes off his shoe and gives it to the civil servant. While she's studying it in her hand and becoming involved with the next car after us that rolls up to pay the money, Felix bangs Lou on the shoulder. "Go, man, go!" Lou is high enough on grass. He tromps on the gas.

"See," Felix said. "Gasoline and alcohol *do* mix. You just have to get past the taste. Where are we?" He's passing the rum. "New Jersey," Lou says, "where you wanted to be." "Where I was raised *and* ruined," says Felix. "The whole state is a mistake." For once he's right. Oil refineries, factories. "Everything here," says Felix, "is nuts and bolts. Robot vomit." Tamara and I are sick of the whole trip by now, Tamara more than me. We tell Felix. He doesn't want to hear it. "No, no," he yells. "Drive faster, Lou. Make the radio louder. *Tell lies!*"

Next there's a BANG! A blowout. We're right in front of a big Jersey State Trooper's car. "This is just what I love," says Tamara, "sitting in a stolen car, with a flat tire, in front of a cop, in the middle of New Jersey. I can't wait to do it all again tomorrow."

"Tomorrow," says Felix. "A fiction of the sleepy bartender. There is no tomorrow."

"There's no Tamara either," Felix's wife says, "you don't stop these games. Shut up, Felix, the cop is coming over."

"A kiss before dying," says Felix.

"You got the stuff to change a tire?" Lou asks him.

"No," says Felix. "We'll have to fake it, man. Show him your *badge,* Lou. Give him the secret cop password."

"Don't talk, Lou," says Tamara. "You're so high it's a felony."

"Biography," says Felix, beginning to play Definitions again. "A list of crimes committed and suffered."

"Men," says Tamara. "The sex that suffers from penis envy."

"Wife," says Felix. "An ex-lover."

"Felix," I said. "That's enough. Stop."

"He can't stop," says Tamara. "That's his big secret.

He can't stop." She gives Felix a bitter look and gets up as if she's so clumsy she can't look for her handbag in the rear window without blocking it, but she's covering the glass so the cop can't see in while I slide over into the front seat to take over from Lou. By the time the cop's reached us it looks as if I've been driving. I'm the most sober of all.

"Don't let him open the trunk, man," Felix says to me. "If he sees it's empty of tools, no spare, he'll shoot us for incompetent."

We get out of the car, and I do a number about the key to the trunk is lost, etcetera, etcetera. The Jersey cop is big and polite, patient as a Marlboro cowboy, but you can see the old sweet number in his eyes: women drivers. Which means he's mad but won't let himself show it. But he won't go away, and after a while we had to open the trunk to pretend to look for tools. Mop! Smoke and fire. Felix has so much grease and oily rags back there, it's spontaneous combustion. We stamp it out, but the cop is bugged. "What's the matter?" he says. "Didn't you know you had a fire? Didn't you smell anything?" Felix says, "We thought it was *New Jersey*, man."

It took Tamara and me a lot of work with the tears and smiles to calm the cop down. After a while he calls the tow truck and they patch us up. That's that, the cop gives us a final glare, kicks his motorcycle and goes. "Say, was there somebody here?" says Felix. But no one laughs. We head for home, Felix sitting in the back, Tamara, Lou and what's left of the rum up front with me. I'm driving.

We get back to the Glue, and the three of us bail out. Lou and I are going in to have a final drink to calm ourselves down, but Tamara angrily says she's going home. Felix is sitting sad and all alone in the car. I said, "Felix, tell me, couldn't you have planned things better? What was your hurry?" Felix says, "I always do everything right away and badly. I'm so afraid the next minute I won't want to do them at all."

Someone puts Mabel Mercer on the phonograph and turns off the lights against the end-of-August heat. A last few people stand up to dance. The black windows facing Perry Street begin to grow light, the dancers flashing from gray to sudden pink and gold as they catch the first beams in the east. I scoop the last ice cubes out of the punch bowl and put them into a handkerchief and hold them to my face and throat. Nancy Colbert shuts off the phonograph when the record ends and turns out the last lamp. Illuminated by the pale dawn, her face white and strained from being up all night, her big white dog, Lavish, finding a cool spot to lie down on the bricks inside the fireplace, Nancy sings "Shades" for the dancers.

My talk with Felix:

"Sometimes I think there's a Law of Absolute Conservation of Misery in our lives," he says. "Some unchangeable first law of human thermodynamics. The amount of unhappiness you're going to experience is fixed. You can only juggle around what doses you're going to take it. Most marriages, you take a little every day. Fatigue . . . disappointments . . . the routinization and death of the sexual impulse . . . the anger building up between you like interest on a loan you can't pay. Watching a face you once loved grow older. Just plain boredom. Clair, you know my marriage. You know how it is with Tamara and me. Some days I think, I'll end it today, I'll take one whole lifetime's share of grief in one big bang—one short, abrupt, condensed, concentrated, unadulterated, pure-pain divorce. I'll drink all her tears, all at once, once and for all, and be free. A whole new lifetime to live with another woman. Maybe a lifetime of pain. Maybe a lifetime of pleasure. But not *this* life. A second life, another spring."

"But the second time. You're not a kid any more. All bets are doubled."

He turns to me. "Isn't that the way you want it?"

"Have you told her?"

Memories that tell me I've forgotten how to be young. End tape. LeClair Pottinger.

11

Monday Morning

"You know those last few hot, steamy days you always get in New York just before Labor Day? That's when it was. Like some kind of dream, man, some heat mirage, always the fire hydrants going, the kids, spooky Village kids up three in the morning, always hot, night, us, alone, the streets empty." Moved by sympathy, wanting to share Clair's death but not wanting to intrude, Felix was telling me about a small death of his own, the loss of a girl he had once loved. Concern for me in the very indirectness of the way he felt he must show it.

I had had another drink and fallen asleep again when the doorbell rang and Felix came in. He was filthy and smelled of booze and grass, wearing the same clothes he had had on at the party. He needed a shave, his strange streak of white hair falling forward into his eyes. The eyes themselves red even through the glinting blue-and-silver shades.

"I just heard," he said.

"You need a drink?"

"The saloons aren't open yet. How are you?"

"Vodka?"

"Anything."

He splashed it all over himself. He couldn't light his cigarette.

"Pour it for me, will you?"

"I'll give you something." I lit a cigarette for him and began to make more instant coffee.

"You OK?"

"Better."

"Not OK?"

"Better."

"Use a piece of the vodka yourself."

"I had some."

"Have one with me."

"Not yet."

I filled a mug half with coffee, one quarter milk, a lot of sugar, one quarter Haig & Haig. I poured the mug into a cornflakes bowl and put it in front of him. Felix sat a moment more. He licked his lips. When he reached for the bowl, he missed. He let it sit in front of him. He smiled at me, smiling at himself. I had to smile too. Sitting over the bowl of coffee and whisky, he was too shaky to pick it up. Leaning over and staring into the dark liquid until he felt steady enough to try to get it to his mouth, he told me about the one time he had been overwhelmed by love. "It couldn't work," he said. "Too many things wrong. The things that were wrong to begin with, that made it all exciting and different, that got us into it—those were the things that caught up with us in the end and killed it off. Even time was against us."

I said I knew what he meant. I remembered when Clair used to sing at the Waverly until one or two A.M.

"That's it," Felix said. "Like that. I was working days, she's working nights, time got all mixed up . . .

"I was always sleepy, you know?" he went on. "I was always groggy, drugged with heat, the endless walking around the night, time too fast to waste it asleep. I was happy, man. Maybe that's what goofed me, that rotten marriage I was in. I wasn't used to it, maybe—being happy. After a while I felt I had to hold my breath, I'd dream I was touching wood, I became superstitious it would end. It was like fever, sleepy days, white nights, the heat . . . Labor Day that year set the all-time heat record since 1894.

"Always I felt like I was forgetting something, but it was too hot and fast, the summer dying, the days like too much light in my eyes, my wife's rat lawyers calling me up and I'm ducking the subpoenas, only the nights are safe and dark. A train was always leaving some station I had to be on, but I didn't know what train or where it was going from. I used to feel if only I knew the right, magic thing to do, if I could hold my breath long enough, it would all come out all right. Everything was like swimming underwater; every second you want to stop, to rest, to come up for air, but you have to keep going without another breath. It was too hot to think anyway.

"I was still doing the real estate gig, and every day I'd come home from work, and six o'clock, six thirty, fall right into the unmade bed, the laundry piling up, dirty dishes in the sink, wearing the same clothes because I couldn't get to the dry cleaners in the daylight hours, the calendar pages stuck and piled up from August twenty-sixth, because I was afraid if time would move. Two A.M. the alarm would go off, I'd get up in a sweat, a borrowed St. Marks Place pad, right, no air conditioner? I'd bathe in the tub in the kitchen, shave to be ready to go to work in the morning, put on yesterday's damp shirt, but in the briefcase a clean one I'd bought on the way home because I never had time to make it to the laundry either.

"I'd sit by the open summer window, a cup of instant coffee, a smoke, I'd look out at the Empire State Building, the spotlights on the TV tower white and gleaming but the building itself black and dark, only a few windows lit up, some stud working in the night, making a lot of loot—who's up that hour except money guys and guys like me?

"Three A.M., I'd pick her up when her place closed. She was a hatcheck. Man, how hot those nights were. You know how it always is the end of summer? No breeze, everything still, dead, the city like a dead brown flower. It was only a few days, you dig? The heat—that year it only ended Labor Day. Labor Day we drove out to Jones Beach three o'clock in the morning, and when we left the end of the day she said this is the last day of summer, and I didn't want to hear it. She was right. What's happened to summer anyway? Some enemy of the human race is running the weather now, it doesn't get so hot any more.

"Yeah, we'd walk around the streets, there'd be all these kids, whole families, man, they had the fire hydrants going the middle of the night. The city dead, water wherever you looked, streams running down the gutters every block. Citizens who sleep well, they don't know about summer nights. They're zonked out, snoring, their taxes paid, unaware, unhip, you know. It's a different life goes on all night, summers.

"The Puerto Ricans opened up the hydrants, they sprayed the water up in the air, you know, with a flat board? The spray like white rain, the kids dancing in the streets under the water, but quiet, quiet because of the people asleep, and once in a while a late cab cruising by. We'd walk right under the water too, come out, our clothes clinging, the people laughing at us but good-natured. They were families, dig? They can't sleep so they take the kids out in the streets for air. They must have been nice families, man, right? No rat father would take his kid out three in the morning because the kid was too hot to sleep?

"Anyway, we'd walk along, three A.M., four A.M., wet clothes, the city asleep, somebody playing a guitar very low and singing in Spanish, the hot streets, the water, always more hydrants around every corner. The spray up over our heads like a kind of white sky.

"I met her the first day of the heat. The radio said ninety-four degrees, and she said, 'It's like we meet in a foreign country, in a hot, tropic place, and soon it'll be a cold, different place, you'll go back to your wife and we'll break up.' Five A.M., six A.M. we'd fall asleep, sweating, hot, wct, wet, the sheets soaked, the Korvette fan creaking away, and I knew she was telling me the truth, but there was a private lie hidden in it too. She had chosen me not despite my being married—I always lay it out in front, I'm married, and then it's up to her yes or no—she'd chosen me because I *was* married. The foreign place we were in was only foreign to her, not to me; she was like a traveler who gives herself to a love affair with all her heart because she knows there's a return airplane ticket waiting for her in the suitcase back at the hotel, and the cold weather she talked about was the time she had set in her mind to get back on her plane. I had started the thing as maybe just another number you do, something on the side to get away from my rat wife, but somewhere along the line everything shifted, I realized she was in this affair for something of her own and I was only a part of her unknown plan. Suddenly I wasn't

thinking any more only how to get out of it without
too much trouble or tears, I was thinking about what
was on her mind; the timetable for that train I was
afraid of missing was one she had decided in front. It
was a strange feeling, exhilarating and heart-in-
the-mouth too. I was out of control for once in my
life, drunk on a woman like I had never been drunk
on speed or booze. I wanted her more than any other
woman I had ever known. Sometimes all you have to
know is that she is not in love with you to make you
fall in love with her in a way you wouldn't believe.
She would only be mine for this little time, and only
the heat, the run, run, run pace of the affair, going
without sleep, time stolen from time without thinking
could keep fear of losing her from stopping my mind.
We'd fall asleep, her body curled in my arms and already the feeling of loss begun, her hidden face I
would never know. I'd be up before she was, getting
dressed in the can to go to work so I wouldn't wake
her, putting on the clean shirt I had in the briefcase,
leaving her a note, 'See you tonight,' and I'd pray,
please more heat, another hot day, God, just one more
day, I don't care if it's like an oven . . ." Felix braced
both elbows on the table and tried to lift the bowl
to his lips. He was still shaking. He averted his face.

"Maybe if we put in a little more milk."

"Anything," Felix said. "Just kill the smell."

"But you're divorced now?"

"While you were away."

"The girl in the heat. Anyone I know?"

"You ever have any numbers on the side from
Clair?"

"Not while we lived together."

"This one went around only with married guys.
You didn't know her."

I added the milk. "Try to get some of it down," I
said.

He gave up before it was halfway to his lips.

"She didn't want to be tied down," he said. "Then
she married somebody else." He sat with both hands
flat on the table against the shakes.

"I never knew you to get hurt by a girl."

"Am I different from you?" He lowered his head

into the bowl, then smiled at me over the rim. "What the hell," he said. "It was over a long time ago. While you were away."

He lowered his head and drank the Scotch coffee without lifting the bowl—a dog lapping up water. The liquor hit his stomach. He fought the heaving, then sprinted to the kitchen sink. He came back. He began to look better. Enough had stayed down.

"Try again."

More of the booze stayed with him. "OK," he said. He smiled and closed his eyes. He picked up the bowl in both hands. The shaking had eased. He finished it off in one long swallow. *"Whoo—eee!"* he said. I began to make him another.

"No," he said. "No more coffee. In a glass. Got a tie?"

I took a necktie off a hook on the back of a closet door and gave it to him. He slung both ends around his neck but didn't tie it. He motioned with his head and I poured some Scotch in a glass. He let it sit.

"What a night," he said.

"What time you leave the party?"

"I never saw Clair. She must have come later."

"But what time?"

"Maybe midnight."

"How was I?"

"One minute I saw you, sober as a judge. The next minute, I'd taken my eye off you, you'd *arrived,* man. You must have put a pint away in ten seconds. You know who I left with?"

"Lou."

"He told you?"

"He turned up, assigned to the case."

"That's a break. I took him to McGruddy's and bought him a drink for old time's sake. You don't remember us leaving? I shook your hand."

"I don't remember anything except thinking I was sober."

"Have one with me," Felix said.

"Not yet."

The glass of Scotch waited for him on the table. He put his fingers around it but did not lift. He let it sit on the table. He looped the tie around his arm as if it were a sling, both ends going around his neck and down the other side. He used his left hand to pull the ends of the tie down. The sling raised and steadied his right arm, letting him bring the glass up to his lips without accident or spill. He drank. "Truth serum," he said. He put the glass down empty. More color returned to his face.

"The cops rough on you?" he asked.

"Not many kisses."

"They got any ideas who did it?"

"Maybe they think I did."

"How the hell could you do it? You were in love with her."

"How the hell do I know what I do when I'm that blanked out?"

"You were in love with her!" Felix said. "And she was in love with you. Don't talk crazy. You didn't do it."

"Have one with me," I said.

Felix gave me back the necktie and poured his own —a stiff new shot. He picked up the glass and drank from it unassisted in one long take. "Yes," he said, letting out his breath. "Those after-hours Hoboken joints." He lit his own cigarette.

"A girl there?"

"I do a little business that side the river. After Lou went home I had to see a couple of guys. You don't drink with them, they don't trust you."

"The cops'll want to see you. A list of all the people you invited to the party."

"I already phoned them. I told them I'll come in later. I wanted to see you were all right first."

"Where'd you hear?"

"There's a picture them carrying Clair out in the *Daily News*." He hadn't wanted to be the one to tell me.

There was ice and soda in his fourth drink, a slice of lemon peel, and he had asked me to put it in a clean glass. The whisky had done its work. A new Felix sat before me. He sipped the drink slowly, at ease, smiling, a cigarette between his lips, his hands steady as a rock. The sun was shining on his combed hair and clean face. "You know," he said, "I feel a whole lot more like I do right now than I did when I first came in here."

"I blacked out, Felix."

His face changed. He was on his feet. "I know," he said.

"I don't remember anything. I didn't do it."

"I know."

"I keep seeing her face. The open eyes."

"I'll never forget that hatcheck," Felix said and took my head in his arms.

"You remember before the party I was telling you about Jennifer?" Felix said. "The one looking for the perfect man?"

"Yes."

"The girl in the heat, the hatcheck. That's who it was. Jennifer." He wanted to go out for a drink. The bars were open by now.

"Plenty to drink here."

"More life in retail booze, you get higher drinking in a store. *Let's go out!* I don't like to stay in. I use the kitchen my apartment for an ashtray, hang my clothes on the floor. Somebody wanted to give me a dog, I said, *'Don't* give me no pet.' You got a dog, you might as well be married and *have* a kid: you got to go home every day to *feed* the dog anyway." He finished my drink and then his own. "Rose-colored glasses," he said. He was running out the door in front of me.

12

Grand Opera

"A Spoken History," Tape 14A. LeClair Pottinger. Begin.

Felix: Felix and I did not really so much have a love affair as a grand opera. We never had a date where you had dinner and maybe a drink after that with friends and then went home to bed. It was one of those passages in his marriage where they were on the brink of divorce, separated on and off, and a lot of heavy lawyer action going on. Everything had to be conducted with great secrecy. I didn't care.

I liked it that he was married. It protected me. When the man is married he has to handle all the guilt. All she has to deal with is the loneliness on those nights they don't speak about, when he is with his wife. But I never felt lonely when I was not with Felix. He burned me out, and when he was away I was always glad to get back to my studio, to spend time alone, wash my hair, go to the museums, do the laundry, and work.

We used to meet at three or four in the morning after I got off work and the Waverly was closing. We'd go to the West End or one of the other bars and restaurants around Columbia University which Felix knew about, nights when he would quarrel with Tamara about women or money and he'd charge out of their place on Riverside Drive. Other times he would take the day off from his dying real estate office. We'd go over to Hoboken, where he was trying to get a little something new started, parking me for an hour or two at Lynn's Klassy Klientele Kafe or the Starving Artists' Gallery, funny little places near the waterfront where the little fugitive colony of Hoboken expatriates hung out. Often we would stay over on the Jersey side of the river, having dinner with painters we'd met at local galleries. We had a whole secret second life over there, connected to New York only by the underground PATH subway line. Those were my favorite days.

The smell of Hoboken near the waterfront: bitter and fresh, a wind off the river, garbage, and the smell of the sea. But it was never enough for Felix. He always wanted movement, noise, the lights brighter, the music louder. Whatever he did, it had to have drama. Sometimes it was Act I, Scene I, and we were A

Pair of Students in Old Heidelberg. We'd walk arm in arm along the streets where you could smell the river, having a beer with other Young Lovers, singing songs at corner tables, borrowing money charmingly from waiters we'd gotten to know—and overtipping them the next time we were there. We were always talking about Not Owning Each Other.

Very often, though, we were Verdi—or do I mean Puccini? Once Felix wanted to leave me and I began to cry and accused him of never having really loved me. He told me it was only For My Own Good, he was married and he couldn't let me go on throwing my life away on him. I told him that if he Did Not Own Me, the decision as to whether I wanted to waste my life on him was mine to make, not his. But he wouldn't agree until I said that perhaps what he really meant was that he wanted to go back to his wife but did not know how to tell me. He began to cry himself, just looking into my wet face with tears pouring down his own. We were on a crooked little street where there was a restaurant we liked, the Bocce, so we ran in there. Suddenly we were in this strange scene, sitting at one of the tables in the back, in a brilliantly lighted room, the way old-fashioned Italian restaurants used to do when they put all their money into the food and none into charm. At last it was as if we were finally on a real stage.

The restaurant got its name from the game, it was built around a real earth-floored bocce alley. The little old Italian men threw the ball down the alley at the side of the restaurant as if they really meant the game and weren't just stage extras hired for the occasion. There they were, grunting and spitting, drinking wine and crying out in Italian when they made a good shot—all in the best Method manner, acting as if they really cared about the game, were 3-D, really alive, had families and lives even when we weren't around. Felix couldn't stop crying, but then he began to laugh too—it was funny to be having a tragic love affair in a bocce alley. And Being No Good for me. "You're right," he said. "I can't stand the guilt. This morning when I came home to St. Marks

Place she was sitting on the steps in front. She said she wanted to die. I said I would come back to her."

"Soon?"

"This is the last time."

Maybe he was going back to his wife because I hadn't asked him to stay with me. We had never spoken about marriage, but he had begun to talk about taking an apartment together. I had remained silent. Wanting us to go on, but not knowing what I wanted us to go toward, I had always been uneasy of any talk of the future. Paralyzed by my old dilemma that I wanted him to be faithful to me, but unable to fool myself that I could be faithful to him, I said nothing. In my daydreams I have been unfaithful every day to my lover of the night before, just as I knew I would be unfaithful in my mind again tomorrow to my lover of tonight. Not being able to say what I wanted from him because I did not know myself, not blaming him —*always this desire to be fair*—I still did not want to hear the words aloud: "I am leaving you. This is the last time." They were like a knife, but I could not say in return, "Stay with me." I let him think I wanted him to go.

One half of me wanted to throw the glass of water into his face, cut his heart; another half was sorry for what he was going through. I put my arms around him. He felt my turmoil. He put his arms around me. Glaring at each other like the bitterest enemies for one moment, the next moment like love's reward, this sudden wave, we felt this inundation of relief and affection for each other because we were going to be able to let each other go. We had loved one another but our business together was finished, the emotional work we had to do done. We looked at each other as if we were both a hundred years old, dryly and amused, two old friends who meant each other well, meeting a last time before the grave. As if seeing each other for the first time.

By this time the gray-haired waiter had come up to us, he was watching with a kind, solicitous look on his face, worried. So we somehow were immediately into another Scene, the one where the two leads meet by accident and Find Each Other in some incongruous situation. Sergio Franco was about to sing "Some Enchanted Evening, Across a Crowded Room"—but I felt a chill. It all seemed about to be starting up again.

It made me feel a prisoner of my own stupid emotions. *I would not have it!* Having come so far, it now must end. It must have frightened Felix too, because he took me out across the street to another little neighborhood bar. But he didn't know what to do, our affair like a murdered corpse between us, how do you say goodbye? So I said that we were only to pretend that this was our farewell meeting: he didn't want to leave me, but his father had persuaded me to let him go for the sake of his brilliant future career. It gave Felix a way to see me, to see himself, to see us both once again in a make-believe light, and he felt better. He wanted to say goodbye with champagne, but they didn't stock it in a little Hoboken neighborhood place like that, so we drank Calvados instead, because Felix said that was a romantic, tragic drink.

And as we drank we found we weren't just pretending goodbye, it was goodbye. We were crying, both of us, and Felix said, "I have never made a woman happy," and I said, "You've made me happy and I will love you always for it," and after that we both let go, showed off and said every lush, lovely, extravagant thing we both—good, fair and decent players of the Game—knew we were not allowed to say, had repressed, cooled out and pretended not to feel in the face of the open but unspoken fact of his marriage and my own secret knowledge that I didn't want to marry him anyway. This had now become a new game too—we meant all these things we were saying about loving and remembering each other forever—and that made us sad. But we also knew we didn't mean them too, and that made us happy.

We kissed each other for the last time and went out, lingering for a moment on the sidewalk, holding hands as we walked back to the car, me wondering at how different everything was from what I'd imagined when I was a little girl growing up and thinking about what my life would be, but we only shook hands when we arrived once more in New York. "So soon?" I thought. "Have I graduated so soon? I'm not ready yet." But I was. Felix had become a love of the past. I let him go back to his wife.

I ran into Blake at the Paradise only a few nights later. When he called me on the phone the next day I was not surprised. Sometimes I try to get him to play Why hadn't he ever called me a long time before? Why hadn't he talked to me with more interest on nights when we might find ourselves (with different partners) at McGruddy's or the 55? "You weren't ready to see me then," he said. It summed up all that could be said. It had been an accident that we had met again that night at the movies, but it was no accident that I was able to see him at last. Felix had been my final rehearsal.

"When you're ready," said Blake to me—literally the first words we ever exchanged the first time we were alone together—"I'll be waiting."

"Are you ready to begin?"

"I ended mine last night."

"What if I never do?"

"It was time for mine to end anyway."

"Mine is over too."

"The guy at *Black Orpheus?*"

"Someone else. I'll always be grateful to him."

"Never tell me who he was."

"He was married. . . ."

"I don't want to know."

Power, aware of itself, all the more real for knowing it was vulnerable too. Blake had asked me to meet him at the Puerto Rican dance hall he called La Perla but that really had a different name. He turned to the bartender and asked for two martinis, with an extra splash of vermouth in his own.

"We're on," he said.

"OK," I said.

I could not breathe.

OFFICE OF CHIEF MEDICAL EXAMINER
OF THE CITY OF NEW YORK

520 FIRST AVENUE
NEW YORK , N. Y. 10016

LABORATORY FINDINGS

Name __Le Clair Pottinger__ M.E. No. __B-83211__ Lab. No __1275/7B__

Autopsy by __Dr. Foreman__ On __4/24__

Specimens or samples submitted: Tongue depressor of vagina
plus saline washings of bite
marks on left breast

Analyses and tests requested: Acid Phosphatase Test—
Microscopic examination

Result:

Vagina:
  Acid Phosphatase: Positive
  Microscopic: Vaginal scrapings reveal
                 spermatozoa present.
  Inhibition: Decedent is Type AB. Inhibition
                 test of vaginal material shows
                 Type O grouping.

Left breast: Bite marks made immediately before
                 time of death. Saline washings
                 reveal saliva to be Type A.

Blood taken at autopsy was hemolyzed.
Cause of death: ASPHYXIA BY LIGATURE STRANGULATION
                HOMICIDAL

MOTILITY OF SPERM INDICATES INTERCOURSE TOOK PLACE AT
APPROXIMATE TIME OF DEATH.

Signed: _R. J. Foreman, M D_

13

Boots

The plants were almost weeds, spindly-tall and sad, overwatered and brown-edged, planted in a four-by-six-foot plot of earth opened in the concrete floor in front of the plate-glass window at the end of the room. On a green desk blotter scotch-taped to the window someone had lettered a sign with black crayon:

> THIS IS A GARDEN.
> IT IS NOT A GARBAGE CAN.
> BE CLEAN.

The black man at the desk was wearing intern's white ducks but had a cop's silver N.Y.P.D. badge pinned over his heart. He said into the phone, "The family from Charleston is here." He listened and nodded his head. He put down the phone but did not hang up. He spoke to a weeping woman and a younger man who looked like her son. "The viewing room is the second door down the corridor on the right," the black cop said. The woman stared at him through her tears. She shook her head as if he had spoken to her in a language she had once known but could no longer understand. "The viewing room—" he wearily began again—

"Thank you very kindly," the young man said in a southern accent. His mother was half leaning, half falling from his arm. He led her through the door the black man had indicated.

The man at the desk watched them walk away until they were out of earshot. He held the phone in his hand until they were gone through the door and then he put it back to his mouth again. "Harry?" he said.

"They're on their way. Tray Four," he said. "The multiple-stab job. Yeah. Show them the good side." He hung up and looked at me.

"Officer, could I see the coroner?"

"You got an appointment?"

"No. But tell him it was my wife they found on West Twentieth Street."

"Dr. Jarvis is the chief medical examiner for the entire city," he said. He was running a pencil point down a list of names. "The medical examiner—the *assistant* medical examiner—who worked that case is Dr. Foreman."

"Can I see him?"

He reached for the desk phone. "I don't know," he said, "pretty busy around here." The phone rang before he got it off the cradle. He answered and spoke about a case recently covered in the newspapers.

A woman had been found floating in the East River. She had been unidentified and had been routinely consigned to an anonymous city-paid suicide's grave. Her head had been surgically cut off after the body had reached the city morgue. The newspapers said it had been a medical school joke; someone in the coroner's office had wanted to use the skeleton head as a *memento mori* desk ornament. The stink developed when a young woman read about the case in the newspapers; there was a description of the body. She had come here and identified the headless corpse as her mother.

The black cop put the phone down and turned to me. "You want to see Dr. Foreman," he said. He asked my name. "I'll see if he can see you. Please sit down." He pointed to some benches along the side of the room where other people were waiting.

There was a man sweeping the floor, and another cop in a white coat came along and they joked about the city going bankrupt while they had a Coke from the machine. The sweeper's idea was that if the city deliberately defaulted, they would be able to stiff the banks who held the city's bonds, thus leaving a lot of money free to give municipal employees a big raise. The cop thought there might be a catch in the idea.

The sweeper said no. "All that glitters ain't necessarily shit," he said, and they laughed, tossing their empty Coke cans among the plants in the garden in front of the plate-glass window as they went out. Dr. Foreman came in. He too was wearing the standard E-Z Kwik laundry suit of white ducks. He was in his late thirties, thinning hair and a face I couldn't get a grip on, hard and soft at the same time, lined and etched by more troubles than he should be carrying. Shiny black waterproof boots up to his knees, the white pants tucked in. "Mr. Blake?" he said, speaking with a brisk, irritated air, looking his question around into the space above the heads of the four or five of us anonymously waiting. I followed him down the corridor.

We passed a door that said Viewing Room. It was closed but I could hear someone crying in there. There was a drone of a hydraulic lift. "The bodies are under refrigeration of course," Dr. Foreman said in his irritated voice, as if I had asked him and he resented having to answer, "but that's down below. In the basement. They come up on a tray for the family to identify through the glass screen—you get these Italian mothers throwing themselves on the bodies of their sons . . ." We were in his office. "I suppose you'll want a cup of coffee."

"No, thank you."

He stood irresolutely for a moment more, tapping his fingers on his desk. There was a white cardboard container of take-out Chinese food near the telephone. The cold rice had begun to congeal.

"Want something to eat?" he asked. His voice was unexpectedly concerned, but he grunted with satisfaction when I said I wasn't hungry, as if turning down his offer of food had relieved him of any further obligation toward me. He sat down in his swivel chair and leaned back to look at me, hands cupped behind his head.

He waited for me to speak. I couldn't. "OK," he said at last. He leaned over to shovel cold sweet-and-sour shrimp out of the cardboard container. He was eating, irritated again, his face somehow red beneath his icebox pallor and thinning hair, impatient to get rid of me. He looked up over a spoonful of rice. "You came to see me, I'm busy, I'm on my lunch, the chief medical examiner is out with the flu, but here I am. You're in my office, you're seeing me. What's so god-damn important you have to see me?"

"You got a drink here, Doctor?"

He stared at me a moment more and then opened a desk drawer. He took out a bottle of colorless liquid that had had a gummed red-and-white label. It showed a skull and crossbones and the word "Poison." He poured some into a glass.

"Why the label? People steal it for a free drink?"

"I label what it is. It'll kill you." He walked over to a sink in the corner. "You'd better have some water," he said. "It's medicinally pure alcohol. Almost two hundred proof."

"Have one with me?"

His mood looked blacker than ever. "Not when I'm working."

He watched me put it away in two takes, drumming his fingers on the desk, staring at me until I was finished. "Another?" he said.

"No, thank you."

"OK," he said, putting the bottle back into the drawer and slamming it shut. "Didn't you identify your wife to the police right on the spot?" he asked. "Changed your mind? Jesus, don't tell me you changed your mind?"

He sat staring at me for another ten seconds. I could not say what I had come for. I did not know myself. Some people came to the door. I could see their figures through the clouded glass. Foreman did not take his eye off me. One of the people outside knocked on the door. "Dr. Foreman?" he said. Fore-man did not turn his head from me. "In a minute," he said over his shoulder, and the man outside went away. Foreman was still wordlessly looking into my face. At last he sighed. I tried not to look at the shiny black rubber boots on his feet. They reached up al-most to his thigh. The white Nedick's ducks tucked into them were stained with blood. His head slowly began to turn from side to side, saying, No, no, no to whatever vision he saw inside his eyes; they were closed against mine.

He opened them. "You want another drink?" he said. The kinder voice was back.

"If you'll have one."

Mad again: "I'm one of those people you may not know about. I don't drink before evening." Another silence, his fingers drumming on the table.

"OK," he said. "You want to know what happened, right?"

"I know what happened, Doctor. I can't believe it."

"Ahh . . ." he said. He let out his breath once more. "A thing like this," he said, "the mind has to defend itself. A protective switch gets thrown in the brain so we don't have to take in too much emotion before we can handle it. Drinking can do it—that's one reason people drink. But the mind can do it all by itself. It cuts off. That's why it all seems unreal, happening to someone else. That's the way it is with you?"

"Every time the phone rings I think there's been a mistake and I'll hear her voice and she'll say, no, no, it was somebody else that looked like her."

"You had some kind of plastic surgery on your nose?" he said. He was looking at my bandage and the discoloration around the eyes.

"I had an operation on my deviated septum a few days ago in France. They reamed out the channel so I wouldn't snore any more. I was going to surprise my wife."

"A welcome-home present?"

"I wanted to show her things could change."

"You were in love with her?"

"I was in love with her only for a short time but it was the only time I was ever in love with anyone. It was the best time of my life and I'd trade whatever time in my life I have left to have the feeling with her back again. We'd been separated. We were going to try to be married again."

"You loved her, all right."

"Not enough."

"You better have a look at the autopsy report."

The "ligature" in Dr. Foreman's report was the wire the florist had used to tie the bouquets Felix had ordered to dress up the apartment for the party. Dr. Foreman said that the shit in the bed meant Clair had been alive when she had gotten into it. "Or was forced into it," he said. Her bowels had let go when the wire had been used to strangle her.

"You don't have to let Toomis know I let you see the report," he said. He sounded more angry at himself now than at me.

"I won't."

He looked away. "Did you understand it?"

"The sperm. Was it mine?"

"We don't know. What we do know—sexual intercourse took place, either with her consent or against it."

"Toomis said it was with."

"He told you that?"

"He said because there was no blood or skin under her fingernails, it meant she didn't fight back."

"He doesn't like you."

"He thinks I did it."

Foreman bit his lip and thought a moment. "Toomis has his opinions. I have scientific evidence. The lack of evidence of a struggle is not conclusive. Maybe a knife was held to her head. So we can't be sure. The other thing we can't be sure—did it take place before her death or immediately thereafter."

"*After?*"

"It's important. Part of the murderer's psychological profile. If the sex act took place first and then he killed her to shut her up, that's one kind of man. Relatively less pathological than the other kind. The other kind, he prefers sex with someone already dead. The killing comes first."

"Doctor, are you testing me?"

"For what?"

"Because I flunk the test. I can't listen any more."

"Maybe it took place during," he said.

I was up and walking around the room, up against the wall, as far from him as I could get.

"*During?*"

He was watching me closely. He closed his eyes and put his fingertips together.

"Murder," he said, "happens forty-eight times more often in the U.S.A. than in England, Japan and West Germany combined. During the Vietnam War more Americans were murdered at home than killed in combat in the ten years we made our major effort there. In an average year, maybe twenty thousand people are murdered in this country. Murder used to be easy to solve, because people mostly killed people they knew. That's changing. New York cops once solved ninety percent of the murders they'd get. Now we're down to less than fifty percent. We used to be a community of neighbors. Love and hate all mixed up, and people killed people they saw every day. The book still tells the cop the first suspect is automatically the husband or wife of the deceased. That's out of date. Now we're a city of anonymous transients. New York has the highest murder rate of strangers by strangers in the country. One person out of three is killed by someone he never saw before in his life. Murders by chance acquaintances, murders for no reason, stabbings in a quarrel in the subway, anonymous bombs, snipers on the roof. Used to be blacks mostly killed blacks; there are twice as many interracial murders today. Murder has become epidemic in this country, and you can blame poverty, television, the gun laws, drugs, Vietnam, whatever. Nobody knows. You know the fastest-growing class of violent criminals? The FBI says women are turning to violent crime at a rate triple that of men. The social contract is breaking down. You're a coroner in New York long enough, you find people get their kicks different ways. That's another reason maybe why she didn't struggle. One of them might have been holding the knife while the other went at it."

"WHAT ARE YOU SAYING?"

"There were two men."

"No."

"Yes."

"Two."

"Yes."

I sat down. He offered me a drink. He was watching me.

"Toomis didn't mention that?" he said.

I couldn't answer.

"I can see he didn't."

"Two men," I said.

"Yes," Foreman said. "Two."

14

A Birthday

"A Spoken History." LeClair Pottinger. Tale 23. Begin.

Spring: Leaves on the trees, green and young, so tender you want to eat them, the benign sun warm as a lover's hand on your back at a dance, nostalgia for the turning year rising like sap in the blood, the long, lyric rush into the orgasm of deep summer just beginning, Blake and I on our way from Ira's Glue to the Fortune Club, below Wall Street, over Battery Park. It's my birthday and he's borrowed a membership card from a producer to celebrate the new suit I've bought to wear. As we get out of the taxi Blake hums to himself from the stack of La Cubana records he hasn't changed on his turntable for months, and I see us in an old movie, a picture Blake and I recently went to see again, the people in *A Man and a Woman,* and how they rode their horses into the sea in the Camargue, in France.

The Fortune Club is the side of Blake we never see in the Village, this is the kind of place he goes to hold his TV meetings and drink with producers, here is the private life he leaves behind every night he comes to McGruddy's or the Glue wearing his nine-to-five suits and a tie which make him look like a tourist. He rarely speaks of these places, and if I ask him, he answers with a joke about "uptown." Something in him does not like his work, but I am shy of this other life of his, the secret self engaged with forms of power unknown to me, directors, agents, sponsors, CBS, NBC, people I don't know, rarely meet and in whose presence I feel diminished and awkward again, small-town—I go along with his jokes too easily. A form of fear. The world north of Fourteenth Street is one I have laughed at, like most Villagers. Since that day at the Fortune the laughter has come to sound unconvincing to me. Sneering at a snobbish party is valid only if you've been invited to it first. At the Fortune I got my first understanding of why Uptown hires our laughter. Court jesters enhance complacent feelings of dominion. We are more clever than they. They are the king.

Seventy-eight stories above the earth, Blake and I sit on thrones in front of arched, floor-to-ceiling windows, all of New York Bay before us, Hoboken—old memories of Felix stir—a smudge of buildings somewhere far away and small, off to the right across the river, the enormous expanse of tranquil blue-green waters in front reminding me that Manhattan is a tiny island, the air and sky irradiated with golden sunshine plangent and palpable enough to swim in; the muted hum of cars and people far below like the drone of bees in the sun. A freighter steams under the Verrazano Bridge, her straight white wake pointing back to Europe, Tangier, Rio. Beyond the toylike and green Statue of Liberty I can see where Brooklyn runs into the sea. Blake orders martinis. My suit is white, trimmed with white fur. When he leans to kiss me on the cheek I blow the long-haired silky white monkey fur against his lips. A *frisson* curls his shoulders and I see bumps form on the naked skin of his wrist as he reaches forward for his glass. The power of flesh and blood—my flesh, my blood, and his. I lay my head back against his cheek so that we are both facing the windows, looking the same way. "The gesture that beautiful women patented a long time ago," Blake calls it, teasing me with a smile, meaning it too.

Cocktails come, so cold the gin smokes off the ice.

Oysters and striped bass, new asparagus, tender as love itself, salad mixed with cognac and lemon so no taste of vinegar mars the palate for the wine to follow: two different *crus* of Blanc de Blanc chill beside the table in frosted silver ice buckets running with ice-cold sweat. The barmen wear gamblers' green-and-gold brocade vests, and the walls of the room are covered with acres of the same brocade. We have coffee, a black cigar for Blake. I have a puff from it myself. The sun moves over in heaven and shines on our table, and as the time comes when even the bankers and millionaires in the room have to go back to their offices, the place empties and our two voices sound small in the empty echoing space, muffled by the cloth of gold on the walls. I have come to see that Blake is one of those men who expand with booze, grow larger. His speech never slurs, he presides over a private kingdom of order within anarchy, into which he is inviting me. The bankers and millionaires are rich, but they have gone back to their offices. Blake is hanging on to a job where they don't like him, but he takes the afternoon off. In the later quiet he signals up a round of stingers, and after that, one more for himself. He pulls my chair closer to his, scraping it across the floor, and we murmur to each other while the waiters disappear and are replaced, suddenly, by a chorus line of beauties in black mesh stockings, waitresses getting ready for the early evening dance on the ballroom floor below. And people in twos begin to drift in with the music. Women in long expensive dresses, their eyes shadowed for night, handsome men who have forgotten about the business of the day.

Blake has taken me into a new domain in which he is at home, an easier, more beautiful world. *Luxe, calme, et volupté,* and booze was the heart. "You know why people clink their glasses?" Blake said. "Wine satisfies four of the senses. Taste, touch, sight, smell. When you touch your glass to someone else's, the fifth is satisfied too." Our glasses ring together. "Sound."

It is alcohol that made the decorator put the bar at the center of all the lines of sight in the room, the way a less intelligent one would have built the restaurant around the view of the harbor or even the fireplace. It is wine and the magic of martinis that keep the bartenders smiling, their chrome, glass and silver implements gleaming as they preside over their mysteries. It is champagne and gin and Scotch, carried in serene and silent importance on huge silver trays, nestling in snowy white linen napkins, gracefully handed down by waiters to customers who look up in anticipation like children watching Christmas toys unwrapped that is the communion here. The silent pause, the unspoken toast, the ritual meeting of eyes over the rims of glasses—people taking the first sip of evening together against the apprehensions of the dying day. It was the mystique and majesty of booze into which Blake was ushering me—a land I knew nothing about. I was from De Haviland, West Virginia. I knew only the dusty, splintered floors of the 55 and McGruddy's, the eternal beers and cheap 90-proof Fleischmann's people drank there, bartenders in beards, jeans and sneakers. My boundaries had always been the rickety lofts of SoHo, the cold-water flats of the East Village, the one-and-a-half-room apartments of Hudson Street, decorated with bullfight posters and Van Gogh reproductions; and never above Fourteenth Street. The Village—a territory geographically no bigger, perhaps just as land-locked and self-referent as the village of De Haviland itself. With Blake I walked into a larger world of accepted risk and the sophisticated pleasures of the earth. He was a lord within it, and I could be there with him. "We could get married," he had said to me New Year's Eve.

Could I handle it? I had always thought of myself as a faithful girl, and in fact was always faithful without thought or hesitation to each man as he came along. But I could never see whoever he was as the last man I would be faithful to. I did not look into the future, but I needed to know it was open, and the way I always knew the affair with one man was over was when I found energy in the idea of having that first lunch with another. Marriage was many things, but one of the things it was was an acceptance that that part of the future had closed. I had never directly answered Blake's proposal.

"Deciding not yet to decide," he'd said, "is deciding. It means no."

"Drink me," said the little bottle to Alice. She did, and was a giant. "Have another?" Blake asks, and I respond to the risk no less than he. "Yes," I say, and become a member of his kingdom. He has the keys. Over the bar, autumnal forest sheafs of wild flowers and wheat grow out of green-and-gold festoons covered with the same brocade as the walls. The insistent music of *A Man and a Woman* has never stopped playing in my mind and I fall asleep, my head on Blake's shoulder, sitting in the window, watching a commuter ferry leave Manhattan in the last afternoon sun and arrive in Staten Island covered by night. Eve sold Eden for an apple. How much would she have paid for Pointes des Asperges au Beurre Fortune Club? We cross invisible borders and never know they were there until we look back.

15
Telex

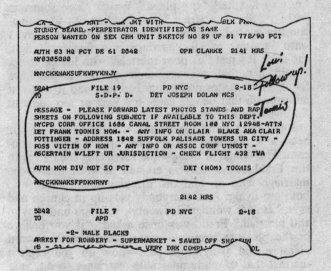

```
LR            HAT - ..  JKT WITH              BLK PA
STUBBY BEARD -PERPETRATOR IDENTIFIED AS SAME
PERSON WANTED ON SEX CRM UNIT SKETCH NO 29 UF 81 772/90 PCT

AUTH 83 HQ PCT DE 61 2842              OPR CLARKE  2141 HRS
NY8305000

KNYCKKNAKSUFKWPYKNJY                                          Lou'
                                                             Followup!
5241           FILE 19              PD NYC              2-18
TO             S.D.P. D.    DET JOSEPH DOLAN MCS

MESSAGE - PLEASE FORWARD LATEST PHOTOS STANDS AND RAP  Toomis
SHEETS ON FOLLOWING SUBJECT IF AVAILABLE TO THIS DEPT.
NYCPD CORR OFFICE 1686 CANAL STREET ROOM 100 NYC 12948-ATTN
DET FRANK TOOMIS HOM - ANY INFO ON CLAIR BLAKE AKA CLAIR
POTTINGER - ADDRESS 1842 SUFFOLK PALISADE TOWERS UR CITY -
POSS VICTIM OF HOM - ANY INFO OR ASSOC CONF UTMOST -
ASCERTAIN W/LEFT UR JURISDICTION - CHECK FLIGHT 432 TWA

AUTH HOM DIV MDT SO PCT              DET (HOM) TOOMIS

KNYCKKNAKSFPDKNRNY

                                    2142 HRS

5242           FILE 7               PD NYC              2-18
TO             APB

         -2- MALE BLACKS
ARREST FOR ROBBERY - SUPERMARKET - SAWED OFF SHOTGUN
MB - 2.             - VERY DRK COMPL          OL
```

16

Marriage

"A Spoken History." Tape 32B revised. Begin.

I remember once when I went back to De
Haviland for Christmas, my mother asked me in her
shy way if I had "any plans." Wasn't there someone
yet? . . . She was afraid I was holding out for someone too special, waiting too long. Maybe she knew I
wasn't waiting at all. Marriage is a fine institution,
she said. It's just "us poor mortals" who loused it up.
I told her that perhaps some people might have
thought Procrustes had a fine bed too, and it was just
unfortunate that people came too long or too short to
fit. I wish now I had never said that to her.

But I can't stand the Billy Graham notion that just
because a marriage doesn't bust up it's a going concern. The image of two people sacrificing their lives to
this Frankenstein they've created between them—the
marriage lives on and on, drinking their blood, and
both are dying. And everybody gets up in church and
says, "Isn't it wonderful, twenty-five years and they're
still married." Freud was once asked: "If you believe
in the pleasure principle—that people move toward
pleasure and away from pain—how do you explain
the fact that so many miserable marriages go on, year
after year, the two partners torturing each other?"
And he said, "Perhaps the revenge is not yet complete."

But in the end Blake and I went to City Hall, the
least terrible way. I would not go home to De
Haviland and wear a long white dress. I also did not
want my mother there. I don't remember much about
it . . . there were pigeons in City Hall Park, they
walked around and then went up in the sky, wheeling
in circles. I wore the white suit with the white monkey
fur because it was lovely, but put on a black lace
blouse so there was no charade about virginity. I
suppose I remember more about that than I thought.

We had about an hour to wait. Lou was best man.
He saw that waiting was making me nervous. He
said, "Let's go out and come back later." He bought
us a drink, and then we sat on a park bench for a
while. I put my head on Blake's shoulder and threw
pieces of hot-dog roll to the pigeons from a frank Lou
bought from a man with a little wagon and a striped
umbrella. It's my wedding day, I said to myself, wondering how I felt, and thought of a picture postcard
I had once seen, a sentimental painting: a simple path
across a field, a low white fence, the path diminishing
beyond into a dark wood. An image of death, but
somehow cheery and satisfying too, appropriate and
important as the day. Then it was two o'clock and
we went up. It wasn't great, the Marrying Sam in a
hurry, bored, but when we came out we were married.
I was married!

Lou stepped up to kiss me, and behind him, Blake
was smiling. He had insisted on the ceremony. He
hadn't accepted my idea that I just move in with
him. Either we were marrried, he said, with all that
meant, or we weren't—with all that meant.

"It wasn't too bad, was it?" he asked, meaning the
ceremony.

"No."

"I'm sorry if it was a bit shabby."

"This is the happiest day of my life."

"Didn't you expect it to be?"

"I want to be a good wife."

"You will be."

"Blake—I'm so excited!"

I had wanted to hear myself say the words aloud.
To change the hypothetical to the actual and feel
what it meant. Going through a ceremony, speaking
the words in front of witnesses—it's not just getting a
piece of paper to hang over your bed. If the ritual is
so meaningless, why do people fight it so hard? In
our bones we know how important it is to swear to
try to be committed.

In my first years in New York I had come to think
marriage was a certain kind of talent that some people had, others did not. The talent for the violin is

lovely, and when someone has that talent, the music is marvelous. But nobody passes a law that says everyone must have a talent for playing the violin. Why do we insist that everyone have a talent for marriage? I had wanted to make of my life—"noble" is the secret word I never dared say aloud but harbored in the privacy of my mind. And if life could not be noble, then I would make it exciting. If I married without talent, life would not be noble, would not be exciting. Just a puddle.

But Blake won me. The moment he looked at me in the Paradise movie house, I danced in my mind— *and yet against my will*—in visions of white. I still feel today that I do not have the abstract talent for being a wife, only his wife. (Fantasies of picking up a man, taking him home to my apartment for the night, and giving him taxi fare to go away in the morning.)

I married because I knew it would change me, and I was ready for change. The intention clear, the decision made, I would signal it to myself first of all by a ceremony. I got married more for me than for Blake. Backward and inexorably we move through life's rites of passage, looking ever over our shoulders at childhood pleasures not yet tasted to the full, reluctantly surrendered. I wanted to look forward at last, look my life in the eye.

"Why did you suddenly agree after all?" Blake said.

"I wanted to hear myself say the words."

" 'I love you'?"

"To swear to be faithful to you."

"And when you heard them?"

"I meant them."

The relief that I meant them.

A week or two after we were married Blake quit his job and we went to Martha's Vineyard. It was there he wrote his first TV movie script and I finished the windows for my first show at Mrs. Korne's. Beginnings. A beginning for him, a beginning for me, a beginning for both of us. Glorious to be alive.

This tape ends. LeClair Pottinger.

17

Blood Test

"You all right now?"

Dr. Foreman had opened a window of his office and I was sitting down. My skin felt cold.

"Yes."

"You sure?"

"Tell me about the two men."

He looked at me. I understood what was troubling about his face. The mustache he wore was hard and black. The face behind it was soft and petulant, like a spoiled precocious child's. The deep lines from nose to mouth and under the eyes didn't go with anything else. He put a nervous hand through thinning hair. "All we know right now," he said, "is that one has Type O, the other Type A. Of course we didn't know that until we did the autopsy. . . . You want me to go on?"

"Yes."

"Except for the degree of motility and the count—neither one of which is conclusive," Dr. Foreman said, "one man's sperm is much like another's. But forensic tests can type the seminal fluid itself. That's where the difference is. It's the same as the blood type. O, A, AB, B . . . whatever. Blood, semen, even your saliva—they're all body fluids. They all type the same. They took a sample of your blood right then and there?"

"Before they took Clair away."

Foreman pursed his lips and studied the autopsy report. He opened his mouth and tapped a pencil on his teeth. "Was the smell strong?"

"Strong?"

"In the room."

"A strong smell of shit."

137

"So they couldn't smell it?"

"Smell what?"

"The smell of seminal and vaginal secretions. The smell of recent coition."

He put the pencil down. "The bite marks on the breast, of course—they could spot that right off. But if the coital smell was masked by the excretory smells . . . How'd the medical examiner on the scene spot the fact of intercourse right off? Usually we don't begin to look for that until we get the body back here and the autopsy is performed."

"The detectives told the medical examiner on the phone to bring some kind of lamp."

He let out his breath. "Ah . . . Yes. Semen in the pubic hair. It shines in ultraviolet light. Lucky for you they spotted it right away. We determined your blood type, of course, but we tested your B.A.C. too— Are you OK?"

I had thought I was. I wasn't. "Excuse me, Doctor. SLOW DOWN. I'm sorry. It's going too fast." I tried to stand. I had to sit down again.

"*Two* men?" I said.

I could handle the idea until I said it in my mind. I could not get used to the word itself. "Two."

"I thought we were past that," Foreman said. He looked mad again, the hard, mustache part of him coming to the fore.

He played with the autopsy report on the desk in front of him, pinning it down against the breeze from the open window with his box of Chinese food. "Your wife's blood type was AB," he said. "Relatively rare. That helped. The inhibition testing showed Type O seminal grouping in the vagina. Positive. No chance of a mistake. The man was Type O."

"WHO WAS THE TYPE A?"

"That was someone else." He put his fingers together like a lecturer in a medical school. "When a young woman is found murdered in New York City our standard procedure is to look for signs of rape. The bite marks on the decedent's breast were severe.

Fresh. You cannot bite someone without you leave traces of saliva. Even if the saliva dries and you think it's disappeared, it hasn't. It's like saying a fingerprint has gone away because you can't see it. The saline washings I did from the bite marks tested Type A. There's no way in nature for a man with Type O semen to leave a bite mark that tests Type A saliva. So without doubt there were two different sexual participants present. In my opinion, maybe four, maybe eight hours before you phoned the cops."

"But the second man—"

"The bites were sexual," Foreman said. "We get too many homicide sex cases in here to be in any doubt. If the bites are only on the breast, or other sexual parts, it's conclusive. Semen or no, there was a second, sexually active man present."

I stared at him. I knew the answer. He answered my unspoken question anyway: "The second man didn't come."

He stood up abruptly and walked to the window. He looked out, away from me.

"Or . . ." he said.

"Or what?"

"Toomis says it was a pretty wild party. Village people?"

"Yes."

"The bites could have been made by a woman."

I was seated again. Dr. Foreman was looking at me. His words had a retaliatory, savage bite. He sounded as if he was mad at me. I knew he was mad at himself. I didn't know why. "You came in here looking for nice, soft answers. We don't deal in nice, soft answers. You might as well get used to the truth," he said. That was why he was mad.

I asked what kind of blood type I was.

He looked down at his papers. "You're an O."

"Does that mean—?"

A harsh laugh. "Just because you have O Type?

It doesn't mean it had to be your sperm. A couple of million men in New York have O, forty-six percent of the population, to be exact. I'm an O myself. The most common blood type of all. But it does say that whoever bit her, it is medically impossible it was you. If that's any consolation.

"As for the biter," he went on, "man or woman, A's not all that rare either. Without prejudice, and for the sake of argument, let's say it was a man. I would bet there are maybe fifty men Type A in this building right now. You're not an A, so you're not the biter. You are an O—so maybe—only maybe—the semen is yours. All by themselves, these tests don't say you're it. They merely say it's possible you could be one of the two, and if you were, you were the one who performed the intercourse. If you'd been a Type B, however, there would have been no way you could have been either one of them. The cops would have ruled you out *prima facie*. As it is, you're a possible. The cops don't like it you say you can't remember how your own wife got in your bed. That's one place the early blood test worked for you. Lucky the ambulance man took your serum sample then and there."

"Serum?"

"Blood serum. The blood test. We tested you for B.A.C. too—Blood Alcohol Concentration. If they'd waited till the next day, the alcohol would have been metabolized. You tested two point eight. You test one point zero, New York State says you're too drunk to drive a car. Two point eight—even after you've slept it off for a while—that's high enough to give anyone a memory blackout. I told that to Toomis."

"Would two point eight make it medically impossible for a man to have an erection?"

"You a doctor?" His irritation was coming back.

"No. But I always heard too much booze—"

"It ever been true for you?"

"Very rarely."

Foreman grunted. "OK," he said. "So you're not too big a liar. A lot of kids are born nine months after a drunken Saturday night. Don't give the cops alcoholic impotence as some kind of alibi."

"Does Toomis know there were two men?"

"Did he have you come to the station house to make a statement?"

"Yes."

"What time did he let you go?"

"Early Monday morning."

"He knew about the semen Sunday night. He telephoned me from the station house." The doctor picked up the container of Chinese food and looked at it. He threw it into the wastepaper basket and went to stand with one foot on the windowsill. "But he didn't get my report about the biter, the second person with Type A saliva, until maybe noon. Lucky for you."

"Why?"

"He gets a little edgy about exotic sex crimes. Did you have some trouble with a black guy tried to kill you?"

"Yes."

"Toomis asked if it was possible that booze could cause retroactive amnesia—he said you forgot to mention the black guy. Could drinking wipe out memories of a day or two before the actual drinking. I told him that these alcoholic blackouts literally kill thousands of brain cells. It's possible. What's more likely, drunks get used to forgetting what happened yesterday. They don't want to think about it. A drunk protects himself. He thinks of life as a series of random, unconnected events. Cars smashed, money lost, angry people—the horror shows that happened last night— he doesn't want to think about them today. He forgets. He doesn't want to see what his memory blackouts mean."

"Thanks."

"Toomis thinks maybe you were protecting your partner," he said and began walking up and back in front of me, across the room from one wall to another.

"Partner?"

"Toomis doesn't buy it that maybe the biter was a woman. You gay?"

"Gay?"

"Toomis thinks maybe you might be in love with the other guy and want to protect him. Or maybe you're ashamed, still in the closet. Christ, sit down. I'll get us some coffee. You're an addictive personality, you know that? You smoke your cigarettes only half-way down, you're lighting another. You want to feel whatever you're on, there's plenty of it left."

"One of the standard assumptions they teach at John Jay cop college, if there's a sexual trio, it can easily be the two guys are half queer for each other, using the woman like a telephone to tell each other some-thing they can't say face to face." We were still in Foreman's office. Two paper cups of coffee were in front of us. I had finished mine. Foreman hadn't touched his. He pushed it toward me. He went on.

"The other hand, many bisexuals make no bones. They need masculine reinforcement of their male identity to play the man. Otherwise they feel the woman is swamping them. A lot of guys, alone with a woman, he's impotent. In a gang bang they're King Kong. That's why gang bangs are so popular. They need to touch some template of masculinity, to feel they are surrounded by men; it makes them feel like more of a man themselves and they're a hell of a lover to a woman."

"Are you telling me two gays killed Clair?"

Foreman shook his head. "There's a scientific dis-tinction between the homosexual and the homoerotic. Some guys like to go second, they prefer a wet deck, they feel more like men in the Biltmore Men's Bar than anywhere else. They're not queer, maybe they never had a homosexual experience in their entire lives. The homoerotic is the elation of masculine morale. It's not flesh, it's spirit, the sense of intense maleness men have when there are no women around. The solidarity of men in groups, the lust of lynch mobs, beer drinking with the boys on Saturday night, not shaving on hunting trips, telling dirty jokes in the locker room. *Esprit de corps* is the homoerotic, in-tensely sublimated—the joyful and selfless love between soldiers that leads them to run into machine-gun fire to save a pal's life even if they will break the same man's

head if he puts a hand on them in the shower. The
homoerotic is team spirit. It wins football games. The
company of men, this band of brothers, 'the guys.'
Many men had it in war—that's why they can't wait
to go to war again. Don't give me the old bullshit
about latent homosexuality. I don't know what that
means except that all of us have a layer of pansex-
uality that can come out in special circumstances.
Prison. The buggering that used to go on between
Nantucket whalers. They had wives and children
ashore, but their voyages to the Pacific would last two
or three years, never a sight of a woman. 'A man's
man.' Clark Gable. John Wayne. Hemingway. The
U.S. Marines. . . .

"The two of them didn't have to be queer. Maybe
neither ever performed an overt homosexual act in his
life. Oh—maybe the guy who held the knife while his
friend performed—maybe he'll turn out to have a
submissive, homosexual component. But when the cops
find them, I'll bet they have this homoerotic element
. . . egging each other on, daring each other to go all
the way . . . feeling all the more male together because
they are *defined* as not being the woman. You don't
like what I'm saying, do you?"

"I understand what you're saying, but I can't believe it."

"Any reactions?"

"If I was there, one man or two, drunk or sober, I
would remember. I can't think any more about what
you're talking about. It's hard."

Foreman was shaking off my words. He no longer
was irritated with me, but he could not turn off his
curiosity. "Look," he said, "let's go at it another way.
You and your wife have been separated. Now it's
love all over again, kisses and roses. But there's also
leftover, residual anger. You're crazy drunk. Toomis
says you're the jealous type. Who knows what kind of
revenge gang scene you might get into? This other
guy, he must be wondering right now how much you
remember. Why you're not naming him."

"I CAN'T NAME HIM. I WASN'T THERE."

"If you were there, maybe he's thinking he'd better shut you up too."

"There was no other guy."

"The forensic says there was. Listen, somebody already tried to kill you once."

"That was a mistake."

"I hope you know what you're doing."

"IF THERE WERE TWO GUYS, I WASN'T ONE OF THEM!"

"OK."

"I'm not a maniac."

"You don't know what you are you drink that much. You have these memory blackouts often?"

"Sometimes."

"That why you forgot about the black guy tried to kill you? Whoever hired him, that guy is still out there."

"He wasn't trying to kill me. They were trying to kill him. He got killed himself."

"How much do you drink?"

"What I have to."

"You drink when you're down?"

"More when I'm up."

"To heighten the emotion?"

"Yes."

"You know anything about manic depression?"

"Only drugstore psychiatry."

"You have many wild ups and downs?"

"Only with women."

"You go through cycles with women?"

"Before I was married. While I was separated."

"You feel high and marvelous at the beginning of each affair, low and depressed when it's over?"

"Something like that."

"Maybe it was the other way around."

"Say it again."

"Maybe you get excited about this woman or that because you are already excited to begin with. Maybe you break up with her, not because she brings you down but because you're so down in yourself that you can't put up with anyone else."

He was watching to see how these ideas went down.

"Drugstore psychiatry thinks mania and depression are opposite emotions. We're beginning to believe now that the manic high and the depression are both the same underneath. That the depression is the more important of the two. The manic mood is forced, often fueled by booze. The exhilaration is a symptom, merely the patient's own cover-up to himself—a defense against the underlying unbearable depression."

"So?"

"Think about it."

"You think I'm a manic depressive?"

"Do you have trouble falling asleep at night?"

"No."

"That would be anxiety. You have sleep problems?"

"I wake up early, three or four A.M."

"That's depression."

In the silence he stirred uneasily. He smoothed his gangster mustache. "Your wife leave you because the sex wasn't good enough?"

"It was good enough. Maybe it wasn't often enough. She left me because of the drinking."

"You don't think you drink too much?"

"I drink too much. But not that much."

"Drunks lie," he said. "To themselves first of all." He took a step closer to me. Before I knew what he was doing, he prodded me in the liver. "You drink because you feel it will get rid of your anxiety. But let me give you a medical fact: you're getting the cart before the horse. The alcohol doesn't cure the anxiety. Booze—coming down off it—*causes* the anxiety. So you drink again. It's OK to lie to me if you want to protect your suicidal habit. But don't lie to yourself. Your liver's not too swollen. Not great, but not too bad yet. It won't take your abuse forever. You drink too much."

"You think I killed her?"

"Do you?"

"No. Drunk or sober, no."

"A drunk's word is not testimony." Mad again, the

seesaw anger almost palpable. "You had so much booze in you, *I* could have been at the party. I could have read the whole Gray's *Anatomy* to you—and two point eight—even after sleeping it off for a few hours! *Two point eight!* You wouldn't remember." He grunted, the seesaw coming down. "It doesn't matter what I think. What's important is what the police think."

"And they think it's me?"

We were on our feet, standing near the door of his office. Behind the black mustache Foreman's face looked weary and worried. He said, "That's the one thing they never tell me. What they think."

I put out my hand. "You've told me more than you should. I'm grateful."

"More than Toomis would like."

"He won't find out from me."

"Try to cut down on your drinking."

"Why did you let me see the autopsy report?"

He didn't answer. Perhaps he did. He said: "The conventional idea is that alcoholics are trying to commit some form of slow suicide. Research going on at Yale and Rutgers, we're beginning to believe something else. Booze is not a death wish. Maybe something went wrong in the drinker's childhood, maybe he's up against some intolerable strain today. It's stupid to think these people are drinking because in some mysterious, unconscious way, they want things to get worse. These people want things to get better. That's why they drink. They are playing doctor to themselves. Maybe they're taking the wrong medicine, but it's for the right reason: they're trying to keep from dying. Listen, you had enough booze in you to plead to a psychotic episode. I can testify, whatever you did, that much alcohol in you, it was not your responsibility."

Once again he was suddenly going too fast, had taken a turn I didn't understand. "I'd have to say I did it? Plead guilty?"

"You'd have to admit there is at least a possibility you did it."

"No."

"A plea of temporary insanity is only technically a plea of guilty. You don't know that you didn't do it. Plead temporary insanity and you're finished with the whole business. A woman with two different men? The jury wouldn't have to leave the box. You got a life to lead."

"No."

He looked at me. I thought he was going to get mad again. Instead, "Give me your phone number. I'll call you some night. There's something I want you to hear."

"What?"

"You'll know when you hear it."

I looked at his pale face, the almost subliminal red flush beneath the white skin, the harsh lines that were too old for the smoothness of the rest of his complexion. I realized what else was crazy about the way he looked. He looked like my father. "Doctor, you're half drunk yourself right now, aren't you?"

He walked away.

18

George Sanders

"A Spoken History." This is the eighth tape. Begin.

I remember that unseasonably warm November day coming back downtown after a talk about publicity with Mrs. Korne at the gallery, our lighting arrangement for the show cleverly worked out, a rumor of critical attention already started, feeling my life planing on top of the wave, life itself warm and sweet, afloat in my own perfume, lolling back like Sheba among the seat cushions, the taxi rocking down Park Avenue on my way to meet Blake at McGruddy's, thinking of all the resentful wives home cooking dinner while their husbands were having "OK, just one more" in the Biltmore Men's Bar and missing three, if not four trains one after the other, on my way to a cold martini, a lobster dinner and us dancing at La Perla after, seeing the sun dying in purple and gold glory on my right at the end of every blue-shadowed east-west crosstown street, wearing a beautiful new, fishtail blue clingingly flimsy fuck-me dress, and the touch of good underwear beneath cradling me in secret luxury, listening to the music of my mind—with all this going for me, my stomach dropped out.

I told the driver to stop at the nearest corner telephone box. Blake answered, almost too drunk to speak. "Whoozh zhish?" I hung up without a word. We had been married three months.

"Where to now, lady?"

"Make it four-oh-seven West Twentieth Street." Home.

It was months since my conscience had come on at me like a tiger—not since our marriage had I felt that silent, murderous rush of the beast from the unconscious jungle. But Blake's inability to recognize my voice, his love of the pleasures of gin, to which he returned the moment he was away from me, wiped out all the ground I had gained. My very perfume reeked in my nose, pretentious and shabby, the self-delusion of an unattractive girl who thinks an expensive new lipstick will distract from her acne. Fear brought back all my childhood guilt at being ugly and stringy, flat, too tall and self-conscious. I could feel myself go back to the familiar old crouch inside, trying to be little like other girls. Wiped out. Denied. I could not allow that.

I told the driver I had changed my mind again. I would not be going to West Twentieth Street after all but to the Riding High, a bar on Sullivan Street where none of the people we knew ever went. It was one of the secret places to meet in the days I was going around with Felix, before Blake. Immediately in my mind, the old anxious songs began again.

I had perhaps become wiser in the ways of the world, but my superego had grown cooler too. It now came sauntering along, smiling and worldly, cheerful if you please, if anything smarter and more sardonic than me, a bit more sophisticated than I had grown myself. A George Sanders of a conscience. "Come now, sweetie," George says, "you *are* married. You do admit your days of hanging around saloons and celebrating with drunks are over, don't you? What's a married woman doing going to these bars alone? Do you really think you can tell me that you're going out only because it's so boring and depressing to be around Blake when he's locked in and drinking? Isn't that when he needs you most? We needn't try to fool each other. It's sex that's giving you this illicit tingle right now, the forbidden act has the adrenaline flowing, revenge has you hot. And isn't it lovely, that old feeling when you *know* you're on your way somewhere there'll be noise and music, wine, and a lot of people, and it's one of those days when all the mirrors are friendly and you look your smashing best? *A meeting with a stranger.* I don't blame you if you don't want to waste it all on a Nick too blotto to see you. But don't try to fool me. *A fuck-me dress, indeed!*"

In just the space of time it took for a light to turn from green to red and back to green again, in that angry, frustrated time during a traffic jam, when you feel all of life is somewhere else you're not and everyone is at a party to which you were not invited, I was treated to a private showing of my own home movies. Silent images of my mother over the ironing board so that I could look prim and proper at school . . . my stepfather trying to stammer out some lecture, unable to say that what frightened and angered him was the knowledge in his own guilty conscience that this little girl was growing up in a sexually dangerous world where men were predators and women wept . . . Miss Harris in eighth grade who had made me cry after one of my rebellious outbursts by telling me how much I had hurt her, she expected finer things from me than from anyone else in the class. . . . All the sad and well-intentioned moralizers in the world were in the taxi with me—the people I had loved and who had made a soap opera of my conscience.

Feeling hung up, bugged, blue, maybe I should

have married that boy who came up from De Haviland to ask me to go back there to live with him, of what value are art and painting, a New York life, *what do they have to do with being a woman?* The taxi had stopped. We were at Riding High. I got out trembling and shaking, George Sanders laughing at me, alone on the sidewalk in front of a bar filled with unknown and menacing men, cold, afraid, a girl all alone, no one to love me, all the fears that a woman is heir to, etcetera, pausing, paralyzed, between two lives. Just in the nick of time salvation arrived, and in true accordance with the cosmic joke, in disguise. Masked as an enemy.

Around the corner comes a skinny white-faced guy in a rusty green coat. He's got a big cardboard sign on a stick, and he's marching with this sign all alone on that lonely street, picketing the world. And automatically he takes his place at the head of the parade of people bugging me inside my head. Because on his sign it says in big red hate letters "SALOONS THE DOOR TO HELL!" and right away I'm hip, this is what George Sanders is really like behind his cool smile: a mean, skinny, hate-filled nut who is frightened of what he desires, an envious lunatic, desperate that somewhere, someone is having a good time. "SALOONS THE DOOR TO HELL!" the sign says, and I shout, "Keep up the good work, brother!" to the poor suffering idiot, and he begins to say, "Thank you, sist—," but by this time the inner music has started up again, I've got the bar door open, Harold the friendly bartender remembers me from the old days when I used to come here with Felix and puts a drink on the wood, a smile on his face for me, the jukebox is loud, the light is calm and whisky-colored, all the men are handsome, most of them with good-looking girls, New York is where I belong, and I've gone in, almost six foot of woman come out of the jungle, laughing at George Sanders, riding high. Harold nodded his head toward the rear.

I've been around enough gamblers by now to know the cliché is wrong. They do not play to lose. There are moments of high, hard, almost lunatic omnipo-

tence in their lives. It is their drug. Once tasted, it is
the recurrence of these moments of illumination for
which they play again and again until they die, no
matter what the odds. I felt now a moment of power
of my own: like a high-betting gambler I once watched
in Las Vegas who signaled for yet another card when
he already had a frighteningly high eighteen down on
the table in front of him and didn't even have to look
to know he had just been dealt the break-taking three
he needed to confirm his godhead, I did not have to
turn around:

Felix. He got up from a table in the corner and put
his drink down on the bar next to mine.

"What's that you're drinking?"

"A romantic and tragic drink."

"Calvados?"

"You remember," Felix said. "Something told me
you'd be in here today. I felt lucky." He waved his
hand, and Harold, who remembered too, took away
my martini and replaced it with a Calvados of my own.

"I haven't seen you around lately."

"Nick and I spent most of September and October
on Martha's Vineyard. We've only been back a week.
You been away?"

"Out of town. A little something going."

"A girl?"

"Business."

"Hoboken?"

"California. And Mexico too. Like that. Nice to
see you again, Clair. I never knew how much I would
miss you." He raised his glass. "The sun also rises,"
he said.

"*De nada.*"

"Harold, two more."

It is unfortunately no longer possible today to take
bullfighting as a thing of a more serious order than,
say, the return of the player piano or the raccoon coat.
It's just another camp of the twenties. But the ambi-

ence dies hard. To imagine driving to a fiesta along the
hot, dusty roads from Barcelona to Córdoba with a
man you no longer love, in a big, black, ancient, hired
Rolls with yellow basket-weave side panels, is to feel
again the old Hemingway Effect—an out-of-date arti-
fact which had nevertheless led me, when I was sixteen and hoping that whatever was wrong was not in
me but in America, to decide to pursue life, art, love
and romance in Europe myself one day.

This is not to say that these are ambitions worthy
only of adolescent girls growing up in small southern
towns. I'm still a pushover for the whole gaudy number even today. Bullfight posters, the strange ejacu-
lated cries of flamenco singers, that trumpet passage
they always play in the movies when the bull runs into
the ring, eating late at night and alone in Spanish restaurants and drinking Spanish brandy still make me
feel as I did on first reading *The Sun Also Rises*:
what a ball to be tense, jaded, desperate and unhappy. Perhaps Felix was in the same mood. He suggested we walk over to the Picador for a paella.

"Let me make a phone call first."

He smiled and gave me a dime.

No answer at home.

"He's off again, drinking, isn't he?" Felix said. He
hadn't asked me why I was alone.

"I was calling my gallery. I'm going to have a
show."

"Let's have dinner," Felix said, "to celebrate your
show?"

"Are you living with Tamara?"

"She thinks I'm in California."

"But you're living with her?"

"Yes."

"Yes."

"Yes?"

"Yes, let's have dinner."

"Why's it OK only if I'm living with my wife?"

I did not reply. An exchanged glance. My heart
like a hammer.

I did not tell him I did not want it to be with
someone from whom I'd expect too much.

The excitement of complicity: without a word, we knew we didn't want to hurry the moment. A walk first, past the expense-account people eating surf-'n'-turf and near-food dinners in the glass-enclosed sidewalk terrace restaurant of the Fifth Avenue Hotel ... past the young marrieds determinedly buying lousy paintings under the street lamps at the outdoor art show to take back to the three-and-a-half in Queens ... past the glittering stream of failed rock stars, bright young urine-analysts, clever people working for the revolution at Young & Rubicam and broken-string guitar players on Eighth Street. Then through the park and under the dark rustling trees, past the young lovers eating cantaloupe on the black lawns, out onto Fever Street, MacDougal Street, and then around the long way, taking Sixth Avenue back (stopping often to have our silhouettes drawn on soft copper "by genuine artists"), west on Perry Street, north on Hudson, and into the Picador.

Posters lined the walls, each one illustrating another classic ritual pose of man and bull. The people standing at the bar beside us were speaking Spanish and drinking bourbon. Felix and I started with martinis the way we often had, but he soon wangled the honest bartender from the straight and narrow six-parts-gin-one-part-vermouth (lemon peel, please, Pablo) into mixing certain murderers Felix had learned about in Mexico. The best was equal parts of Fundador, vodka and Pernod.

Eddie Fornes, the owner, came up to say hello and shake hands. He remembered us. He was very polite. He'd once run some secret millionaires' private club restaurant in Madrid before he got in trouble with the Franco cops and had to skip. We bought him a drink, and Felix put a slug in the jukebox. Paso dobles began to play, and Eddie had the guy make us a paralyzer he had invented back in Spain: champagne, crabapple juice and vodka. And then they led us, laughing and singing, to our table.

We had paella, of course, and something made with hot Spanish sausage and clams. There were chicken livers sautéed in sherry, tureens of shrimp and oysters,

veal served still sizzling in wine. And in the air the
lovely faint suspicion of garlic.

There was wine, first a white one, and after that I
don't remember. The jukebox played on and on. In
the bar the Spanish people laughed. Espresso appeared, cigars came too, and brandy. Felix said he
loved me. I wanted this night to make me forever different, irrevocably to cauterize the open place in my
flesh where Nick had touched me, to break his hold
with the burn of a rival's flesh. Even if Blake would
never know, even if this infidelity were the first and
last time for the rest of my life, it would glow like a
burning coal forever in the darkness of my mind, a
jewel of my own, a memory I would never lose. It
separated us. It was what I wanted: I would not return to Blake as untouched as he had let me go. Tonight with Felix would put a distance between us. In
that distance I could live. Felix read the roll call of
names on the posters on the walls above our heads:
Jerez . . . Toledo . . . Valencia . . . Albacete . . Madrid
. . . Córdoba . . . Barcelona . . . "Places we'll go together," Felix whispered. "Yes," I said. We both knew
we never would.

Postscript: the erotics of anger.

Old lovers may remain old friends but they remain
old enemies too. Recollections of stifled disappointments and lies, resurfaced rejections clash and dance
in atonal harmony with fond and happy memories.
Released at last from the strain of having to love each
other, the unspoken half of the relationship comes onstage. We enter a new area of desire, cruel perhaps,
but naked too.

Women have always lamented the famous split in
men between emotion and sex. Perhaps they have been
wiser than us all along. Why else have they always
been the more erotic race? A man has a limited, single
goal; he has the power of that singleness too. Women
want sex, but we want the man to like us, to love us
too. Our drive is diffused. This is the war between the
sexes.

In the fairy tale we read as children the grateful
genie grants the fisherman three wishes. The result is
disaster, and the fisherman's last wish is to have the
first two undone. The irony for women is that if we
get our wish, we may rue it too. The more tender he
becomes, the closer, sweeter, warmer—the more we
succeed in taming him and putting him in the family
way—the closer we come to the incest barrier. We do
not know that is what it is. It is not expressed as fear.
It expresses itself as sentimentality.

We begin to think of him as protective, tender, kind,
safe, unexciting, nonsexual—and that is how he thinks
of us too. Blake's favorite joke—the one I hated and
over which we had our last quarrel before he walked
out—was that the definition of a bachelor was a man
who comes and goes. That quarrel was one of my
mistakes. The joke was his effort to add a little arro-
gance and cruelty to the oversweet mixture of marriage and feel himself a man. "The thrill is gone . . ."
goes the old song that both sexes sing. Why? We have
seduced the man, but we are in the trap too. Boon
companions, best of friends, a family. But lovers no
more. His erect cock may not have been near us for a
week, but we don't mind. His arms hold us tenderly
as we lie against his breast and watch TV. Love is all.

It had better be. It is all you get. I never doubted he
loved me, but the longer we lived together the more
he lost desire. Months went by, only once in Martha's
Vineyard, and after that nothing at all. I have come to
think that his drinking is not tied to his damned father,
whom he never stopped talking about, but to the loss
of his mother, whom he never mentioned at all. He
drank too much when I met him. I did not expect to
reform him, but why did it accelerate the longer he
lived with me? Women think whatever goes wrong is
our fault. Why was he drinking so much if he loved
me? I now think it was *because* he loved me. He had
put me in the place of his mother, whom he loved
more than he could know. Unable to handle the idea
of sex with me, he drank in order to lose me too.

We have long protested being demeaned by men
who "want only one thing." In our need to make every

man love us, no matter how casual or trifling the moment (or the man), we give him the power to withhold what he never considered part of the bargain to begin with. Nine men out of ten are incapable of love. The shame of whining after love from a man who does not know what it means, or thinks it weakness if he does. Better to get in touch with our anger at these men instead. *If they are proud to be called studs, let them be used as such!* Better to spend our nights in bed with them than our days alone waiting for that tenth man who may never come along. Love is a promise that may never be fulfilled, but if it comes, it is the enemy of sex. Excitement is real, you feel it in your blood, an avalanche. Anger, even hate, brings excitement to sex. Anger distances the man. He becomes our sex object. The biter bit. The hangman hung. Men little know of women's volcanic angers.

Anger brings a sharp and malicious edge to appetite. The sexual power of the stranger is knowledge every woman has, and has been taught to deny. Perhaps we no longer think of sex as forbidden. We know it is dangerous. A lifetime's training in inhibition is not undone by slogans in *Ms.* Magazine, Bob Dylan lyrics and the pill. Sex wears a monkey face and screams in a monkey jungle. We are afraid to allow a man we love to see the grinning, lightning-lit, promiscuous and unashamed face of lust we wear in our dark and secret dreams. With someone you don't respect, anything goes.

Sex with servants, sex with the man in the mask.

Tape ends. LeClair Pottinger.

19

San Diego

City of San Diego
San Diego Police Department

FROM: Det. Joseph Dolan Shield 1789, 17th Det.
Sqd., S.D.P.D.
TO: Det. Sgt. Frank Toomis, N.Y.P.D.
SUBJECT: Information on activities of Clair Pottinger
AKA LeClair Pottinger AKA Clair Blake
AKA LeClair Blake

1. On Sunday, April 4, the undersigned received a
Telex request from Det. Sgt. Frank Toomis, N.Y.P.D.,
for information on past activity and movements, this
city, of subject named above, who was a victim of a
homicide in New York City on night of Saturday-
Sunday April 3–4. N.Y.P.D. Homicide File case
76438. Dets. Frank Toomis and Lou Farrow assigned.

2. The undersigned responded to subject's last San
Diego address, 1842 Suffolk Palisade Towers, and interviewed subject's former roommate, Inez Farejo. As
a result of this interview, the following information was
developed. The subject moved from Los Angeles to
San Diego about 21 months ago, during which time
she shared this apartment with Farejo. Subject answered an advertisement in newspaper Miss Farejo
had placed asking for a woman to share the rent. Miss

Farejo stated that subject seemed to have only one male acquaintance, whom she saw frequently, giving his name as Harry Maxwell. Subsequent investigation showed his address to be 35 La Vista Drive, La Jolla, Calif. When asked if Maxwell was subject's boyfriend, Miss Farejo stated she believed he must have been more of a business associate. Miss Farejo was asked by undersigned to give her reasons for this judgment. Miss Farejo stated that subject had never shown any romantic involvement with Maxwell. In addition, Miss Farejo stated that starting about one year ago, subject became very popular with a number of different men. This was in strong contrast with the first six months of subject's co-residence in the apartment. Miss Farejo further stated that she had recently quarreled with subject over these men, and was thinking of asking subject to find a new apartment. This became unnecessary when subject suddenly told her (Miss Farejo) that she was moving to New York. Subject had never told Miss Farejo that she was originally from New York or that she was married. Miss Farejo states that subject was secretive and generally uninformative.

3. In reply to a direct question, Miss Farejo stated her opinion that subject's connection with the men who suddenly began to appear at the apartment was sexual. Most of them stayed overnight, sharing the subject's bedroom. Miss Farejo said she rarely saw the same man twice in subject's company, which puzzled her because they (the men) often showed signs they would like to know subject better by questioning Miss Farejo about other boyfriends, what was subject's favorite perfume, etc. In the first six months, subject had not entertained a single man in the apartment for any reason, other than Harry Maxwell, mentioned above. Miss Farejo stated that Maxwell never spent the night with subject at the apartment.

4. Undersigned responded to 35 La Vista Drive, La Jolla, to interview Harry Maxwell. Upon arrival, undersigned found that Maxwell's apartment was sealed

by the Police Department, it being the scene of a homicide.

5. The undersigned responded to the 9th Det. Sqd., La Jolla P.D. for further information concerning the seal on Maxwell's apartment. While at the 9th Det. Sqd. the undersigned learned that Maxwell was the victim of a homicide the afternoon of Saturday, April 3. He was shot in his apartment, twice behind the left ear. Door was not forced and there was no sign of struggle. Apartment was not robbed. This case is being carried under the 9th Pct. UF54 No. 9083, Det. Luiso, 9th Det. Sqd. assigned. The undersigned interviewed Det. Luiso, who states the case is under active investigation. Det. Luiso further states that Maxwell was a political activist who had been arrested several times on suspicion of marijuana-possession charges. No record of convictions. Maxwell's apartment was searched, and Det. Luiso states that a suspicious white substance was found mixed with salt in a 5-lb. box of Diamond Kosher Salt. White substance is being separated and analyzed by forensic laboratory as of this date.

6. Maxwell was an industrial chemist at California Cyanamide, Inc., 4587 Pueblo Blvd., San Diego. He was known as a quiet, efficient employee. No adverse information developed against him at California Cyanamide.

7. Undersigned received a phone call this morning from Det. Luiso, 9th Det. Sqd., La Jolla P.D. Det. Luiso states that further search of Maxwell's apartment developed an open parachute found crumpled up in a ball under a wad of laundry in Maxwell's closet. Parachute is being sent to forensic laboratory.

8. Miss Farejo said subject had left most of her clothes for the maid. However, subject left apartment two days before she had told Miss Farejo she would be leaving. Clothes closets showed signs of hasty packing. With Miss Farejo's permission, undersigned went through the apartment. Some underwear, cosmetics,

women's stockings and other incidental items were left
behind but did not seem to undersigned to have any
significance. Behind a dictionary in subject's desk
drawer, undersigned found one reel of tape recording.
Tape was in an unsealed white business envelope with
word "Johnson" written in pencil on envelope. Miss
Farejo stated she is not familiar enough with subject's
handwriting to say with certainty if the name was in
subject's handwriting on evidence of just one printed
word. Inventory of clothes, cosmetics, etc. left in apartment plus reel of tape are enclosed with this report.
Please advise of desired future disposition of clothes,
etc.

9. A recent snapshot was found in the apartment,
identified as subject by Miss Farejo. Undersigned made
a copy of photo for investigative purposes of San
Diego and La Jolla P.D.s. Original enclosed for confirmation of subject's identity by you.

10. Miss Farejo further stated that subject was employed at Speaking Volumes, Inc., this city, mfrs. of
tape recordings of books for blind people. Miss Farejo
was under the impression subject was a part-time
employee because she remained at the apartment very
often for days at a time to paint. A stack of 18 oil
canvases were shown to undersigned by Miss Farejo.
They had been kept in storage in the basement of
the building, and Miss Farejo said she recognized them
all as having been painted by subject. Miss Farejo
stated that she had never known subject was a painter
until one year ago. Subject had shown no interest in
art during the first six months they had shared the
apartment. Miss Farejo states that subject explained
her sudden interest in painting by saying quote When
I can't love, I can't fuck. When I can't fuck, I can't
love. When I can't love or fuck, I can't paint. When I
can't paint, I can't fuck or love. End quote. Responding to a direct question from undersigned, Miss Farejo
stated it is her strong impression that subject's interest
in painting coincided with beginning of time when she
began to bring men home to the apartment. Photo-

graphs of 18 oil paintings are enclosed with this report. Please advise of desired future disposition of original canvases.

11. Miss Farejo further states that she was under impression that subject was part-time employee because she traveled frequently for nonbusiness purposes. Miss Farejo was under impression that subject must have had a private or other source of income because the rent was high and could not be easily met on a part-time salary. Undersigned asked to see the clothes left for the maid. They were expensive garments, with Dior, Yves St. Laurent, etc. labels. However, subject never discussed money with her. Subject owned and drove a Jaguar Imperial, Calif. lic. YFK 8738. Miss Farejo said subject had sold her the car for $1000 before she left, stating that she (subject) did not have time to dispose of the car otherwise. Miss Farejo showed undersigned the bill of sale, correctly executed. Investigation showed the car had originally been bought from Pacific Motors, La Jolla, for $9,898.89, and paid for in cash. Miss Farejo also stated that subject drove in her car often to Ensenada, Baja California, staying away overnight frequently. Miss Farejo asked subject if she liked the beach at Baja and subject stated to her quote, I don't have enough patience to sit in the sun. End quote. Miss Farejo is a female Hispanic, 5'6", 115 lbs., dark hair, brown eyes, 28 years old. Identification unit checked for past criminal record, negative result. Is employed as an Art Director by Friday & Scott Advertising, this city, earning $18,-000 per year. No other information available on Miss Farejo.

12. Undersigned responded to subject's last place of employment, Speaking Volumes, Inc., 24 Sutton St., this city, and interviewed Mr. Joe Robinson, Executive Vice-President. Mr. Robinson states subject was employed as a free-lance producer for about one year, earning approximately $8,000. Subject was a good worker, and was additionally valuable because she had a good speaking voice and would record herself

on the tape-recorded books the company produced, which resulted in important economies. Subject was asked several times to work full time but refused, stating she didn't have time and was only working at Speaking Volumes because she enjoyed the work. Subject kept to herself and did not associate with any of the other employees. On two different occasions subject's coworkers hinted to Mr. Robinson that subject had a drinking problem, but Mr. Robinson states he never saw subject under influence of alcohol. It is the judgment of undersigned that Mr. Robinson took a fatherly interest in subject, and he spoke of her work and character in the highest terms.

13. The undersigned responded to the Intelligence Unit of this dept. and interviewed Det. Walter Stevens concerning Harry Maxwell. Det. Stevens states that Harry Maxwell has been under suspicion for some time of financing several politically active groups through sales of narcotics. Det. Stevens states that none of these groups had any known connection with headquarters in Baja California. Maxwell was also under observation by the F.B.I.

14. The undersigned contacted the San Diego office of the F.B.I. and conferred with Agent Boyland, who advised that both Harry Maxwell and LeClair Pottinger have been observed on numerous occasions together. A tap on Maxwell's telephone was begun January 12, but was discontinued at end of 30-day court order authorizing tap. No suspicious references were recorded except for frequent mention in telephone conversations between Maxwell and subject of quote the man from New York unquote. F.B.I. further reports that Maxwell and subject had several meetings with unknown men at Traveller's Airport Hotel, San Diego. Agent Boyland stated it is his opinion that these men may in fact have been the same man, since he seemed to be wearing various disguises of wigs, mustaches, etc. Detailed descriptions of this man or men included with this report.

15. Undersigned responded to the TWA ticket counter at San Diego airport and interviewed Ticket Agent Helen Lasky. Miss Lasky's records showed that subject arrived at ticket counter the afternoon of Saturday, April 3, and stated she must get to New York immediately. Miss Lasky stated that she remembers subject very well (when shown photo taken from subject's apartment) because there were no seats left on next plane to New York and subject urgently requested she be given first standby. Miss Lasky further stated that, at subject's request, she phoned all other airlines to see if subject could get on earliest flight to New York. When this was unsuccessful, subject availed herself of a sudden cancellation and took Flight 245 to New York, leaving immediately. Ticket exchange was effected. Subject's old ticket was canceled and a new one issued. Old ticket (No. T-23857B) was for Flight 299, San Diego–New York (connection at LAX), leaving Monday, April 5, at 5 A.M. New ticket was Flight 245, San Diego–New York (connection LAX), leaving 4 P.M. local time, Saturday, April 3. TWA records show this flight arrived JFK–New York on time, 2 A.M. local time, Sunday, April 4. Subject's plane ticket paid by AmExpress card 041 AB817 0 100AX. This card issued to Clair Pottinger, 1842 Suffolk Palisade Towers, San Diego, Calif.

16. Subject responded by telephone to American Express issuing office, Los Angeles, Calif. A search of records shows subject has used AmExpress card extensively since issued 18 months ago. Monthly charges averaged $2000–$3000, mostly for foreign travel. Various cities in South America were most frequent destination, including Mexico City, Lima, Quito and Rio de Janeiro.

17. The undersigned has given information regarding the New York City homicide of subject to 9th Sqd. La Jolla detectives for their information and advised of subject's connection with Maxwell. This information was also given to F.B.I. with advisement of sub-

ject's death in New York and prior connection to
Maxwell.

18. Notify undersigned if any further assistance or
information is required.

Joseph Dolan

Joseph Dolan
Detective

20

Johnson

Toomis read the report three times and then
picked up the envelope the detectives had found in
Clair's San Diego apartment.

"This name Johnson she wrote on it," he said to
Lou. "It mean anything to you?"

"Common enough name."

"No friend or acquaintance of Blake's you know
named Johnson?"

"Never heard him mention any."

Toomis took the tape out of the envelope and
bounced it in the palm of his hand. "Go ask the lieu-
tenant we can borrow his tape recorder," he said to
Lou.

He read the report a fourth time, and then Lou
came back with the machine. They listened to Clair's
tape.

"A Spoken History," Tape 32 starts now.

When I was little and planning to run away from
home I began by saving my money. When I left Blake

I had no money saved at all. I had been smarter about money as a kid than as a grown woman.

My mother's silent lesson had been that you don't talk about money, so I didn't talk about it. I merely thought about it all the time instead and saved as much as I could. As a child I took the jeers about being a tomboy because I was "good about money," but marriage regressed me. With a sigh of relief, as if giving up a lifelong constraint, I fell into habits of thinking about money and not thinking about it, both at the same time. "Things will work out"—which meant Blake would work them out. I didn't have time to think about problems with money. I had a more insoluble one.

Blake. He was ever present in my mind, like the roar of a waterfall; but there is no solution that will make Niagara go away. Part of the relief about leaving him was that I didn't have to worry about his drinking any more. I tried not even to think about him, and began once again to worry about money instead —thus giving a kind of falsely "real" focus to my anxieties.

All my thoughts began with I would not take any more from him. If you take someone's money, you take the strings and bullshit that go with it. What I think now is that I was fooling myself. With the utmost self-deception, I was depending on him to come for me before all the money was spent. Or, if it was all spent, then I would have no choice. I would have to go back.

Part of my way of fooling myself was to phone Felix from Los Angeles when my new show opened at the Korne Gallery. I asked him to go see it for me and to tell me how many had been sold. He asked if I was too broke to come to New York. I said I was afraid. Felix thought I meant the critics.

"The windows got good notices that first show of yours," he said.

"I'm still working in glass. The critics don't like it if you don't change."

"Painters always repeat the same theme. Picasso and his blue clowns. Warhol and his Marilyn Monroes." He paused. "Or do you mean Blake?"

"Yes."

"He's gone."

"Gone?"

"To France. Couple of days ago. Didn't you know?"

"For good?"

"He subleased the apartment."

I told Felix I had to hang up.

"We'll talk about it when you get to New York," he said. "I want to see you." He sent a telegram to my phone number the next day saying a paid ticket to New York was waiting at the American Airlines desk.

We had made a date to meet at the zoo. He was eating popcorn and looking at the seals when I came in through the Fifth Avenue entrance. He had on a long suede coat almost the yellow of his head, and the white streak in his hair glinted blond and gold here and there when he stood with his back to the sun. A blue turtleneck beneath, his beard shaved, the old familiar smile of pleasure in seeing me. It reminded me how much I had loved him. He looked at me over his familiar blue sunglasses, walking toward me in that way he has, with his arms slightly rotated forward, the vulnerable open space of the inner elbow and the palms of his hands facing out.

I said, "Other people when you see them again, they're supposed to look smaller than you remember."

"I got some heels put on these boots. I wanted to be as tall as you."

I kissed him for that, his head down shyly, the kiss landing on the forehead, the strong-planed face in which you could almost see the marks of the sculptor's thumb in the clay. He was gold and white, blue and yellow, the colors of the unexpectedly sunny day on which we met. He looked laughably young without the beard, some kind of kid's unsure mischief in his eyes. And his beautiful smile. I was glad to see him. I had gone to the gallery right off the plane.

"I didn't think you'd come," he said. "Every time I see you it's like the first time. I always forget how beautiful you are. I'm glad you're here."

"I'm glad too."

"Then you're not mad at me?"

"Don't think that."

I leaned in to him, to kiss him again, but he turned, his face turning, coming up closer, his nose going past my eyes, his eyes looking into mine, his arms flying around my neck, my body turning with his, accepting the momentum of his own.

"You wouldn't kiss me if you were still mad at me?" he said. "Everything is going to be different now. I should have filed for my divorce years ago. I'm glad you kissed me."

I took a step and we began to walk. He asked if I had heard from Blake. I said no. Felix said he had Blake's French address. Did I want to write to him? No. I did not say I had phoned the apartment myself.

In the lunatic way of children who do not trust what other people tell them and are uncushioned for disappointment when the bad news turns out to be true, I had phoned, hoping Felix was mistaken. That Blake had not left or had come back. To say I wanted us to try again. I had one last gasp of urgency when the man who answered said he had Blake's address in France—he was supposed to send the rent checks there. Three thousand miles away, the address care of *poste restante*. You can't phone a mail drop. The energy drained away. Later I sent Blake a postcard so I would not think of him again. Felix and I looked at the bears and the lions, and then we came back to the seals again. The sunlight was a little white, brittle but warm on our backs. We held hands. I tried not to think about money. We were happy.

Later we sat under one of the green-and-white-striped umbrellas on the cafeteria terrace. Felix went in to get us two coffees. He had a half-pint bottle of Calvados in his coat pocket "for old times' sake." We put some in the coffee, and Felix moved our chairs so we were sitting in the sun. He had a piece of cake that he picked apart while we spoke, the mischievous, shy smile lit by the sun on his face. He was throwing crumbs to the pigeons. I leaned forward as we spoke, in under the shadow of the umbrella, so that the light would not be in my eyes and I could see him better. The pigeons circled across the sky, swinging in great wheeling crowds. They were very pretty, but they made a hell of a noise cooing and gurgling over the cake crumbs. It was early in the day, and with the chill in the air, there weren't too many people around.

"You doing anything special in Los Angeles?" Felix asked.

"I wanted to go far away."

"Anybody there?" His voice was only unsuccessfully casual.

"No."

"I mean, a man?"

"No."

"And you're worried about money."

"A little. I don't want you to lend me any."

"I just wanted to know," Felix said. "Tell me, you given up on Nick for good?"

"He gave up on himself a long time ago. Like his father."

"Why didn't you love me?" Felix said.

"The turns you give a conversation."

"Clair, tell me."

"I did. I do. I still have mixed feelings about you."

"You never told me you loved me."

"I told you. You didn't want to hear it."

"I never thought you meant it," he said. "Don't get mad. If you loved me you wouldn't get angry with me."

"Listen," I said. "Listen, we have mixed feelings about everybody. I've always loved you."

"You loved him more."

"You never wanted me to love you. That was our bargain. That's why you liked to be with me."

"It was a dirty bargain."

"It was yours."

"*Yours too!*" he shouted. "If I ever talked about anything, even just moving in together for a summer on the Cape, you looked out the window."

"That was all a long time ago." I felt stifled, angry, but afraid too.

"We won't talk about it," Felix said, afraid too. "It's getting you mad. I'm sorry."

"I'm not mad."

But "If only you could have loved me," he said, like a broken record.

I held myself in. "I did love you." My breath was short.

"Please, Clair, don't get mad." And he looked at me with his eyes that had always searched my heart, and for one crazy second I thought maybe there is a God, a God who'll stop me from getting madder at him, but there is no God and I yelled at him.

"You're right. I never loved you. I couldn't fool you. You're right!"

"Clair, what are you saying?" His smile gone.

"I never loved you," I shouted at him. "It's that simple. You knew it all along. That's why you never left your wife for me, why you never turned on with me for real until I met Blake. That's why it happened! You don't love me. You're only jealous of Blake. Why shouldn't you have gone back to your wife? You knew I never loved you. I wasn't able to fool you!"

He stared at me as if I had a knife in my hand and was going to stab him. "How could I fool you?" I cried. "I couldn't fool myself!"

I got up to go. But I turned to him one last time. "Why couldn't you have believed me when I told you I loved you? If you could have believed it, I would have believed it myself!" And I walked through the pigeons and out of that goddamned park. I took a taxi back to the gallery. Still no sales.

Typist, this tape ends here.

Toomis shut off the tape recorder. "Recognize the voice?"

"It's her, all right," Lou said.

"You look blue."

"I'm not blue."

"You look like you were in love with her. Maybe you should take yourself off the case."

"Frank, shut up. I can be objective about her."

"We'll see."

"You're talking about my job. Come on. What've we got?"

Toomis looked at Lou over the lighted match held to the end of a cigar. "If you're so goddamned objective, you know what we got. From what we know from Mrs. Korne, she had her first show six years ago, right after she got married. A little publicity, some nice mentions, only two sales. This second show she's talking about, it's two years ago, right after she leaves Blake. Same story: not much money. So two years ago she's broke, worried about money. Now—Now she's OK. She's got these expensive travel habits, to say the least, and her airplane tickets aren't being paid any more by this Felix. She's living in a way you can't support by a part-time job reading books to blind people. It looks like she's in the coke trade—coke mixed with the kosher salt at this dead guy's place, Maxwell. Maybe she's a big importer. All that South American travel in Dolan's report. Maybe she's working for somebody else. Also, for all we know, maybe she makes a habit of flying in for the afternoon to have these sessions with this Felix. Another nice friend of yours. He use anything?"

"I never heard he was."

"What gets me, all the babbling about God, she gives herself an excuse, the goddamned whore. Why do tramps have to dress up their sex with a lot of poetry?"

"How would I know?"

"I'm really asking, Lou. You're half a hippy yourself. Why can't they leave religion out of it?"

"Who's not objective now, Frank? You got religion on the brain. You got it in for the girl."

"She's not a girl, she's a junky, or mixed up with junkies, or a pusher, or a bringer!" Toomis shouted. "I don't like it about your friend Felix, Lou. It's not clear from the tape what's up now, but they used to be more than just pals. We'll talk to him again. Maybe they still got something going between them. Did you know it?"

"Felix is always secret about women he goes with.

He was married then. When she was married to Blake I never heard a word about her."

Toomis walked to the window. Lou watched him mash his cigar out in a tin ashtray. "OK," Toomis said. "She makes this tape. The story of her life. She works where? In a blind people's book place. So she has access to tape machines. Maybe she makes more. Play it again. The beginning."

Lou rewound the tape and pushed the button. "A Spoken History," said the woman's voice on the machine, "Tape Thirty-two starts—" Toomis mashed his finger on the stop button. "Tape Thirty-two," he said, "Where's one through thirty-one? You ever find her suitcase or suitcases?"

"I checked TWA baggage," Lou said, "and got the overtime list from JFK, from when she landed through eight hours after. Eleven lockers turned up unpaid, overdue after twenty-four hours. But nothing for us. I checked them. The guys who killed her, it figures they got the suitcase. Including the tapes. OK, so they're the story of her life. Why are they so valuable to someone else?"

Toomis said: "I got a better idea. They didn't want the goddamn true-romance tapes. The suitcase was filled with sweet white powder she got from Maxwell. Or stole from him."

"She killed him?"

"He was dead, wasn't he? The La Jolla P.D. lab separates out the 'suspicious white substance' from the kosher salt, you bet your sweet little ass it's going to be coke."

"And the black pusher Sam who tried to kill Nick," Lou said. "He figures in this—"

"—*because he's in the dope too!*" Toomis finished Lou's sentence. "This case is about the shit trade, all right. Sam's try on him, her being put away—they're connected. Maybe they tried to put the bump on him because they didn't know how much she had told him about their business. Husband and wife make up, she confesses her past, he kisses her and all's forgiven. Except from their angle, one extra person knows. Remember, when he calls her from France she says she can't meet him in New York right away? She got to finish up some business in California first? The business she got to finish, she got to get together one last load of shit her last run, that's her unfinished business. I wouldn't be surprised your fancy movie friend with the advanced morals got himself a nice suitcase of coke somewhere. Maybe he even knocked her off for it. Maybe she shipped it to him ahead air freight, and they were going to rip it off together, finance a new life. Maybe I won't have to fire you off the case after all."

"Come again."

"You're Blake's friend. Stay close to him."

"So he calls me up and says, 'Hey, Lou, guess what I found? Clair's suitcase was under the bed and maybe ten kilos pure cocaine in it.'"

"He doesn't have to know why you're hanging close to him."

"We don't warn him? They could try again."

"If he doesn't have the suitcase, there's nothing to warn him. They got it. She's dead. They'll forget him."

"Look: she arrives on a last-minute flight. The seat cancellation tells us she probably didn't have a chance to phone New York what flight she's on. The middle of the night she stashes the stuff somewhere and thinks she'll make the drop tomorrow. Meanwhile she gets killed. Her business associates—they'll think he's got the suitcase."

"We owe him anything?" said Toomis.

"Frank, they killed her. They'll kill him!"

"He held out on us about the black guy, didn't he? Her—I don't care about her being killed except it leads us to her partners. A scummy doper dead, we're one ahead. I don't want that shit going on sale on the street. I want the guys she was carrying for. Let them come after him. You'll be there."

"What about the rape?" Lou said.

"Who said it was a rape?" Toomis said.

"Jesus, there were two of them—"

"The medical examiner says it is possible one of them was a woman. Funny kind of rape."

"Frank, I knew her . . ."

"Did you know about the mask?"

"No."

"Just how much do you know—to be exact—about her bedroom habits?"

"I don't like that, Frank."

"Is that an evasive answer?"

"I don't know anything about her in the bedroom."

"You don't want to face it about your sweetheart, do you? Let me tell you. Any broad that'd carry dope, she'd take on two dykes, two guys, one dyke and one guy—a nice little party on a rainy afternoon before going to the pictures. A nice bangola first after the party's over, then they give her the business, grab the suitcase and go home."

"I can't see Blake setting up a trio with his wife."

"One, he's drunk. You don't know what he'll do drunk. Two, he's passed out. Maybe the whole thing takes place with him snoring it off right there in the goddamn bed. Goddamn freaks, they make me puke. My friends are moving out of New York, Lou. Me, I'm stuck in Queens. There's a nice black doctor and his Barnard College Lena Horne wife. They bought a house in the next block, I can't sell mine any more love or money. I'm married. I got a family. I don't want my kids buying dope on their way to school. Blake will have to take his chances."

"I don't like it."

"Hate it. Do your job."

Toomis's fingers drummed on the table. He took off his hat and wiped his bald head. He put his hat back on. His eyes gleamed. "You know this Johnson you were asking about? The name on the envelope with the tape?"

"What about him?"

"Play the end Mrs. Blake's tape again."

Lou put the tape through the machine once more. The men listened. Toomis spoke aloud the words they heard. "Typist, this tape ends here." He smiled at Lou. "Phone Dolan in San Diego. She had the envelope half-addressed, but she left in a hurry after she knocked off Maxwell, or heard about it and knew she was next. She never mailed it. Tell Dolan to find the typist. We find her luggage, I bet we find the coke and a bunch of tapes and her whole diary, neatly typed up by a certain Miss Johnson."

Toomis looked at the color photos Dolan had sent with his investigative report from San Diego. They showed the oil paintings that had been stored in the basement of 1842 Suffolk Palisade Towers. "What the hell does this tell us?" Toomis said. "Eighteen naked guys. One of them with a head in a pillowcase. The next with a face painted like a hawk. One of them like the Lone Ranger . . . Eighteen naked guys and every one of them wears a—" His voice stopped.

Lou finished the sentence. "Wearing a mask," Lou said.

"She brung it with her," Toomis said. "As soon as she's inside the door, two years away, and she can't wait to try her new fuck games with her husband."

"She was a painter, Frank. She used it a prop for her paintings. . . ."

"Grow up," Toomis said.

21

Urn

We drove through a gate down an avenue of trees and went into a low white stone building. There was taped organ music, and after a while a conveyor belt started up with the whine of an electric motor. Panel doors slid open and shut behind the coffin. There was a sound like a subway express train behind the doors. I don't know what I expected. Not that. Clair's mother tapped me on the arm and opened her purse. Her name was April. She had a half-pint flask of Scotch and gave me a drink. I had said we did not want a minister. No one spoke a eulogy; Clair's last ceremony took place in silence. When we had come in, there was no one else in the room except an usher in a swallow-tail coat. When April and I stood up to go, I saw that Lou had come in and was sitting in the back.

They gave me an urn. April and I left.

"Why did you decide to do it this way?" April said.

"Clair and I once had a talk. It's what she wanted."

"Funny conversation."

"It was our wedding day."

"When I was a little girl growing up we lived beside a river. We got up so early it was still dark. My father used to like to drink warm milk from a bowl. I remember the bowl was chipped. The big meal was at noon, supper in the early evening. My mother sometimes hummed to herself, but she never sang. She was not a talkative woman at all. My father was much older than she was and I could never feel as if he was really my father. He was like a grandfather, more like someone in a history book at school who told about the frontier. Once he told me, when he was a little boy *his* father shot a panther on the roof of the house. I used to pretend to myself that they were not my real parents. I once told that to Clair. She said she did not have to pretend. Her real father had gone away."

We were sitting in the living room of the apartment. I had not turned on the lamps. Darkness helped. I was thinking about Clair. April was remembering aloud. The gray evening came into the room; Clair's painted-out white canvases hung on the black walls, softly shimmering, rectangular ghosts in the last dim light. The only color came through the open door of the bedroom: long bars of blue and gold from Clair's stained-glass windows. April stood up and took the urn from the table between us and held it in her arms. She held it to her breast. She stood with her back to me. Over her shoulder: "Why are the paintings white?"

"It was Clair's way of erasing mistakes. Then whatever shadows of color showed through the white, she'd use to give spontaneity to the new painting she'd do on top."

"And the faces in the stained-glass windows? Why did she paint them white?"

"They were a mistake too."

April came back to her seat. She put the urn back on the table. "In the nights," she said, "I used to wish for a little brother or sister to play with. I was an only child. Once when no one was looking I stole one of Mother's preserve jars and put a little note in it. I let it float away on the river. Then, on nights when I lay in the dark hoping my mother would not die, I'd think of the river going on and on, my bottle floating on it. A little ship, a little message, something anyway, going somewhere, something that seemed to be leading the way out for me . . . a little spot of brightness I could see in my mind, you know, going off and disappearing across the black nighttime fields.

"When I grew up I went to Wheeling and studied at the art museum. We were all Marxists then—the Depression—socialists at least, and women wore those funny men's hats. One year it was the vogue to go to see the Bobcats—our local baseball team—play as often as you could. The big thing was to show that women were just as much at home as men in the man's world—which we thought was the *real* world then, you see. I was working in a department store when I went home one Christmas and met John Pottinger. He was from Baltimore but had come to De Haviland to teach in the high school. We married and I never got as far away from home again until this trip. He left me, you know."

"Clair told me."

"I never told her."

"What?"

"It was Clair's birth drove him away. He couldn't stand children, the responsibility. She used to ask me about him. She had an idea about him, that he was some strange and romantic figure. How could I tell her the truth?"

April paused. Her eyes lost their focus and she thought again about her life.

"From the window of the hotel last night," she said, "I could see the Hudson River. It reminded me of the river I knew when I was a little girl. I began to wonder, if you trace rivers back to the Continental Divide, do they all connect up someplace back there? Last night I dreamed that the bottle that the little me sent floating down her river in West Virginia so long ago came floating down the Hudson to New York and I found it. But in the dream I was too afraid to open it and read the message inside. As a matter of fact, I tried to think this morning what was the message I sent out so many years ago, but I couldn't remember. Something like, 'Help, I'm lonely,' I suppose."

The last light was gone. I turned on the lamps. April said she had to think about getting out to the airport to go home. I asked if she'd like a drink.

"Clair phoned me once. She said you drank too much."

"Sometimes."

"I told her men drink. Her father did. I told her not to fuss."

I said I was sorry Clair's stepfather hadn't come. April said that was the way he was: births, deaths, marriages, he felt the emotional work of the world was women's work. I asked her to tell me about Clair's own father.

"When I was living in Wheeling," she said, "I wasn't so sure I ever did want to get married. Young people today talk as if they invented sex, but it did exist before they came along. I had decided that by the time I had had four or five affairs—as we used to call them—and never felt the Blinding Flash, as my mother used to call it, True Love, you know, well, I could pretty well be sure that all the moonlight-and-roses stories my poor mother used to tell me when I was a little girl were just more of the lies they tell kids. Isn't it fierce, though, the way people feel it's their duty to just out-and-out lie to their children? I mean, their little innocent daughters, just out-and-out filthy, black lies about what life is all about?

"Anyway, I was figuring, after I'd had my six affairs, that I'd give up looking and find some Daddy

Warbucks to keep me. I didn't want to go back to De Haviland. I had a figure then, those days, I was jolly and loved a good party. And I could do it with style. That's not a bad life, you know. Why else does every little housewife go to a costume party dressed up as a streetwalker every chance she gets?

"But you guessed it by now: just when I had met and got done with Number Six, when I reckoned to myself I'd seen through all the lies, I got trapped, I fell in love. *That* one wasn't a lie after all. But someday I'm going to write a book and show how men invented love to trap women. Love leads to every misery a woman has, every indignity she has to suffer—including the double standard. Women have love and men have the double standard. Oh, it's lovely to be in love, to feel the excitement, you're warm all over—I remember . . . But sometimes the price you have to pay—

"Anyway, John Pottinger and I, we made it. He was a good, sweet man to me until the children were born. That's when he began to drink. Suddenly one day, Clair was four or five, he just never came home. He sent me a letter from Baltimore. He said he knew I loved him, but if he stayed with me, in the end his drinking would make me hate him. He didn't want his daughters to grow up with a drinking father, and he could not give it up. Sometimes I wonder. If I had known the effect on John that having children would bring . . .

"Well, anyway, I married my second husband, Harley, when Clair was fourteen. He drinks a bit too, but not like John. I think we're doing better at marriage than most. Or anyway, I am. One or two things (I don't think Clair knew about them) used to make me feel maybe Harley was more like John Pottinger than I knew, that maybe he doesn't care as much for this marriage business as I do. But what can I do for him? I give him all the room and happiness I can. After that, it isn't going to do him any good for me to worry and feel guilty.

"Harley never made much money, but that's all right. We have a little rinky-dink rowboat on the lake with a malted-milk machine motor for the summer.

And we always have a little wine around the house to keep us warm the winter. You drink yourself; you understand. Every once in a while we have a fight and bust up a couple of days, but even that keeps things moving for us.

"So here I am, I'm fifty-three, just this past December, and it's been a hell of a life. And I suddenly have a daughter of my own—and she came to me one day and said she wanted to go to New York to live. She wanted a life of *her* own. You know what I told Clair the night before she left to come to New York? 'Your stepfather and I, we don't have much to give you, but I'll tell you this: enjoy yourself, wear pretty clothes, and don't fall in love too soon. Remember that your mother is on your side no matter what happens, and never be one of these little milk-faced girls who decides she's in love with a man just because she tumbles into bed with him.' "

I drove out to the airport in the taxi with April and told her I would fly down in a few days for the funeral. She was taking the urn back with her. She said maybe they'd bury it on a piece of property they owned near the river.

"Will you let her father know?"

"I don't know where he is. Clair never got over it, you know—the way John Pottinger left us."

We were standing at the airline ticket counter. There was some trouble because the security bomb-detector machine flashed red at the metal urn. They wanted April to ship it in the hold of the plane. She told them she was going to carry it with her, and why. They froze.

She said, "Why are you smiling?"

"Clair was more your daughter than she knew."

"I think she knew."

"Funny about your name."

"Funny?"

"Except for you, April isn't my lucky month."

She walked onto the plane holding the urn in her arms. I went back to the apartment alone. A time to reexamine my life.

The litany of my days is common enough. Like most

people I knew, I was a democrat who did not believe in Democracy, a liberal sick of progress, an atheist who would have preferred the mysteries of faith. I could not even start with the assumption that my life was my own. Like most men, I was doing work I had not chosen. Like my father, who had reached his dead end in some vague middle management, I too found myself beached somewhere in middle show biz. The assignments I was getting were not to do new work but rather script fixes and rewrites; I was facile enough to invent episodes for TV detectives, not talented enough to do anything more.

Like my father, I had given up on my wife too soon.

By the time I had grown old enough to know him, my father no longer spoke of love and I never raised the subject of did he love his wife. When he mentioned my mother to me it was always in tones of politeness, regret. I did not question his silence, but it left me wondering. Like drinking itself, love was endless, and while I did not trust it, I never felt I had contained it. My ambivalence was its greatest attraction. I had come back from France determined to invest at least as much of my life exploring the further meanings of love as I had spent exploring the enigmas of booze. My greatest hope was that I didn't understand love. Whatever I did understand I despised.

I had wanted to construct a small and ordered world, a community I could believe in even if it would be a community only of two, and if the rules and values would have to be egocentric and private, at least they would not begin with "absurd capital letters." I had come back to answer at last the question begun during my undergraduate drinking sessions with my father. *Succeed in what?* I wanted to believe, not in marriage but in my marriage to Clair. To succeed in that. But I had left it too late.

Without her, the only way I knew out of the airless and onanistic room of the self—an object too contingent to occupy the thought of sixty or seventy years —was booze. The world had no purpose, the search had more meaning than the goal, the happiest times of my life had been drunk and roaring. I have read

Sartre on the existential moment, and discussions
about living for today are common enough everyday
chatter, but the only way I have ever been able to
shut off anxiety about tomorrow, regrets over yesterday, or the tedium of right now is with a drink. A
quiet martini at ten thirty in the morning in a cool
and dark bar, a little music playing, cold water running in the rinse sink, a fresh supply of new, white,
hard-edged ice cubes mounded in a silver-and-
chromium bucket, nobody around but the white-
jacketed bartender off at the other end, humming as
he slices lemon peels for the lunch trade, and all the
commuting world hot and hurtling by outside the
window on their way to their offices—it's a soothing
and intense experience. The first martini narrows time
down to the moment in which it itself exists; four close
the gap between thought and action, between reason
and emotion, heal the subject/object split, reunite the
self that feels with the bored self that watches. But
like the Wall Street broker after the crash who has to
change his habits, not because the years of riotous
living have taught him the moral superiority resident
in seventy-nine-cent meat loaf but because he can no
longer afford champagne and caviar, I had to stop
drinking. Alcohol enlarged the world and made it
whole, but the bar bill had been presented at last,
and it had been more than I could pay. Drinking
had made Clair leave me twice, once for California,
this time for death. The phone was ringing as I awoke
in the dark. I let it ring, then shook myself awake,
held a moment more by memory and sleep: the empty,
shimmering white canvases on the dark walls, the
smell of paint in the air—Clair was as close as if she
were merely in the other room, blowing on her chilled
fingers, stamping her foot against cramp, finishing up
the stained-glass window that now loomed above my
head. Goodbye to Clair. Goodbye to her light. I would
never see her face again. She was painted out. On
the phone Lou said, "You ever hear of someone
named Johnson? A friend or associate of Clair's?"

"No."

"Toomis says maybe you can drop in the station house to talk to him again the next day or two."

"What about?"

"Nothing important."

I asked why he had been at the cremation.

"I was hoping to see maybe a face didn't belong there. You never know." His voice changed, softened from the official grew halting in embarrassed concern. He had come to the cemetery because he had been worried about me.

"Let's have a drink and maybe dinner tonight," he said. "Maybe it's not good for you to be alone. What are friends for?"

book four

HALF-REMEMBERED FIGURES

22

A Portrait of Nixon

Time. Paralyzed time. Three months gone by as if I had waked in the middle of the night in my own room, but the bed on the ceiling, all the other furniture up there and me too; and with no reason for the end of gravity. Silent, brute, impossible fact: everything calm, quiet, my shirt and pants folded on the chair, but wrong, upside down, no way to know what was up, what down, or why I was not falling into space. As if I had waked again the next morning to find everything back in place, the ceiling up, the bed on the floor, but still wrong, and still no explanation. And now no longer any evidence it had happened. A dream I knew was no dream; what had happened to Clair could not have happened, but it had.

Bulletins from another front: Eleven major corporations had moved out of New York City since the beginning of the year, 16,000 more jobs gone. The transit unions were turned down for a ten-dollar raise by the mayor's budget committee, *The New York Times* ran an exposé on the secret ten-thousand-dollar pay hikes given the day before to forty of the mayor's political appointees, on the same budget committee. In retaliation the subway men said they were going to strike; Avis and Hertz immediately raised their rent-a-car rates. In Central Park a recently discharged city cop on a stolen ten-speed bike had whizzed out of the bridle-path bushes just after dawn one day and put a bayonet into a horse's belly. Then he had mugged the rider, a Fifth Avenue advertising man, for $600. In the following three weeks, less astute students of horse-flesh, who could not recognize the difference between an expensive mount privately kept and ordinary hacks rented out to the public by the hour, had murdered four more horses, robbing their riders with disappointing results. The wreckers who were tearing down the old apartment house around the corner on West Twenty-first Street were fired one morning because the California land company that owned the property decided nobody would buy the new co-ops even if they completed the building. The Six-o'clock Happy Talk News on Channel 7 ran a human-interest forty-five seconds on the father of three who had been the last rent-controlled tenant in the old building. He had been induced to move out by being offered one of the new co-ops at a bargain price. He had taken a job wrecking the old building to earn his down payment. Now he had no job, no place to live. The federal government cut its aid to New York's drug programs; in turn the city was forced to close fourteen rehabilitation clinics, putting 19,000 junkies back on the streets. Police estimated these returned users would commit $4 million worth of burglaries and muggings in the next year to pay for their resumed habits and would commit close to 400 crime-related murders. The savings to the government of the United States of America was $400,000. On the corner of Fifth Avenue and Forty-second Street a hunchbacked man handed me a green flier. "The national economy is healthy," it said, "but the people are sick. God is love, but Jesus suffers." He did not say what he wanted me to do about it. On the corner of Fifth Avenue and Forty-third Street a teenage Korean disciple of the Reverend Moon handed me a red-white-and-blue flier. He told me, "God bless America." When I asked why, he could not speak. "God bless America" was the only English he knew.

Bulletins from my own front: none.

"We got guys working on it here in New York," Lou had said when he dropped by for a drink one night. "We got investigations going forward by the L.A.P.D. and the San Diego cops too. But we don't have much yet." They were following up on Sam, the black pusher who had tried to kill me. Nothing there either.

—and then I asked Felix what kind of business he was running in Hoboken.

I had been in attendance at the summer-solstice gala the beautiful Miss Colbert had given for her big white French poodle, Lavish, but had decided not to drink; I had left sober, an uncharmed and uncharming guest, when the obligatory glass-smashing scene began. In bed by midnight; terrific pounding on my door around one.

"Hey, Nick? What the hell you doing in there? It *disappoints* me, finding you in bed alone."

I yelled through the door for Felix to go away.

"Would I be a friend I let you waste your Saturday night asleep? Open up. *Always* brightest before dawn."

Lou was with him.

"This official?"

"Don't be sore, Nick," Lou said. "Felix said he was going to find you. I come along. We thought maybe you'd like some company. You hungry?"

"Sure."

"The Village Embers," Felix said. "Barbecue. I can eat like a regiment. Come *on!*"

I hadn't been able to sleep anyway.

Walking toward the Embers; leaves on the trees on Cornelia Street opened up for summer. The leaves black on the undersides, silhouetted black against the street lamps, full and deep green on the side that faced the electric light. The endless brownstones and apartment houses of New York had fascinated me from the first. I would walk through the streets at night, held by the lights in thousands and thousands of windows behind which millions of lives were being led that would go on whether I knew the people or not—mysterious lives, people who had jobs, families, furniture, pursuits, interests, friends, talents, none of which were dependent on me knowing about them at all. It was an image of infinite possibility: "fascinating strangers" as my father used to say, whom I might meet at the office today, at a party tomorrow. In the years I had been away in France the city had changed; the windows were now barred with heavy iron grates, few late lights burned. New York's promise—that at any moment I might so easily meet someone who could radically change my life forever—gone.

Lost in thoughts of Clair, I did not notice Felix and Lou were slowing in their walk. Up ahead a solitary taxi had cruised to a stop at a red light at the corner of West Eleventh Street. From doorways and shattered storefronts on both sides of Sixth Avenue fifteen or twenty twelve- and fourteen-year-old black kids had silently appeared and were swarming toward the cab. From behind us three more came running. One of them pushed past Felix; he whirled fast as a dancer, knocking the kid down. Up ahead the taxi did not wait; the driver accelerated through the red light and was gone. The wolf pack stood restless and unfocused in place a moment longer. The night was silent except for the sound of a kid cursing Felix. By ones and twos, heads began to turn. The pack was looking at us.

"Trouble," said Felix.

"Don't get separated," said Lou.

We moved closer together.

The kids split up into two gangs. Half of them crossed the street, their heads watching us all the while. They began to move around our flank. The other bunch walked directly at us.

"Right on, you mothers!" Felix said.

"Pull your gun, Lou, the bastards!" I said.

"Be cool," Lou said.

The kids were twenty feet from us. The cursing stopped. Silence. They moved closer. We did not move at all. As silently as they had appeared, the kids faded away.

Something in me was relieved but disappointed too. I was shaking with unexpended energy, like an outboard motor running at full speed with no water to push against.

Felix was looking at me. "You got a lot of heat in you."

"I'm sorry," I said.

Lou was looking at me too. "You wanted a little gun action? Kids like those, once they start to mix, they don't back off. I don't want to be in the *Daily News* tomorrow, the cop who shot a kid."

"It was a stupid thing for me to say."

Lou looked at me a moment more. "You got a lot on your mind."

My fingers were balled up into fists. I let them go. "Maybe it's time to think about leaving New York for good."

Felix spat on the ground. "Back to France?"

"I feel like a foreigner here. At least there I'm supposed to feel like one."

"Home," Felix said. "The scene of the crime." His voice was intense. He seemed to be going through a reaction of his own. He was more keyed up than usual but more tired too. He kept yawning. He made an abrupt gesture in the air, half irritation, half anger. "We are *not* cruising at speed," he said and short-stopped us into Ira's Glue. Ira himself was behind the bar. Felix ordered beer and a shot of bourbon for himself.

"Jee*zuss*," said Lou, coming down off his adrenalin too, and said he'd have a bourbon himself. Felix went off to make a phone call. Lou and I were alone. He said did I want to have a drink.

"In a while."

I apologized for not being cooler about the black kids on Sixth Avenue.

"Don't think about it," Lou said. "You got a lot on your mind. Everybody's always saying this one is cool, that one is cool—I mean, what is cool? Usually it means you don't give a shit. What's hard about being cool like that? Real cool—that's just the opposite. Take Felix and Jennifer. You ever meet her?" He was talking so fast I realized he was embarrassed by how stupidly I had taken the incident with the street gang.

"Some kind of affair with her and Felix in the summer heat?"

Lou smiled. "Man, it was all heat. All on his side. I'm surprised he told you about her."

"The day after Clair died."

"Maybe he wanted to tell you a story about himself you wouldn't feel so bad. She was one of his defeats."

Lou finished his drink. He asked again if I'd like

one. I said I'd wait. He went on again about Felix and Jennifer.

"The difference," he said, "between Felix and some guy people say he's cool, you go out to Valley Stream a Saturday afternoon, make it to the supermarket, watch the scene there. Here comes some poor cat, he's caught, he's got the wife with the list walking in front of him, he's pushing the little wagon and he's got the rotten kid in the basket. And he's pushing it. I mean, at least the wife's got the wall-to-wall to brag to her friends, the kid's got an ice cream and a dirty face. What's *he* got? He's got the job to push the wagon. Later they're going to have the new married couple from across the hall over for dinner, and after that maybe take in a movie, go bowling, maybe a Valley Stream pizza parlor after that. I mean, that's his life, people live like that, you know. So this guy, he meets his friend in the supermarket, he's also pushing the wagon, and they say how are things Harry, and the other one says, 'Yeah, like, cool, man.' Of course he's cool. He's dead. But that's not Felix and Jennifer. She gave him a hard time, but you'd never know it from him. You had to hand him that. He had it for her. Being cool when you're burning like him, that's cool."

Mel Parigi and Big Mary were having one of their quarrels in the corner. Felix was still on the phone, but he sent them a hello drink, finished his own, hung up and dialed a new number. The poet Anatole Fugelman came in with Matti Cosworth.

"What'll it be?" said Tito the Puerto Rican hamburger man. He went to the big black cast-iron roller of marbleized butcher paper and tore off a six-foot strip to cover the tablecloth. He liked to write people's orders on the paper so there'd be no arguments. Anatole said he'd have the usual and began to write a poem on the paper.

Tito looked at Matti. "And you?"

"I need something skinny to eat," she said. "I have to lose seven and a half pounds before my breakfast date with Robert Redford."

"When's your date?"

"Tomorrow morning at nine A.M."

Felix was still on the phone, but he sent Matti a drink for that one and then turned his back to us, hunching over the instrument in intense conversation. In a quiet voice Lou went on with his story about Jennifer.

"Felix was making it with her on and off this last year or so. What it was, she was just plain one of these women didn't want to settle down yet. Felix would chase her, catching her wasn't hard, but then she'd get bored, start a new scene somewhere, then she'd get tired the new cat and come back to Felix. She used to say he was the only man understood her. I guess he did—but who'd want to understand *that?*

"So how does it end? Two, three night ago I was here in the Glue with Felix. We've sort of gotten to be friends again, you know? What the hell. Anyway, a guy comes in never liked Felix. He gives me a wink and comes over. Here's trouble. Felix is cool. He looks at him like he's studying an ant, a germ. The germ says, 'Hey, Felix, Jennifer just got married.' Felix doesn't say anything. He just goes on studying this amoeba. The germ winks at me again. He says it again: 'Felix, Jennifer just got married. I was at City Hall with them. You know that TWA pilot? She's flying to Puerto Rico on her honeymoon with him right this minute, your number with her is over.' "

Lou shrugged and smiled. He went on: "Felix ignores this ridiculous scene, the germ fat and happy, he's giving it to Felix. Felix doesn't let on anything. He tells Ira he wants a new drink, make it a double. By this time the germ is jumping up and down. He knows his news has to have gotten under Felix's skin, but he's not getting any reaction. He wants to see Felix blow up, he's just a worm, he hates Felix, all the action, all the girls around Felix. The germ looks at his watch. 'In fact, Felix,' he says, 'right this minute they're probably having a drink at the hotel right now, a frozen honeymoon Daiquiri.' Felix turns to the germ and he doesn't look at him. *He surveys him.* He says nothing. He finishes his double and calmly tells Ira he'll have another. The germ can't take it. 'Felix! Felix!' he yells. 'Don't you get it? They're probably in the

sack right now, the marriage consummated, you'll never
see Jennifer again!'

"Felix picks up his drink. He smiles at the germ. He
drinks half the drink. 'Next time you see her, tell her,'
he says, and he says the coolest thing I ever heard in
my life, 'tell her she has any children, *we're through.*'
And he finishes his drink."

Lou was looking at me, smiling triumphantly at
his recollection of Felix's aplomb. Enormous chasms of
deceit swam before my eyes, too deep to look into
without becoming dizzy. The violence of the kids in
the street had spoken to me, and I still felt an answer
in myself, the thrill of the berserker, a satisfying rage
for revenge. It frightened me. I was afraid of what I
thought, but I said it anyway: "Then the affair with
Jennifer—*it ended only a few days ago?*"

Lou looked at me. "You knew her?"

"Felix told me it was finished while I was still in
France."

"When did Felix ever tell the truth if a lie was fun-
nier?"

I was suspicious of myself, suspicious of everyone
else. I wanted to ask Lou more, but old patterns of
passivity were shifting, revealing older patterns I did
not want to know. I was sick of my blackness. I said
nothing. Felix was coming back from the phone. Lou
moved away a bit so we'd look less conspiratorial. Felix waved a hand so we would not be embarrassed.

"Listen," he said, "I never mind what people say
behind my back. It's what they say bad to my face I
can't stand."

He looked from me to Lou. "You were talking about
me, right?"

"Only about how you feel when a love affair comes
to an end," I said—a drop of poison. But Felix heard
no double meaning, he merely used my answer to go
off into private memories of his own.

"Yeah, yeah," he said dreamily. "Even the best
things come to an end. *That's why* they're the best.
Ira! *Calvados time!*"

He leaned over the bar and poured his bourbon down the sink. Ira brought us three Calvados. Felix picked up his new glass and tasted it. "Yeah," he said, "there's something about drinking Calvados on a long, sad, rainy Sunday afternoon with a girl you're breaking up with. One of my favorite times. You both know the affair is over, you *turn on* to romantic, tragic drinks, the last minutes together are sweet, the pretense of forever gone . . . It's exhilarating."

He turned to Lou. "You ever end that way?"

Lou looked white in the face. "Felix," he said, "I have a great admiration for you, at least half of which may be genuine. But you know your trouble? Nobody ever went to bed before you. Let me tell you, you didn't arrive on earth trailing clouds of glory to invent sex for the rest of us." He slammed off to the Gents.

"What's wrong with him?" Felix said.

"Maybe he thinks you're putting him on."

"How can I tease him about having an affair?" Felix said. "He never has any."

Mel and Mary had finished their desperately quiet argument in the corner. They got up to go. Mel tried to fake us out with an extra hearty good-night wave, but Mary kept her face averted. Felix watched them go out together. Through the plate-glass window we could see Mary walking along the street, her face strained, her head rigidly turned from Mel's pleading gestures.

Felix looked after them. "Whenever I see two people like Mel and Mary, they don't know how to let each other go, my advice is always the same: Get married *immediately!* So when you get divorced you won't be too old."

Late. Felix said he didn't want to eat after all. Lou and I said the hell with the Embers and had two of Tito's hamburgers. Ira turned off half the lights and took off his apron. He put a toothpick in the side of his mouth and came over to stand with us, half off duty, one leg hiked up and resting on the chromium sink. Felix told him to have a Calvados on us. Ira went to find the bottle. Lou was talking to Fugelman about poetry. Felix flipped his sunglasses up on top of his head again and peered around the Glue's half-gloom for anyone else he knew. I didn't like his eyes. His glass was empty. He drank mine, ordered a new round of Calvados for us all.

I said to Felix, "You going for my title?"

"How's that?"

"I don't remember you a strong juicer."

He spread his hands in front of him. A deprecatory smile. "I been using it to kick. It puts the slows on."

"Kick what?"

"I been weekending a little."

"I thought you hate pushers."

"Now you know why."

"You got it in control?"

"Just a little penny skin-popping. I'll kick for good starting tomorrow. I'm coming down now, dig? I'll be all right."

"That's why you're so fidgety?"

"Lou makes me nervous."

"Why?"

"So we make up past misunderstandings. I don't like a cop should be my best friend. I run into him at McGruddy's tonight. I'm leaving. I got to see some guys. He asks where I'm going. I tell him I'm coming to see you. I got other things to do tonight, but don't want to tell him that. It's lucky, because right away he says he'll come along too."

"He thinks I need cheering up."

"I'm hip."

"He's coming back," I said. "Put your sunglasses down. Don't let him see the pupils your eyes."

"Thanks. I forgot."

"Don't forget to kick."

Lou picked up the new glass on the bar in front of him and sniffed it. From behind his blue shades, Felix winked at me. "What's this shit?" Lou said. He was angry, as if he had seen the wink.

Felix was standing a little straighter, his dreaminess gone. "We thought you'd like some more Calvados," he said.

"I don't want Calvados," Lou said. "Why are we drinking Calvados?"

"Because it's a romantic and tragic drink," Felix said.

"My ass is romantic and tragic," Lou said. He looked closely at Felix. "Is this another one your numbers, Felix? What's with all this Calvados and this romantic and tragic all of a sudden?"

"I thought Nick might like a romantic and tragic drink because tomorrow's Sunday." The adrenaline was pumping in Felix's veins. He had been slurring his words earlier. His speech was clear now.

"Are you hinting something?" Lou's anger was surprising.

"What's to hint?"

I didn't want to think it myself. The idea that Clair and her death on a Sunday might somehow be part of this talk was impossible.

"Just stop with the romantic and tragic, that's all," Lou said. He pushed his Calvados away.

"You want another bourbon instead?" Ira asked Lou.

"I'll stay with beer." Lou turned to me, irritation still in his voice. "One thing Felix says is right," he said, finding a way to change the subject without seeming to veer off too obviously. "Why is Sunday such a downer? Just to think about it and already I'm depressed."

"That's all I'm talking about," Felix said. "The Sunday Neurosis, nothing more."

"Sunday's always a good day for business," Ira said. "Soon as we open one o'clock, they come hurtling in like snap, crackle, pop—shot from guns."

Lou said "Shit" and walked away from us and put a quarter in the jukebox. Before he could come back: "Felix, I got to ask you something."

His eyes narrowed. "Lou's coming."

"Call me when we cut out of here. I'll be home. I got to know what kind of business you're running over there in Hoboken."

The look of relief came up like the sun across his face.

Diana Ross was singing. It was close to four A.M. I wanted to get home. I did not want to get home. I wanted Felix to phone me. I did not want Felix to phone me. Tito finished scraping the grease off his griddle, turned off the blue Schlitz Beer signs in the window, and the signs over the Gents and Ladies. Fugelman and Matti left. Tito finished putting out all the other lights and Ira locked the door. "Last call," he said to us, and we stood bathed in the muted red-and-gold glow of the jukebox neon. While we watched Tito slowly crumple up the paper tablecloths and begin to stack the chairs upside down on the tabletops and mop the floor, Lou spoke about regret. His voice was quiet, unconsciously taking on the rhythms of the music. Felix winked at me. I avoided his eye. "Every Sunday of my life," Lou was saying, "I get the feeling my golden time is running out. I'm guilty against myself that I haven't lived enough, enjoyed myself as much as I thought I would. The weekend is like a golden girl, and the clocks tick her away and we feel we haven't been man enough to possess her. Behind her smiles she hasn't given us all the sweetness, all the honey and fire she holds and gives someone else. She laughs at us. We know it's all there, like a woman's breast behind her skinny silk dress, so near, so unattainable. If you want a woman hard enough, and you can't have her, you get mad at her. I feel the same about weekends. I wish they had never been invented."

He shook his head wonderingly. "When I was a kid, just growing up, everybody was always asking my ambition. How the hell does a kid know? I had none. I didn't know what I wanted to be—a doctor, business, maybe join the Marines? How the hell did I know? Then one day I got hold my older sister's copy *Vogue* Magazine. It had a list, pictures of the Ten Best-Dressed Women of the Year. I must have been thirteen, fourteen years old. I looked and looked at those pictures—paralyzingly, majestically beautiful women, their incredible clothes, their eyes distant and turned inward, those dreaming, self-contained women, sleeping on and on, looking out of the photographs without seeing me, denying I exist, and they live in a better world, steeped, drowned, lost in lotus pools narcissism, and I knew what my ambition was."

"You fell in love with all of them?"

"I hated all of them."

"I don't understand the story," Ira said. "What kind of ambition is that?"

The music ended. We stood a moment more in silence.

"Nick," Felix said, "you haven't touched your Calvados." He drank my glass and his own too. We walked around Tito's mop and bucket and yelled good night. My heart was pounding.

"I'll call you, Nick," Felix said without emphasis. He had waited until Lou said he was coming with me and then muttered about he had to go see some guys. He jumped into a passing taxi without another word. My phone was ringing as I put the key in the door.

I looked at Lou. The phone continued to ring. Lou looked at me. He smiled. He went into the other room, closing the door behind him. I put my face down beside the phone so that I could speak immediately as I picked it up: "Felix, if you hear the extension click, hang up."

His first words were "You think I did it."

I sat down. "That's not what I asked."

"Lou's in the other room?"

"There's an extension."

"Ask me the real question."

"All I asked was, what are you up to in Hoboken?"

"Give me the one after that."

"Don't talk crazy."

"Toomis tell you I didn't stay long with Lou after we left your party together?"

"Yes."

"I told you that myself. When I came to your place for a drink."

"Yes."

"Ask it, Nick."

"Forget it. No."

"Ask it, Nick."

"Who were those guys you saw in Hoboken? After you left Lou?"

"You're asking if I got an alibi."

"I'm just asking what you do over there."

"OK," said Felix. "You asked it. Now ask the big one."

"The cops are going to ask you, Felix."

"I can handle the cops. You ask me."

I couldn't speak.

Silence.

"Nick?"

"Did you hear a click? Felix, did Lou pick up the extension?"

Silence.

"No."

"Silence."

"You'll feel better. Ask it."

"I can't say it."

"Say it."

"It would be better we drop it. I'm half crazy, Felix."

"It was a crazy thing that happened. The answer has to be crazy too. Nick?"

"Yes?"

"You think I did it."

"No."

"Act like a friend, Nick. Say what's on your mind."

"Don't, Felix."

"Say it."

"Don't push me into something we'll both regret."

"Say the words out loud, Nick."

"Why?"

"You say something in your mind, it seems to make sense. You say it out loud to somebody else, you see it doesn't make sense at all."

"We better hang up."

"Don't worry about Lou picking up. I can hear sound levels drop the extension is picked up. What put these ideas in your mind?"

"You knew Lou was in love with Clair."

"He was the only one thought it was a secret."

"You were teasing him about Calvados being tragic."

"You think I would make a joke about Sunday being the day Clair died? You think I did it to tease Lou?"

"The teasing put it in my mind. The Calvados . . ."

"What about it?"

"There was a bottle of Calvados . . ."

Felix waited.

Silence.

"There was a bottle of Calvados?" Felix's quiet voice encouraged me.

"On the bedside table, when she was killed. Clair never drank Calvados. You shouldn't have made me say it, Felix."

"Was that all?"

"Yes."

"I mean, was that all there was on the bedside table?"

"A bottle of gin. Some vodka. The way you kept insisting we drink Calvados . . . it had some terrible association for me . . ."

"You ever see me drink Calvados?" Felix said on the phone. "I mean, before tonight?"

"No."

"—and didn't every guest at the party go in and out the bedroom if only to use the can? Maybe they drank Calvados?"

"Let it drop, Felix. I'm sorry."

Silence.

"Nick?"

"Yes?"

"I didn't do it."

Silence.

"Nick?"

"Yes?"

"I didn't do it."

Silence.

"Do you want me to tell you about Hoboken?"

"Don't tell me anything. I feel like a fool. I don't want to hear about Hoboken."

"I want you to know."

"I believe you. You don't have to tell me anything."

"You know the Weathermen?"

"The Waldorf bombing a couple of months ago."

"They call it armed propaganda. I'm in business with them."

"Business?"

"They got to raise money. I buy cigarettes legal down in North Carolina. I run a little storage and moving company in Hoboken, in front. During the day, you call up, my trucks come and move you. At night, another truck comes in from down south, tax-free cigarettes. I warehouse them in Hoboken until the Weather guys can run them into New York. Jersey cops don't have the speed New York cops, so the Hoboken warehouse is safe. The cigarettes cost me a buck ninety a carton in Raleigh. The Weather guys add maybe another quarter, thirty cents when they bring them over the river and sell them in the city. The Jersey cops don't care. The cigarettes aren't even being sold in Jersey."

"Did you hear a click? My God, Lou is listening. LOU, ARE YOU ON THE LINE?"

Silence.

I could hear Felix listening. "Take it easy. Nobody on the line."

"I can't believe it, Felix. You're not political."

"Who said I was? I do a simple trucking operation, bring cigarettes up north. The Weather guys take the risk. They buy them from me, they put them on the market. Figure it out. I make seventy-five cents a carton, a truck can maybe bring in fifty thousand cartons a crack. Nearly forty thousand bucks, cash."

"This is one of your jokes."

"Let me tell you a real joke. You can believe I'd kill Clair but you can't believe I'd do a little cigarette running."

"I have to hang up now."

"You believe me?"

"Yes."

Silence.

"Nick?"

"I can't talk any more."

"Nick, tell Lou what we were talking about."

"That you run cigarettes?"

"About I went to my garage in Hoboken after I left him. He'll confirm I was there. They already checked me out on that. I didn't see any guys in Hoboken. I was with a girl in Jersey till I came to see you. When I saw about Clair in the *Daily News*. The cops already spoke to the girl."

Silence.

I had to ask one thing more.

"Felix?"

"Yes?"

I took a deep breath. I forced myself not to hang up. I felt I was about to explode. I couldn't say it. I asked something else. "How did you know so fast?"

"Fast?"

"What I wanted to talk about?"

"What else could it be you didn't want to mention it in front of Lou? I'm not sore, Nick. You been through what you been through, you got to have goofy thoughts. So you asked me. You didn't go to the cops. It was a friendly way to relieve your mind. Thanks." He hung up.

Felix could not know there were two men involved in Clair's death, but I did. Children are not easily shocked, because they accept whatever they see or hear as if it had existed in the natural order of things since time had begun. In the same way, as if I had known from the time I was born, I knew without knowing how I knew that the two men who had killed Clair had to be strangers, unknown to me, crashers at the party, because if I knew either of them I would know them both; and the second would have to be me. The idea was no surprise, it gave me no sudden thrill of intuitive completion. I just knew it. Knew it as unquestionably and unsurprisingly as I knew my name, that two and two are four, or that it now was night. I had always known it.

An idea that would not down; released, it took on a life of its own. In a mounting and childish paroxysm of rage that astonished me but was not lessened because in some remote corner I knew it was childish and only self-pity, I cursed Clair. If she had not died this would not have happened. Tremors of fury shook my body, but the mind had separated, splitting off to fall back to a place where it watched and was unmoved. *If Clair had not left me!* I felt exposed and vulnerable, hating myself for suspecting Felix, suspecting him all the more, and yet sick to death of what my thoughts meant. Sickest of all for what I had not had the courage to ask him. I was frightened because I was angry, angry because I was frightened. *I hated Clair for dying.*

The door behind opened and Lou came into the room, hesitating until he saw that I had hung up.

"I'm glad," he said.

"Glad?"

He motioned with his head to the telephone. "That you have a new girl. Stupid of me to have come here. You should have said something. Get back on the horn and tell her she can come right over. I'm leaving."

He sniffed the air. "You had a drink?"

"No."

"You been letting Felix drink yours all night. Don't start now all of a sudden, for Christ's sake."

I asked him the question I had not asked Felix: "Lou, this Jennifer, who just got married. Who used to go around with Felix. Was she married before?"

Lou smiled. "Why? Is that what Felix said? Just more of his bullshit."

"Maybe she was married a long time ago and got divorced and now she's only remarried?"

"I met her before Felix did, when she first came to the Village. I know all about her. She never even lived with anybody before the day she married this new guy."

From the back room she used as a studio I had brought out the rest of Clair's painted-over canvases and hung them on nails, surrounding myself with her presence. They covered the walls of the living room and overflowed into the bedroom right up to either side of the stained-glass window portrait of the two of us which Clair had made and painted out too. Her broad, flat brushstrokes had covered the canvases in translucent wash; behind the whiteness, vistas of drowned landscapes beckoned, half-remembered figures peered out and called to me. Clair considered these her failures; they were more moving than any she had finished. They lived in me like the language of jazz or string quartets when you do not understand what is being said but find yourself when the music stops disturbed and thrilled, applauding—what? I did not have to understand to know. A memory of my own slid from a recess of my mind, superimposing itself on the pearly Rorschach blur of a canvas as if Clair had painted something there she wanted me to see. Enigmatic, horribly beautiful, suffused by soft light as if from within, the image of a mask floated in front of the masked white canvas, the black mask Toomis had made me wear. I wrote Clair's name in the dust of a window pane. Could the mind remember something the brain forgot?

Over my shoulder I said: "Lou, I think I was one of them."

The postcard came as if to confirm my thoughts but contradict them too, unexpected and amazing, and yet, I felt as I held it by the edges, inevitable too. Sunday night had turned stifling. When I went down for the mail on Monday, the morning was opening up like the door of an oven. Con Edison had broken down for the second time in a week and the air conditioning was out; but my sweat was cold. I took the card back up to the apartment. The stamp was canceled with the new, efficient, money-saving "U.S. Postal Service" mark that doesn't tell you from what city it was mailed. I was careful not to handle it. I used four pushpins to center it on one of the canvases in front of my chair. On the front was a smiling technicolor portrait of Richard M. Nixon against a background of the presidential seal and crossed American flags. On the back the card carried my address in large, anonymous, mechanically perfect block printing. The message was hand-printed in the same way. It said:

SHE WORE THE MASK

The card was unsigned.

23

Los Angeles

Typist, this is Tape 31, "A Spoken History." Notes for revision:

Identifying with the men and against yourself. The tyranny of asking What will he think of me tomorrow? Tape begins here, but skip a space first.

"Taxi."
"Where to?"
"You know a decent hotel downtown?"
"You must be new to L.A."
"Yes."
"Ain't nothing downtown L.A., lady."
"Is there an airport motel?"
"Las Brisas isn't far. It's outside the flight path. They got a pretty good disco going Friday, Saturday nights."
"OK."
For a week, the longest conversation I was to have.
The record dropped. Roberta Flack sang "Until It's Time for You to Go" on the tinny little portable record player I had picked up in the airport gift shop. I lay across the bed, huddling in my raincoat against the air conditioning. I smoked some of the pot I had

brought with me from New York. A bottle of California white was always cooling in water running in the bathroom sink, and I used it to ease the pot's hot scratch in my throat. The brown, white and maroon plastic curtains were always pulled against the California sun, but the reflection from the pool just outside my window got in through the cracks, and I watched glimmers of subaqueous green-and-white light dance on the ceiling. Daytime soap operas followed one another on TV. I kept the sound turned off. The soap people moved through their hospital and law-court agonies to Roberta's songs. The clock radio was turned to the wall. Detached and floating, nobody in the world knew where I was. When the chambermaid came in every day to check that I had not killed myself in the night I went to the drugstore. I lived on chocolate ice cream and elaborate, highly detailed sexual fantasies that made me forget anxiety and the fear of being alone more powerfully than all the gin that Blake could ever drink.

I smoked. I watched the light on the ceiling. I daydreamed and drank white wine. I thought about the opening of my new show at the Korne Gallery and hoped I would sell. I watched the money shrink. Self-defeating, gutless compromise: I had taken only two thousand from the bank. Enough to buy a cheap record player and some wine, not enough to start a new life. Enough to irritate Blake, not enough to make him hate me. Not enough to burn my bridges. I tried not to think about him.

> Call me on the phone? Just forget it.
> Write me a letter? I'll never get it.
> I'm gone for good,

sang Billie Holiday on the portable record player. Being three thousand miles away from New York helped. It was like time.

I finished the wine and sent out to the supermarket for more. Three days. Four. As if it had been waiting for me all my life, I knew the role by heart. The great

community of women, forlorn heroines, deserted by
their men. They had peopled every movie of my life,
the schoolgirl gossip I had grown up on, my mother's
song. The image was sad but somehow glamorous too,
as if learned from old jukeboxes and record-album
covers.

> Gone for good,
> Gone for good,
> Don't look for me,
> I'm gone for good.

Billie sang and Roberta, too, told me I was not
alone. It was fun. The depression did not start till the
fifth day. Billie and Roberta had not warned me about
that.

Food, pot, wine, music, sleep, the light on the ceiling—everything disappeared. The record player
stopped, but I did not start it again. The world turned
silent. It began each time with an ice-cold and hollow
lump in the center of my stomach and spread through
my body in icy shakes. The shakes ran down my arms
and legs, to my fingers and toes. When I held on to
the bed to keep from shaking apart, the bed began
to shake too. I was aware of a voice that cried out
*Mama, I want my mama, mama take care of me,
mama help me,* without being aware it was my voice.
From somewhere in the dark the chambermaid was
speaking to me. ". . . the floor?" She had to help me
up. I did not know how long I had been lying there,
a sofa pillow beneath my head. My muscles were too
cramped to stand. I no longer changed my clothes. I
slept in the raincoat. I did not see how anything would
end. "What would end?" I asked myself. I did not
know who had asked the question or what it meant.

On what day was it that I was first visited by
tremors of joy? *Blake was in the room.* Like music in
the air only I could hear, again and again he came to
me.

"Aren't you going out again today, Miss?"

"I'm waiting for a phone call."

"You have to eat."

"Bring me some ice cream."

It was the chambermaid. I bribed her to hurry with her cleaning. I did not eat the food she brought, flushing it down the toilet before I let her in. I was waiting for Blake to touch me again.

His presence took me at any strange hour it willed, again and again and again; when the feeling passed, it was as if he had deserted me and I had died. The beginning of these delusions—I have them still—that Blake is—guarding me? testing me? watching me?—that he is near.

"Yes?"

"It's only me, Miss. The chambermaid. I have your ice cream."

"Thanks."

"The front desk asked about you. You haven't answered your telephone."

"Yes."

"They said when I see you, would you settle your bill? You didn't leave a credit card. You owe for the past three days. . . ."

I added rent for three days more so they would not phone again. Even as I counted the money into her hand I was in a hurry for her to go. When she closed the door I looked for his face in the darkness. Darkness itself had become sweet.

No.

I began by washing my face and flushing the last of the pot down the john. The chambermaid was surprised by the sudden long conversation I held with her. She did not know I was practicing how to speak, like someone coming out of a cave. These trite talks about California and the weather told me how far I had gone. They reminded me I was lonely.

It was a weariness to go out, but I sat beside the pool and watched the swimmers. Movement helped most of all; Felix used to say that energy feeds on energy. "The more you do, the more you can do." I used another of his remedies too, going into the motel bar to see people, to flirt with the bartender. I would drink Calvados. It had gotten us through our last days —"a romantic and tragic drink," he'd called it. We live by poses, attitudes struck: I was a woman alone, drinking in a hotel three thousand miles away from home. Calvados softened my mood from anger and bitterness to nostalgia and melancholy. I could live with that. I rented a car. An aimless ghost, I drove up and back across Los Angeles, from Bel Air to Beverly Hills, from the Pacific Palisades all the way up Pacific Coast Highway to Malibu. When the world died, men brought me back to life.

Wherever I went there would be magnificent and beautiful men hurrying into stores, bars, hotels, houses, driveways, men so wonderful, so handsome, so radiant and distant in their brilliance they made me want to run after them and yell *"Stop, stop, I don't want to lose you!"* Men so unattainable you wished you had never seen them.

I couldn't walk through the motel lobby without some semi-movie star brushing up against me, on his way in the opposite direction, as if I were invisible. A walk around the grounds of the Beverly Hills Hotel brought out a magic parade of slim-hipped, tight-blue-jeaned heartbreak machines. Everywhere I looked there were dazzling men all around me, ducking into apartment doorways to meet someone else, arriving for parties I hadn't been asked to attend. Men in groups held special fascination. I had never gone along with Blake when he used to fly to California to see his television agents, but I remembered their offices were in Century City.

"Go to the end of Wilshire Boulevard, lady, and turn left."

At the end of the day I would drive out to the Gateway West Building's parking lot to watch the tall, white-toothed, blond and suntanned men of California come pouring out of their offices. Something shifted and moved within as I stood beside the rental car, fumbling with my keys, watching them walk in crowds to their cars. They would see me and they would not, dividing around me like a stream around a rock. The world was ablaze with men and only I was alone. At night I would sketch platoons of men on menus and paper napkins.

Marriage had made me virginal again. Fear had set in with the end of marriage. When I had first come to New York and entered the bar life of the Village I had learned how to meet men casually, easily; who was picking up whom did not matter at all; the trick was to decide for yourself yes or no while he was still getting up nerve for his approach. Los Angeles told me I had lost this ease. I still carried Blake inside; the fear of presenting myself to him, devalued in my own eyes, even if he would never know, paralyzed me. I had tried to break my identification with Blake by going to bed with Felix, but that was only a memory, unreal as a dream. The fractured bone mends, the cut flesh grows over the wound. We do not look different in the mirror. Bake held me still. The connection was unbroken, and I did not want it to break. I could not be unfaithful even though he was at the other edge of the world. I was his wife. I wrote my name on a piece of paper. "Mrs. Nicholas Blake." Didn't the very words tell me I was not alone?

No.

When Blake and I had begun, the divorced man with whom I had gone to see *Black Orpheus,* and with whom I was sitting when Blake turned and saw me, had lived up to his promise and moved to California. John Fennel; he had sent me an announcement of his second marriage from Beverly Hills. He was in the phone book, but I was too embarrassed to call. Two days more of wandering, two days more without a human word. If I could have worked, it might have helped. The disadvantage of working in iron and glass for a woman getting divorced: your tools are too heavy to take with you when you run away from home. Take up watercoloring instead.

The energy turned back, turned black, turned against me. I felt the depression begin again, the emptiness of the motel room begin to beckon, the sweet certainty that Blake was near; I called John that night.

"Blake with you?" he said.

I said I was alone.

He tried to cover his silence by inviting me to his house for dinner, to "meet the wife."

Married and unmarried people should never mix. You cannot be sentimental about it. If you separate, if your friends marry, you have to drop them. And they have to drop you.

"Why've you come out to California, Clair?" he said with a joking smile. His car was in the shop for overnight repairs, but he said I would get lost in the Hertz if I tried to find his house alone. He had come to pick me up at the motel in a taxi. "After all these years you've decided you miss me?"

"I think a lot about the last time I saw you."

"Don't tease me, Clair. You know how I always felt about you."

We were having a drink at the Las Brisas disco bar. The band had just started to play a cha-cha for the elderly tourists, the traveling salesmen and the girls who made up most of the clientele. John and I talked about old times, but he did not have to say it: when we got to his house he'd prefer there'd be no more talk about his "former life" in front of his new wife.

"Here's to the Village," he said. "Those wonderful days when even being broke was fun." I could not hear the rest. Suffused by a feeling of a sudden, swimming happiness, thrilled as if I had been plugged into a central source of power, I had just heard Blake's voice.

Skin turned to ice. I looked at John, saw his lips move but could not hear his voice. I did not dare look around and find Blake walking toward me. I would be overwhelmed, too dizzied by joy, if it came all at once. It was no delusion. He was here. I waited.

"Something wrong?"

"I swallowed a piece of ice the wrong way."

"Funny old habit of yours. You still like to eat ice?"

"Yes."

"Poor baby. You have tears in your eyes. Here, drink some of my water."

"Yes."

I drank. The band went into a new song but stayed with the cha-cha beat. A few more grandparently tourists, pink and white from too sudden sun, stepped out onto the floor. I could feel my heart. John was looking at me. I kept my eyes rigidly staring into his and smiled. He relaxed. "I was just talking about our rebellion-in-the-Village days," he began again, snapping his fingers in time to the music. "What a healthy thing it was then, cha cha cha, but how even healthy things turn sour if they go on too long. I hope you won't laugh at me, Clair. Maybe I've changed since I've moved to California, but I still remember the wonderful time I felt I was having then . . . even though I was miserable about the hard time you were giving me and about that marriage of mine breaking up. . . . There was a little actress you didn't know about, and she and I would—

"Oh, well, never mind, just believe me, I understand it all. I've been through it all, you see. It's just that I've grown up at last, Clair. I find now there are other things I enjoy more. I love seeing you, Clair, you and I always had something special together, but it would be difficult for me to see my other Village friends nowadays. Some of them are always floating through California—making a pot run, I guess— and they call me. They still think they're going to change the world somehow. God bless 'em, may they stay under thirty forever! They're wonderful, I love 'em. But Liza and I, well, what we enjoy is having a few friends in for an evening, coffee, a really *fine* armagnac. Conversation is an art, you know. One that's been lost. TV killed it. Oh, absolutely killed it, cha cha cha, you know?"

He went on: "Liza and I do this cooking-with-wine bit, gourmet cooking. Sounds corny, doesn't it? But it's really fun. We don't believe in letting the squares ruin something fine for us just because they do it too. It's embarrassing to say about yourself, but I believe that's maturity. Knowing what you like. Ah, well, you know the joke: 'Some of my best friends are Villagers.' I remember when we first met, you and I. You were living with those two girls on Jane Street, and I had a small pad on Little West Twelfth Street. Little West Twelfth Street—yes, that's what it was called. Greenwich Village, I love it! Funny how you change, isn't it? A goofy thing, those days, just the name of a funny street and you were happy."

He did a dance step or two in time to the music as we walked across the floor and out to my car. He took the keys from my hand. "If you don't mind," he said, "I'll introduce you as the wife of an old friend. It's more or less true, right? I'll say that Blake is flying out to join you here in a day or two."

"OK."

"Is he?"

"Yes."

"Liza's a fine girl. You'll like her. But a little nervous. You're rather formidable you know, Clair."

"Yes."

Through the window of the bar I could hear the orchestra playing. Blake had never come.

Cha cha cha.

As he drove, John talked about how much easier it was to live in California than New York. Of course the suburbs are a joke back east, he said, but here in Los Angeles you can get out of work and be home and swimming in your pool in less time than it takes people in New York to get from their East Side jobs back to the Village on the crappy subway. And then he began about the trees and the sunshine. I looked at him. He shut up. I remembered what he had said about trees and sunshine when his first suburban marriage had broken up.

When we got there the new Mrs. Fennel came out in the baby-blue stretch pants with the elastic under the instep and wearing the Yves St.-Tropez apron. A fluffy California blonde, and she's got on *all* her beads. There are candles on the table. John makes a big nervous number about what'll I have to drink, cha cha, like we're hearty English fox hunters just come in from a cold day in the shires, and I tell him give me anything. So Liza says, "John, dear, show Clair that new drink you invented. This is the *spécialité de la*

maison," she tells me, and the next thing, John gives
me an embarrassed look, half-proud, and he ducks
into the kitchen, and sure enough they have the
standard wedding-present Waring Goddamn Blendor
in there, and the *next* thing, the lights are low, the
bayberry candles are on, cha cha, Herb Alpert is
playing some golden-trumpet-and-one-thousand-violins
Mexican taco music, we're sitting in the dark drinking a sickening banana Daiquiri and Liza is telling
me, "You see, we discovered that just a touch, a *soup-
çon* of honey, gives it that extra, exotic flavor."

With this I look at John, cha cha, but he jumps
up and says how about another drink, and while he's
in the kitchen making it, Liza and I sit and listen to
the Herb Alpert serenade.

Next, John comes out, and Liza goes in to cook.
By this time I tell him to forget the Daiquiris, just
give me rum plain. From the kitchen we hear rushing
feet, clattering dishes, a glass breaks, and once Liza
yells out to herself. Something slams and slams again
—then a long nervous silence. Finally Liza comes out,
white-faced, her hair beginning to come down in wisps
all around her face. She and John have a whispered
conversation while I pretend not to notice, and he
looks red, but he puts on his jacket, borrows my car
keys without explaining, throws the keys up in the
air and angrily catches them in a fist and says without
looking at me he'll be right back. He goes out and
Liza goes back into the kitchen. I know enough not to
say, can I help.

Silence. Long enough for me to think I'd better try
to giggle her up a little. She may think John only knows
me slightly, and nobody has said a word to make her
think I'm not happily married myself, but I am from
that other world John had silently asked me not to talk
about. I go into the kitchen to suggest maybe we go
out to eat, but she doesn't see me because she's got
every dish, pot, pan, basin and teacup piled up and
dirty all around her, on the floor, on the table, the
chairs. She's got a tureen filled with what looks like
farina and goldfish in her hand, searching for some
empty pot to pour it in, but there isn't a clean one left,

and while she's standing there the hollandaise sauce on the stove boils over, and she looks up wild, with tears in her eyes, and finds me staring at her, cha cha.

I get a look that turns my pancreas green, but she manages to follow it up with at least a winter smile and says things'll be all right in a minute. I tell her sure, and by this time John comes back and gives me a look like I only work here I don't live here, and disappears with a big paper grocery bag into the kitchen with her, and in a minute I hear her crying.

I'm left all alone in the other room listening to the clock tick, watching the candles burn down, smelling the burned dinner and desperately licking the last dregs out of the empty Daiquiri glasses. John comes out of the kitchen. He says, "Maybe I look like a clown to you, Clair. Maybe I am a clown. And this is a clown's house—"

"Yes?"

"But I love her."

I stood up.

"Where are you going?"

"Back to the motel."

"Liza'll have the dinner ready in a few—"

I had the keys to the car in my hand. He stood irresolutely in the middle of the room and then said he'd drive back with me to the motel or I'd get lost in the dark. When we got to Las Brisas I told him to go into the bar, buy a bottle of Calvados, come back to the room and take off his pants.

"All those years in New York," he said when it was over, "it was always No. Now it's suddenly Yes. Why?"

"Next time don't tell me how happily married you are."

He had spent the last few dollars he had with him for the Calvados. I gave him ten dollars for the taxi home.

And after my quarrel with Felix at the zoo I had dinner with Lou. I told him to buy us some Calvados and took him to bed too.

Cha cha cha.

Lou and Felix. Mother Sex versus Father Sex. Little-Girl Sex versus Real:

I have taken roommates when I wanted to be alone, moved in with Inez when I could have afforded my own place, gone with men I did not like, stayed with others long after I should have left—wondering all the while how I found myself in this awful place, with that terrible person, giving myself a dozen different reasons but all the while totally forgetting the compelling one: I am afraid when I'm alone. It took more courage to leave Blake than anything I've done since. Physical courage and taking risks are hard. But men who brag about danger never tell you that it's over so quickly. You take the chance, run the line, it's over; you forget it, exhilarated. Being alone goes on and on and there is no guarantee it will ever end.

Why do men find it so easy to leave women, and why do women suffer so when they go? Why do men want sex without emotion and women insist that emotion come first of all? Last night I ended it with a man who epitomized all the arrogant high-school-quarterback bastards who never used to be able to see me when I was a kid. When I meet these men they have a magic for me still, but I resent it, and I had taken him on to fuck him and forget him, get him out of my system and never have to think of him again. "I love you, goddamn it, don't you understand? I LOVE YOU!" He beat the table with his fist and shouted, but I was no longer interested. He was one more of those men who think no woman can believe someone like him could love her. It is beyond them that you can believe it but reject him anyway. Love is the drug, they are the unending supplier, and they don't understand when you say you've kicked. We use one emotion to speak of another, use sex to get something else. He was using the word "love" to express rage and anger, like the rapist who uses sex to tell you of his hate and revenge. I think I am like the rapist: I have more often used sex to get the emotion I wanted than for simple erotic fulfillment. I no longer am interested in getting men to love me. The emotion I want is to possess them. And then I am released.

I possess a man by making myself part of him, forcing him to see, not his fantasy of himself, but me. The form changes, but the content remains the same: changing his awareness of me is the emotion I must have before there can be sex. Unless I do I will not go to bed with him.

What is this emotion I used to ask of men which stifled them if they stayed and in the end angered them so they had to go? The question cannot be answered if put in these terms, the wrong words are being used. To speak of love is not enough. It is too vague. With Blake I used to say I was looking for a certain "masculine tenderness." Women want emotion first because we feel sex is all we have to give. What men have to give is their emotion, and unless they do, they will leave us. I have learned that asking him for tenderness does just the opposite: it causes him to leave. If you ask him for excitement, adventure, sex alone, he will stay.

I used to suffer from a kind of repetition compulsion. I made the same sexual journey over and over. I am attracted to the mystery and strangeness in a man, the thrill was in his wildness, his difference from me and the hope that his unashamed eroticism would get me past my own little-girl inhibitions. Immediately when I found this lightning in a man I would set out to convert it into something safe, cozy, known, warm, friendly. Tender. I would work to change the love I had for my father to the love I wanted from my mother. From actively wanting to join him in creation of sexual heat, I would passively want him to cuddle and hold me. "Stay with me always," we say to the stranger whose cold unavailability is what caught us to begin with. (The banker who falls in love with the dazzling chorus girl. He marries her, makes her dye her platinum hair back to its natural mouse-brown, dresses her in American Golfer clothes, and then wonders why he is bored.) Like the terrible fairy tale of the three wishes, death is the third wish that comes true. We begin by wanting sex with the stranger who is as distant and unattainable as our father used to be. We end by changing it into the tie to life itself that once we had with mother.

It is a mistake to ask tenderness from a man. It confuses him. He loses his hard certainty of himself as a man, and he goes. It is the reason men withhold their emotion: the emotion you are asking of a man is one he cannot give and remain a man. "If you leave me I will die." Is that a woman talking to a man or a child praying in the dark to her mother? That is why we think we will die if the man leaves us. We have evoked the mother in him. When we were little we would have died too if she had left us. But if the man gives in to our wish, loses his male quality, becomes soft and tender instead, we will love him back, yes— but he will no longer be sex.

My rage at Blake the night he walked out to go on drinking was not because he did not want to fuck. The words I said to myself were, *"I will not sleep one more night alone."* I needed him not as an erotic idea but because I was afraid to be alone in a room when it was not my choice. I needed, not his sex, but his tenderness. He knew I wanted not the father in him but the soft and maternal, and if I called that sex, he was not fooled. Something in him knew he was being twisted, that if he gave in to me he would be finished as a man in my eyes. I used to wonder why I felt like a traitor; even though I loved him, I would far rather he just held me in his arms in bed than make love to me. His drinking was frightening because it unlocked a door and let out the unreachable untamed male who did not care for me. Gin unmasked his other face, cruel, uncontrolled, self-centered, powerful in its madness, unavailable to love or tears. And yet, in my heart of hearts, that is how I think of men.

Is it banal enough to say men divide women into categories, the madonna and the whore, one they marry, one they fuck. But don't women do the same? I was attracted to the handsome gambler in Las Vegas. I would spend a week with him but dream of marrying him never. He was Type A, Clark Gable—hard, dark, sexual, arrogant, demanding, genital. Like your father, he is the stranger who enters and leaves your life from the outside. Type B has always been in your life. He is Leslie Howard, Ashley Wilkes, whom Scarlett knew from the day she was born: soft, dreamy, poetic, maternal in his kindness and concern.

Type A is the hard male fantasy of how men think women want them to be. Type B is the tender, feminine reality we need them to become for us in marriage. At first Blake's remote quality frightened me; the way he would turn up with one woman after another with no explanation given except change made him sexual. But I married him because underneath he had a safe, known and old-fashioned quality too; my mother understood him from the moment they met. The *Reader's Digest* fiction is that you can combine both qualities in one man, have the sexual and the safe, Type A and Type B, genital sex and pseudo-sex—father sex *and* mother sex—both in one man. It is a young girl's belief. Another lie her mother tells her, like "It's just as easy to fall in love with a rich man as a poor one."

Sexual excitement lives on unresolved ideas of aggression. It does not survive the battle that turns friendly. The magic of sex is that it turns death and male hostility into love; but then the magic ends. The sharp, intense excitement that keeps two people fixed on each other is gone. We do not marry the boy next door because he has been our friend all along. The word "fuck" itself encapsulates the problem. "Jack Kennedy fucked a lot of women in the White House, but Nixon fucked the entire country." To our liberal despair, the word is used at least as often to mean anger and fraud as it is used to mean sex. I believe now this is an exact expression of the ambivalence we all feel. It is why this double use of the word is so satisfying it will not die.

I am drawn to the stranger, to Frank Lloyd Wrong, because I am thrilled by my fear of him; I want to make his power my own. Sex—fucking—is how I do it. Savages incorporate the lion's courage by eating his heart. I literally take in the most dangerous aspect of men, their cocks; in the morning I am no longer afraid.

He is a stranger no more. Men have the idea that if they want to fuck you, it means they don't love you. It is the necessary split they need to remain sexual. But if a man tells me he wants to fuck me, I know it can be the beginning of love. Only he is surprised when it is.

Robbed of his mana, fucked out of his magic, shorn of his power; I have made his strength, his lion's heart, my own. The lucky aspect of my shyness is that I come over as difficult and silent. When the man sees my vulnerability in bed, my own tenderness, he is relieved. He melts and responds in kind. *He is tender, but the wildness is now in me.* Like the banker who is bored by the ex-chorus-girl wife, I want him to go. I have changed Type A into Type B, Clark Gable into Leslie Howard, father sex into mother sex. And while the great fear that grabs me in the middle of the night is that my mother will die before I can make up to her for all the neglect and pain I gave her, in the meanwhile all I want to do is get away from her. I play an old record for him at breakfast. "Gone for good, / Gone for good, / Baby, I am long gone for good!" Billie Holiday sings.

Father sex is before. Mother sex is after. You marry the father. You live with the mother.

When I think of someone I hate, I like to imagine using him as my sexual tool, hiding my fear of him, disguising my anger, luring him into bed by making him think it is his idea, abandoning myself at white heat to make him want me as he has never wanted anyone before—and then dismissing him. I can laugh at him to myself. My victory is that I never need to see him again, and if he stays awhile, it is merely as a toy. Even as I imagine this scene, speak these words onto the tape, I feel a thrill. Hate and anger toward various men have given me the most intense orgasms of my life. That is sex, Type A sex, with nothing soft or maternal about it. In this too I am like the rapist: I use sex to get my revenge. Tender is the knife.

When I first left Blake I shied away from men. The more I let this happen, the more I became afraid. Every sexual challenge I did not meet diminished me,

robbed me of self-confidence. My feeling of sexual pow-
erlessness was at the heart of my depression. I lived
like a nun. Now I have come to recognize my two
different reasons to go to bed with a man. I do not
have to wait for Type A to come along; my tastes are
difficult, the men who arouse those feelings in me are
rare. But in certain dark moments I want merely to be
held, to be touched and soothed, comforted and protected and told everything will be all right by someone
who stands outside my fear. Men who will do this are
not rare at all. Merging with him, I incorporate him
into me. Type B thinks sex is what I want. Because the
genitals are involved, he thinks it *is* sex. Perhaps it is,
but only in the sense that there is sex between an in-
fant and her mother's breast.

I went to bed with Lou because he had always loved
me, because my show at the Korne Gallery was a failure, because I was worried about my life and about
money, because it was four A.M. and I was alone.
Grateful to him for the comfort his flesh gave me, I
compounded his confusion by faking orgasm; but men
like Lou are never the kind with whom I can come.
Sex with them is mother sex, their tenderness is all I
want, and if I can get it only in bed, a little screaming
and shuddering seems polite—small enough price to
pay. Lou asked me not to go back to California, to
divorce Blake and move in with him, but I was right
not to stay. I could never be faithful to gentle and
friendly Type B; I can never imagine myself living
again without holding myself open and available for
ruthless Type A to take me places I've never been.
Marrying Lou would have made his third wish come
true. It would have been cowardice for me, death for
him. How many times have I heard a woman dismiss
a man by saying he was too eager to please? How
many times have I dismissed a man in my own mind
by saying he was "too nice"?

Men are cunning who say, "I only want to sleep
with you, that's all." When I am afraid, that lie is a
more powerful seduction than he is aware—even
though not in a manner that, if he knew, would be
flattering to him. He thinks I have surrendered to his

stud appeal. What he doesn't know is that just to have someone near is all I want; on his strong and maternal breast I can sleep. And if I have to use sex to pay the price, the cost is low. I have been made whole, courageous again, more times than not by these men with whom I could not come. Mother sex, pseudosex, sex without orgasm or faked, can be more comforting than most men, dreaming their macho dreams, can understand.

I now believe real sex is a transaction between strangers. Men used to prize a girl's maidenhead because that was the fact and symbol of her power. Taking it aggrandized them. Strongly sexual men are bored by call girls. They are turned on only by women who say no. *No* is the woman's power, which he wants to possess more than her sex. Incorporation and power again. Sexual encounters are called conquests. But men do not understand that women can use sex to conquer too. I open the door for him the next morning with a smile. He has lost the strange, untamed erotic appeal of the father you know can never be yours and has become the loving but oppressive mother from whom you always wanted to get away. How old was I when I began to save my money to leave home?

The pull women feel toward men whom they can mother, men with problems, inadequate, nonfrightening men, may be love. I am not sure. What I am sure of is that sex with them is mother sex, the roles turned around. Real sex is something I feel only for men who are unafraid, men whom I respect (hate is a form of respect)—intact, powerful men who arouse in me that tiny thrill of fear. I have heard this described as the unconscious wisdom of the female race—evolution's imperative that the strongest, best males get the greatest chance to breed. I don't agree.

I am drawn to powerful men because they represent their own triumph over what I fear. With them I can give my nameless anxieties a palpable body. Conquering that body, I triumph over my fears. There has been a transfer of power in the night. I already know who, when the end comes, will want to stay, and who will want to go.

If a woman does not realize this is the mystery of sex, if she has not conquered her instilled fears against exploration to know there is more than one man who can give her surcease from the fear of being alone, she becomes men's victim: "Don't leave me." Once she does know it, her appetites grow. Sure of her sexuality, knowing that she does not want his mother love but his father sex, no longer accepting the man's definition that every erotic encounter must end with her defeat, a silent Copernican revolution takes place. Nothing seems changed, but everything is different. The planets and the sun have not shifted in their courses but are seen from a new point of view. She is at the center of her own universe at last. The world becomes an infinite challenge in which the woman must win. Men must scheme and plot, seduce, promise, threaten, risk rejection, wine, dine, cajole and lie. I need only understand that sex is like water: nothing written there tonight will remain in the morning. Only allow him to understand my Yes and the irresistible game begins again, a war I will always win.

Games are a heightened kind of life, with formal pleasures: they have a beginning, middle, and above all, you know when they are at an end. And then they begin again. Fear becomes excitement, and I live in it. Every day is brilliant; I am alive as never before. The air is suffused with endless variety and possibility, every new man brings out a facet of myself I might never have known. I do not fear the ticking of the clock or the setting sun. I look forward to the night. Glory to be alive, and the only thing to fear is love itself. How can a husband compare with the passing stranger whose face I've never known? He is the orgasm you never had. Two people in bed together make six in all. Her fantasy of herself, her fantasy of him; his fantasy of her, his fantasy of himself. The two real people are least of all—only the fleshy screens on which the others have their ghostly being.

And yet despite all I've just said, none of it is true if it denies I am still tied to Blake. The difference is, I no longer want to be. He is like the high, sweet, swooning habit the addict wants to kick. If he should ever come for me, if I should look up right now and see him walking toward me in his funny old gray double-breasted businessman's suit and polka-dot tie, would I soon want him to go?

I have learned that I need from men, from marriage, what no one man can give. The split is complete, but the illusion dies hard. Half of me wants to believe I can be married again. The other half knows I cannot.

24

Messages

"I like it," Toomis said.

The picture postcard of Nixon was on the desk in front of him. Idly he pushed it with the paper knife into right-angle alignment with the In-Out tray. He brought his shoulders forward, lifting his heavy haunches from the seat pillows so the pistol on his hip settled into a more comfortable position against the back of the chair. Despite the heat he still wore his jacket and tie.

Lou sat in the visitor's chair beside the desk sipping an iced Coke. The T-shirts he wore had a Big Apple picture on the chest, a bite taken out of it. Underneath, the slogan said "New Yorkers Know Something Else." Blake had come and gone, leaving the postcard behind.

Lou pulled his wet T-shirt away from his body and blew down his chest. "What's to like?" he said. "The prelim lab report gives us nothing except nobody's fingerprints are on it except Nick's and one or two smudges that most likely belong to the mail carrier. That kind of draughtsman's printing, you can't tie it to anyone's handwriting. You want me to buy you a postcard like that? I can find a thousand mom-and-pop candy stores right here in New York—to say nothing of L.A. and points between—they don't throw away out-of-date merchandise until it rots."

"The first thing I like," said Toomis, "is the picture is Nixon."

"Always a fun guy."

"Don't tell me jokes," Toomis said. "The card is a joke itself, right? Some kind of beatnik, hippie joke?"

"You don't have to be a hippie to dislike Nixon, Frank."

"Me and my friends, maybe we were wrong about the guy. But we don't think it's funny to send pictures of a man after all he was a President of the United States. You and your friends, the circles your friend Blake moves in—they'd think it was funny, right?"

"You think Blake sent the card to himself?"

"Someone who thinks like him did."

"I don't get it, Frank. The guy who sends the card, he knows about the mask. He's in on it. He should be figuring he's cool, the case is forgotten, it's three months, let it all rest and blow away. No, he begins sending mysterious messages."

"How long you a detective?"

"I left the uniforms eight months ago."

"So you expect every job to be a professional job, the perp gets off the plane, he goes to the door, he rings the bell, the victim answers, bang, the perp gets back on the plane. He don't write no love letters, right?"

"It's strange, Frank."

Toomis grinned at his partner. "What's strange is, here is life looking at you, Lou, and you want it to be like something in a detective manual. What we got here is an amateur. Some kind of nut with a conscience. He doesn't want to feel he's the only one his conscience is bothering him, but here's your fancy friend, walking around town, he says he can't remember anything, booze blacked out his memory. Let him feel some heat too. He wants to tell him they're both in it together. And that this wife he talks about loving so much, she's in it worst of all. What we got here is the policeman's friend, the crime of passion. This card

is amateur stuff, like the stupid way black Sam sets
up the job on your friend, he gets himself iced instead."

"You think whoever sent the card, maybe he sent
Sam too?"

"I hope Blake thinks it's a possibility. I hope it re-
freshes his so-called lost memory. The next card he
gets is liable to be from Frank Campbell come to his
own funeral. You're still sticking with him, right?"

"You want me to keep it up?"

"We'll talk about that in a minute."

The motor in the air conditioner moaned. Both men
turned to face it. They held their breath. A low hum
filled the air, and then with a soft hiss as if it were
their own pent-up breath being expelled, the machine
began to blow chilled air in their faces again.

"Thank God," Lou said.

A uniformed cop came by. He brought the final
lab report. There were no identifiable fingerprints on
the postcard except Blake's.

"Let me ask you something," Toomis said. "The
other night, you, Felix and this Blake go out for a
hamburger and he tells you the end the night he was
one of them. Was he drunk?"

"He was sober when he said it."

"Why does he retract when he comes here to give
us the postcard?"

"He didn't retract, Frank. He only said he didn't
want to repeat it for the record, because he didn't
know why he said it at the time. It was just one of
those guilty feelings. A hunch ain't a confession,
Frank, not without a lot of circumstantial behind it."

"But if we believe it, it confirms a line of investigation, right? If I knew to believe him or not, it would
save us a lot of work. He still drinking?"

"Yes."

"Pretty good?"

"Like three strong men."

"Against what? His wife's dead?"

"Whatever made him say he was one of them. Maybe it's still on his mind. Maybe he doesn't want to face it."

"You believe him?"

"In what way?"

"You think he was in on it?"

"I don't know. Remember you put the mask on Blake? You said he wore it?" Lou pushed the postcard around so the printed message faced him. "The guy sent this, he was there. He ought to know who wore the mask. He says she wore it."

"The postcard is the first thing makes me think maybe she didn't," Toomis said. "I was just trying that out on him. 'No, it wasn't me wore the mask, it's my wife, she likes to wear them.' Why should the guy sends the card tell the truth? He wants to write what bugs your friend the most. If he didn't want to bug him, he wouldn't send it the first place."

"You figure like that?"

Toomis did not directly reply. "What's he using for money finance all these two-seventy-five-a-blast martinis with a twist he goes for?"

"He says a check came in for some script he fixed up he was living in France."

"You know his agent?"

"Sure."

"Check on the money. Don't let him know. There's a suitcase of dope floating around she brung with her. Make sure that's where his money's coming from." Toomis got up and left the room. Lou sat beside the desk and drummed his fingers on the desk blotter. When Toomis came back he had a Coke with him in a paper cup. He put the cup on the desk and studied the icy beads of water that ran down the waxy container. "The best thing I like," he said, "is there's movement in the case. Somebody is out to fool us, play games with us. Either way, it means somebody is thinking. What I like most is when amateurs think they can fool cops. Let me ask you something else. What do you think this girl Felix says he was banging that night over in Jersey?"

"You just jumping around, Frank, or you going in a straight line?"

"Just tell me what you believe the alibi's worth."
Lou spread his fingers open in front of him. "So far,
a million bucks."

"Only so far?"

"Felix can bring in a dozen girls tomorrow they'll
swear they were with him any night of the week you
want to name. You bring her in front of a Grand Jury,
put the heat on, maybe she'll tell you something else."

"You don't believe her?"

"No."

Toomis grunted. "I like you said that, Lou. I don't
like these feelings I sometimes get you're too loyal to
your friends. So you tie Felix to what went on that
night?"

"He's got other reasons he needs an alibi."

"The cigarette business?"

"The Waldorf bombing a couple of months ago."

"You're not saying Felix is a political?"

"I had a talk with the Hoboken cops. They been
keeping half an eye on Felix's warehouse two, three
months now. They think a shipment of cigarettes came
and went that night."

"What's that got to do with the Weathermen bombing the Waldorf?"

"Felix brings cigarettes up from North Carolina. He
warehouses them in Hoboken until he's ready to distribute in New York. So far, nothing illegal, no problems. The problem the Weather guys got, they need
money. Hot dynamite ain't cheap."

"They distribute for Felix?"

"The Jersey cops figure Felix sells wholesale to
the Weathermen in Jersey. They add maybe a quarter
a carton on top for bringing it over the river and selling in New York. They can make maybe ten thousand
dollars a shipment. A lot of dynamite."

"The Jersey cops tell you all this?"

"Not officially."

"This half an eye they got on his warehouse. Why
not two full eyes?"

Lou rubbed his thumb and forefinger together in a
caricature of counting money. He smiled. "They got
mortgages to pay their palatial Jersey woodland estates

far from crime-ridden Manhattan. What the hell they care? Those cigs aren't even being sold their side of the river."

Toomis sighed and leaned back in his chair. He smiled into the air. "So maybe Felix has an alibi for that night, maybe it ain't a real one. Either way, we got something on him the cigarette business, but cigarette business ain't our business. We don't have anything solid to tie him to the kill. Don't answer me a cop, Lou. Answer me a guy who knows Felix. You think he could have been the other guy?"

"Yes."

"Why do you say that?"

"Because he was in love with her and she walked out on him."

"What's new about that? She had a number with him a long time ago, before she was married. She thought maybe she'd pick it up with him again when she comes back from California two years ago. It didn't work, so a few days later she goes back to California."

"She also had an affair with him while she was married."

"While?"

"Yes."

"How do you know?"

"She told me."

"When?"

"I was in bed with her the night after she had that fight on the tape. With Felix in the zoo."

"She ever tell Blake about this business her and Felix?"

"I didn't know until she told me. They kept it quiet. She said Nick never wanted to know her past."

Toomis looked at him. "So he tells us." He paused. "Tell me, why didn't you let me know all this when we first heard the tape?"

"What the hell, so I made it with her two years ago. It didn't seem important to bring up till now."

"What's now?"

"Now we're checking Felix's alibi. Information maybe he was more involved with her than we thought, it's right in the middle of the case. I don't figure what I know about her and him can stay private any more just because the way I learned it."

"Blake know about you and her?"

"I never told him. If she did, he's never mentioned it to me."

"But if she did tell him, the kind of guy he is, he'd never bring it up with you?"

"I don't think he would."

Toomis grunted. He went to stand at the window, a big man with big sloping shoulders, his shirt wet beneath his suit jacket, so wet it had begun to wet his suit jacket too, and the dark-blue summer-weight cloth clung to the wet hollow of his back. "I been wondering you'd get around to telling me, Lou. I had a talk with the squadron commander this morning. One of the witnesses at the party, he says he remembers seeing you and the deceased having dinner together a couple of times two years ago that period she was in New York. You know, Lou, Felix's alibi with the girl in Jersey maybe holds up, maybe it doesn't. Either way, you left the party with him, but he cuts out on you shortly thereafter. Your alibi goes with him. We don't know your movements the time of death. The squadron commander wants you off the case. No hard feelings."

"Technical suspension?"

"Nobody said suspension."

"Am I under suspicion?"

"You'll be assigned something else to do. Now, why don't you just tell me how you spent the night after you left the party and Felix said so long, he had to go to Jersey?"

"For the record?"

Toomis made an apologetic shrug. "Look how it sounds, Lou. Two guys were involved in a sex crime. Two guys were also at that party, they were fucking the deceased, unknown to the husband. You and Felix."

"I suppose you looked up my blood type? That I'm Type O, same as Nick?"

"Just routine," Toomis said.

25

July Days, August Nights

Tom's new status was announced by The Car outside my door. He had flown in from California and wanted to see me. He arrived more than a little late, more than a little loaded, and he sent the chauffeur upstairs to get me. He had phoned from Los Angeles to say the rough cut on the picture I had doctored for him in France was great. He did two minutes on the provincialism of New York writers and why didn't I move out to Malibu, where he'd bought a house and had met a great bunch of movie people. He ended by making the date to see me. He had bought a book and wanted to talk about maybe I'd do the script. He said he was sorry about Clair, asked if I had a new girl, and told me not to bring one anyway. "One of your Greenwich Village dirty-ankle sandal-wearers?" he asked rhetorically. "Looks like she buys her clothes the Occupational Therapy Boutique Bellevue Lunatic Asylum? Forget it." He had his own standard West Coast animal with him—taller than he, blond of course, a certain deadhead serenity, $900 of Halston on her back and a southern accent flavored with Greer Garson broad A's. I wondered what was wrong with her hands until I realized she had been to MGM Charm School, where they teach screen aspirants to keep the thumbs tucked in, achieving the long, tapered, aristocratic look by which such great ladies as Joan Crawford and Barbara Stanwyck had once displayed their breeding to the millions.

Tom himself was wearing a dandy cowboy suit, made not of blue denim but of faded-blue shantung silk woven to look like denim. "I bought it right off Courrège's own back when we were in Paris," he said, smiling down at the inconspicuous little sterling silver "C" emblem on the breast pocket. "He had it tailored for himself in his own shop. They get a certain authentically washed-out look using that strong French cheap bleach and Seine water scrubbed by peasant hands between two rocks—you can't get that kind of softness with Clorox and a Whirlpool washing machine. I got back to L.A. I told my tailor, 'Open up all the seams so we don't lose the original cut, and put it back personalized to fit me.'" Underneath the suit he wore a flame-red Halston shirt of his own, California fashion—four buttons open down to the sternum, the big collar folded down outside the suit jacket. A silver champagne cooler gleamed at our feet in The Car's expensive back-seat gloom, filled with the obligatory Movie Star Great National Drink, Dom Pérignon iced too cold to taste. Tom himself glittered and winked with sharp metallic lights. He was encrusted with enough gold to raise real estate values for two blocks around: gold cuff links, gold ring on his little finger, gold buckles on his Gucci boots. A gold watch and gold metal strap on his wrist, gold charm and medals on a gold chain around his neck, a gold key chain clamped on the gold metal mesh of his gold-buckled belt; and he sliced the end of his cigar with a little gold knife. He had become one of those West Coast producers who laugh a lot to tell you they have long ago conquered whatever it is that is still worrying you.

"Well, well, well," he ha-ha'd, "you wouldn't come out the Coast to talk to me, I was coming to New York, I thought we'd talk here. Let's get a drink first. No Village sawdust saloons tonight, Nicky. This is first class." He immediately ordered too much to drink when we got to the solid gold dungeon he favored for his New York drinking, and shouted for the fiddle player to come over. "Just stand here and give us the theme from *The Godfather* till I tell you to stop. And here"—Tom shoved some folding money into the fiddler's breast pocket—"a picture of my father you won't forget who you're playing for." He made the fiddler drink a glass of champagne. "And you, waiter, have a drink too. Five bucks you drink another glass."

Tom's own song was how stupid it was of New York writers to conform to the idea that being broke was being pure. "No need to be shit on, boy," he shouted at me. "Want a cigar? Have a cigar. Drink something —*drink*, you bastard, and enjoy yourself. Don't worry about the money. Money is what I got. I signed a three-picture deal with Columbia. There's all the money you want in America today. Money for anyone who wants it. Anyone not too lily-livered and shit-eating pure to go for it. Anyone who's *man enough* to go for it."

I got up for an intermission and went around the dining room corner to the service bar. I asked the bartender for some aspirin for my hangover and wondered if it was too early to ask Tom for a thousand in advance on the script he wanted me to do for him.

Waiters were running toward our table as I came back. Tom was wild, laughing, flushed, red with booze and victory. He had one hand stuck way up in the air, clutching an immense wad of money, paper and silver. Money was squirting between his fingers, raining from his fists, dollars floating like autumn leaves, American Express and Diners Club cards getting into the fiddler's eyes, falling among the champagne glasses, sliding to the floor beneath his feet.

His other arm was around the blonde's neck, the fingers remembering to get their money's worth, working out on her pearly starlet flesh as if directed by eyes of their own. The waiters were kneeling around Tom picking up money for him. His breath was coming in long rapturous sighs. He ignored the waiters, he wouldn't bother to take the cards and greenbacks they were trying to hand him. They gave the money to the blonde. She was cool. "Now, honey, don't get excited, sweets. Don't lose all this—behave yourself, hear?" she crooned at him, shoving the green stuff into his pockets. "Now, don't excite yourself so, sweetie pie." She never showed a thumb.

"Money, money," Tom was saying, his voice hoarse, just a gust of breath. He ignored the girl. He was talking to me as if she did not exist. "Money is like a woman. You give yourself to money, till death do you part, money gives herself to you. She's proud, money. She wants marriage, not an affair. And she wants to marry a real man. You got to be man enough to love her, meet *all* her conditions, before she gives herself to you. That's why my women get so hot when I give them money. When I give money, it's like another man gives love."

He began to look around wildly. "Waiter, waiter!" he suddenly roared. "The check! The check! Waiter! Add ten dollars to the fifteen percent for yourself. Waiter! Make it a hundred. Fill in the numbers for me. Make it a hundred for yourself and I'll sign it. Waiter, cheat me, I'll sign it without looking—write whatever you want, it doesn't matter. Waiter, you poor bastard, I've got money, cheat me, *cheat me*. It doesn't matter, ha, ha, ha!"

He had let the chauffeur go for the night. When we got to the door, it had started to rain so we needed a cab. Tom couldn't wait. He began to run down the street after the doorman, whistling and waving his wad of money in the air, yelling for a taxi. Suddenly he was back, jumping out of the back seat of a chauffeured Cadillac, but not ours. He was still brandishing a fistful of tens and fifties. "See, I found this car, the chauffeur wants to make a little money on the side. Let it rain on the poor people—you got money, you don't have to get wet." The blonde giggled a little but waited in her slow, creamy way for him to hold the door open for her. He put his arm up around her neck, pulled her head down to his level. He licked her throat. He bit her ear. Rapturously he kissed her full lips. "Money's got sex appeal," he screamed. "Money, IT IS SEX!" And as the girl leaned forward, stooping in front of him to go in through the limo door, Tom suddenly hoisted her skirts, and laughing uproariously, threw perhaps a thousand dollars between her magnificent nyloned legs.

I never got around to asking him to advance that thousand. When I phoned the next day to talk about

the script job, he stalled. I later heard he went back
to California telling everyone he had seen me in New
York but didn't feel he could safely hire me again because I was drinking too much.

26
July Days, August Nights
(Continued)

My bell had rung late in the afternoon and he
had been at the door, nervously holding a hat he never
put on. He wore a suit and tie but needed a shave;
hair darker than my own. He asked my name and said
he had read about Clair's death in the newspapers
when it had happened.

"I'm John Pottinger," he said. "Her father."

"Took you long enough to come see me."

"I wasn't a very good father when she was alive,"
he said. "You can't ask me to be better when she's
dead." I had thought he was defensive and angry. He
turned out to be very shy.

He needed a drink and I gave him one. After a
while we went out for another. On our walk to Mc-
Gruddy's I asked what caused the breakup between
him and April. "Goddamn," he said, "it was the Christmas tree."

"A fight?"

"The last straw."

McGruddy brought us another round. Pottinger
drank the way I recognized: the first fast, the second
slow. Over the third he told me about his marriage.

"April was such a flip, sometimes I couldn't stand
it any more. I told her and told her, and one night I
told her again. 'Here it is June,' I said to her, 'and I'm
going out now and I'm not coming back till you take
down the Christmas tree.'"

Pottinger was silent for a moment, looking down

into the glass in his hand. "The saddest words in literature," he went on, putting his drink away, "are Swann's. Thinking back, the end of his life, remembering how at first he didn't have a mind for Odette, but as time went on he got hooked, remembering how much he sacrificed for her, gave up his social position, spent his money, how he got hung up and tortured with that insane jealousy thing, and he finally thinks when he's dying, 'And the waste of it is, she was never my type.'

"April never was my type either," John Pottinger went on. "I never thought I would marry anyone but the kind of girl I grew up with—white gloves, straight, clean hair, a cashmere sweater and a little string of pearls around the neck. I came down to De Haviland to teach school, and then I met April. April, she used to have a song she sang, 'Got myself a big brass bed, gonna paint my toenails ruby red.' You know what her actual, quote, first goddamn words to me were? 'Something in me always wants to be made pregnant by a handsome stranger.' Unquote. Imagine my mother hearing a girl say that?

"I used to think my life was going to be lawns, spring and winter terms, quiet summers to do a little reading, a little money in the bank. But April showed me there was more to life. I liked the way she lived, you understand, but I never got used to it. It was always like I was on vacation, passing through, something temporary, in a foreign country, not real life. It was exciting, but I never felt I lived there. Not in that marriage. I used to think maybe I should go back to school, take a postgraduate degree, and April had me taking bongo lessons."

We ordered more martinis. "Frankly," Pottinger said, "I didn't like April. I loved her, I was excited by her, but I didn't like her. Most people will tell you that it's more important to like than to love. At least, that's what they build their marriages on, no matter what they say. The comfortable old-shoe theory of marriage. That's what most marriages called successful are based on—liking. But you're too goofed up, nervous, angry, frightened, trying too hard, betting too much, just too goddamn high to be cool with someone you absolutely love. Isn't that so?"

We left McGruddy's and made it to the Glue, the 55, the Bistro. In the Minetta, Pottinger became very excited. "Look, look!" he said. "Will you tell me what I'm doing here?" He was standing in front of the portraits of the famous losers that hang on the Minetta wall—Jake Spencer, Max Bodenheim, Joe Gould and the other gods of Disrepair. "I shouldn't be here," Pottinger said. "I should be working for the Eastern Shore Life Insurance Company in Silver Springs, Maryland, for God's sake!"

"You live there now?"

"Not in years."

"Will you have a drink?" I asked him presently. "Sure. And you'll have one with me?" "Yes I will." "Listen, are the lights *very* yellow in here?" "Yes they are." "Golden?" "Yes." "Thank God—I thought they were." "Have a drink." "Yes I will. And you." "Thank you. And let's have one to the yellow light." "And another to April, goddamn."

We put money in the juke. Lou and Anatole Fugelman came in and Ira himself from the Glue. The beautiful Nancy Colbert bought us a drink and we bought her one right back. Carly Simon sang about rainy-day love on the machine, and John Pottinger made his last flight of the night, halting at first, stumbling in his speech, crooning the words at times almost to himself, intense, incoherent, drunken, drinking, driven, driving, and breaking through at last and in the clear.

"Yellow lights, gold lights, wink and blink, blur and shine in your brain. Yellow lights in the plate-glass window, Nick, music on the juke, and outside, Nick, MacDougal Street, where I never thought I'd be, and all the beautiful young women and all the handsome men, like a beautiful musical comedy, goddamn. Ice tinkles, someone laughs, the door opens and closes, people come and go, the lights are gold, Carly sings, April waits in her big brass bed, rub me till I'm cherry red, April, April, Christmas tree or no, I'm coming home, April, all of a sudden April, I remember April why I left Maryland the Beautiful for April, god-damn!"

I took him back to the apartment when the Minetta closed and put him to bed on the cot in the spare room where Clair used to paint. He had asked me not to mention to anyone that he was Clair's father.

"Why are the paintings blanked out? You get mad at her?"

"She did it."

"Mad at herself?"

"And me too."

I asked why he had come to see me.

"I don't know. To get a feeling I was close to her."

"It's too late."

"Always is."

We breakfasted on vodka and grapefruit juice around noon. He said he was in a hurry to get to the Greyhound terminal. Some place he had to be the next day. He never told me where.

"You know April is long remarried, don't you?"

"Not when I'm drinking."

"Anything else you want to know about Clair?"

"Not much to ask. Never much knew her, you know."

He left the apartment, still holding his battered old hat in his hand.

"She ever talk about me?"

"When she was little she used to think one day you'd come back for her."

He nodded wordlessly and went away.

27

I feel happy, looking forward to the evening as I always do when Z. is coming for me. He arrives wearing a tall silk opera hat, white tie and an old-fashioned black opera cloak lined with red satin. I don't understand. Had he said anything on the phone about dressing?

"I'm sorry. I didn't realize—it'll only take me a minute to change—"

"It doesn't matter."

He is annoyed. He won't take off his cloak or hat and says we're late. The hair at his temples is grayer than I remember. It confuses me. When I saw him last, wasn't it black? We are in his luxurious old Rolls.

I pull my little wraparound skirt down at the knee so I feel less naked and shabby. Z. says nothing but holds my hand. It is comforting, but he is still wearing his hat. It makes him seem remote, formally distant from me. We are driving through streets that look like a city I've never seen before, passing a large, unknown body of water. I don't recognize the chauffeur.

The first room is a kind of illegal gambling casino built into what looks like an old, abandoned warehouse near the docks. People move feverishly. Some play roulette, running from table to table. Others are betting for high stakes at card tables. Z. takes my arm protectively and we walk toward two big doors at the end of the room. Two servants in Louis XIV costumes are seated at a little table checking names off a list. Z. does not have to tell them his name. As usual when I am with him, the feeling is that we are special guests, long awaited. Z. nods, and they unlock the doors, bolting them behind us.

Heavy maroon velvet curtains have been drawn in this room to shut out eyes in the street and the noise of traffic. It is a secret place. The lighting is subdued, a rich, somber darkness in which people's faces swim into the light like blurred white flowers and then disappear into shadows again. The people are well dressed, the men in dark suits or black tie, almost as splendid as Z., the women gowned by Oscar de la Renta, Givenchy, Halston. A few people are languidly finishing dinner, seated at little tables lighted by candles. Bowls of fruit and buckets of iced wine wait on sideboards. Some people are idly gossiping at the bar. Two alley cats are fucking in the center of the dance floor. Three or four couples who have been dancing to a muted sax, bass and drum stop to watch, their arms still draped around each other. Everyone is silent. I haven't heard a human voice since we came through the locked doors. The tomcat has his lips back, his teeth bared, as if smiling. The female is in heat. The male's long narrow red tip slides in, the female shudders as she receives his thrust, the male drives forward on his strong rear legs, his front legs up on her back, gripping her. The narrow arrow of red hard flesh disappears into the female and she closes her eyes. The drummer beats a little flourish and some of the dancers politely applaud. Somebody throws a tablecloth over the two cats, but I am aware that their bodies are still moving beneath the white folds as the dancing resumes. My pulse is heavy in my breast.

I try to make out the people. Is that A. and B. dancing together? I think I recognize C. and D. standing against a wall. E. is talking to a beautiful woman. He says something to her and she turns to look at me. It is F., but she gives no sign of recognition for me. Another beautiful woman in a ravishingly cut long, slender black tube of silk that reaches to the floor comes up beside E. and F. and places her hand in a friendly, allied manner on F.'s shoulder. They look at themselves and their beautiful clothes in the mirror. F. says something to the other woman, a blonde. They both turn to stare toward me. I don't know the blonde. They are like schoolgirls who want to let someone know she is being left out. They are laughing and whispering together. My confusion grows. F. is usually so friendly, even somewhat shy of me. My stupid clothes have given her an advantage she must have been dreaming of for a long time. She smiles at Z. He smiles back. He never told me he knew her. I move toward him possessively. I feel betrayed but dependent on him for help; I feel like a kid who has lied about her age to crash a grown-up party and has been revealed as all too pitifully wearing her mother's clothes and high heels.

A big tall man, deeply suntanned, joins F. and the blonde. There is a certain hard, Aztec cruelty in his unmoving face. He must be a Mexican. He has brought his dog into the room, a large cream-and-tan German shepherd. F. and the blonde are attracted to this man but are pretending not to be. I can see it in the way they do not directly look at him. They steal glances when they think he is unaware. Heads are turning. A. and B. have stripped naked. A. is on his back, his legs knotted around B.'s neck. B. is lying above him, kissing him on the lips, his cock sliding into A.'s asshole, taking him as if he were a woman. The blonde moans and leaves the Mexican's side.

She has a vibrator in her hand. She turns to face him, a smile for him in her eyes, she wants to take his attention away from A. and B. and win it for herself. Facing him, knees bent with her legs spread wide apart, her cunt open and exposed, she slowly puts a vibrator in, rotating it between her palms, offering it to him to thrust in deeper for her. The Mexican looks away. She walks off the floor with a look of hate for me.

Where is Z.? I don't know what is expected of me. Why does the blonde act as if I am her rival? How can I compete with people like these? Z. has disappeared.

Is that him on an odd kind of elaborate chair on a little platform at the other end of the room? The chair is placed beneath an old oil portrait of a man who looks half like Z., half like George Washington. I cannot be sure of Z.'s face, it is in shadow, but I recognize the strange, tall silk hat. He has not taken it off. I know that in the darkness his eyes are watching to see what I will do. He has never taken me to a place like this before. He is testing me.

There is a noise and I look around. F. is on one of the tables where people were eating. She lies across the tablecloth, between the dishes, the fruit and the wine. The Mexican has released the dog, which has jumped up on the table and positioned himself between F.'s wide-open legs, his nose sniffing her cunt.

Now the dog's red cock is sliding forward out of the fur sheath beneath his belly. It is narrow and long, the tip quivering with desire. The Mexican blows a tiny silver whistle. The dog immediately puts his nose deeper into F.'s pussy, rasping her clit with his rough tongue. Bowls of fruit fall to the floor, a plate breaks. People have gotten up from their tables to watch more closely. Z. has not moved from his chair, but I see him raise his opera hat in a signal to one of the valets. The servant comes forward and puts a velvet pillow on F.'s breasts to protect them. Now F. looks directly at the Mexican again. He puts the whistle to his lips and blows twice. The dog puts his ass down low enough to shove his immensely long cock right into F.'s cunt. She smiles triumphantly, looking at me. But the Mexican ignores her.

He is smoking a cigar, his eyes on me. He is trying to tell me something both F. and the blonde already know. Then I understand. He is impotent. The lights go out and a spotlight flicks on, circling the room. It comes to rest on me. Somehow I know it is controlled by Z.

I drop my skirt to the floor, wondering if I can control my trembling, but knowing what I must do. I am naked. My confidence grows. I get up on the back of a high armchair. The light is so bright I cannot see the faces of any of the people. I feel anonymous, powerful. I sit on the high back of the chair and open my legs.

There is a bowl of fruit on the table. I take a banana and peel it. The banana feels like flesh in my hand, warm and soft, hard and erect at the same time. I want to show the Mexican I will not harm him. I take the banana and slowly begin to put it in.

The banana is soft and fleshy, more vulnerable than he.

I can take it in without breaking it, I can take it all in and still keep it hard, so he need not be afraid; I can take it all in and keep it soft, so it will not hurt me. One inch inside, two. And out again, parting the lips to let it ooze out. In again. One inch in, two, three. Out. In again. The people who are not fucking have begun to clap rhythmically. One inch, two, three inches in, four—five more inches of banana still in my hand, the tender, glistening flesh uncrushed, unbroken, still erect. Five inches in, six inches. It is plump and soft, hard and firm, both at the same time. The Mexican's eyes never leave me. The whole banana is in now, filling me with its fleshy comfort, cramming me with a feeling of joy and power. The Mexican's pants begin to bulge. I have done for him what no other woman could.

I am lying on my stomach. He is getting undressed. While he does, F. and the blonde are using vaseline and mineral oil as a lubricant for my penetration. I realize they are preparing my asshole. I have never taken it in the ass before. I am too tight. I am frightened, but F kisses me and says I can do it. She and the blonde are my friends now. They admire me. They wet their fingers in their own cunt juices and trail them across my perineum to my asshole to get it even wetter. They don't want me to get hurt. F. is kissing me, her tongue in my mouth, the blonde is leaning forward, her heavy, pendulous breasts rubbing across mine. She puts my breast in her mouth and says she loves me, F.'s thumb is in my asshole to begin to open it, I am coming continuously in long, ocean-rolling contractions. The Mexican now has replaced the blonde at my asshole. When I look back I am relieved to see how long and slender his cock is. F. and the blonde kiss me one last time and lead him onto the couch behind me, and when the piercing tip of his cock goes in, I let out a cry of joy.

He thinks it is from pain, but F. and the blonde know it is from pleasure. They look at me proudly, F. kisses him on the mouth while the blonde palms

his balls to keep him hard. He grows erect again w
he sees he has not hurt me but that I welcome h[.]m.
I turn and lie on my right side.

He lies down behind me. I reach back to part my
cheeks so he will know how much I want him. Slowly,
oh so slowly, he pushes against my puckered ass lips
until my anus softens and opens of its own accord.
His bulging head slips in and stops as my sphincter
grasps and holds until I can get used to the hard intrusion. F. has come to stand in front of me. She is
sucking on my breasts, playing with my clit while the
sphincter muscles relax and his read, entering,
moves farther up into me, pushing aside the rectal
tissues. I am melting, melting, the hard muscles
turning soft, my body opening, all the oils and juices
of my body pouring out of every hole. His shaft is
implacable, moving deeper and deeper, parting secret
muscles buried deep in the body, filling me with
sensations of intensity; I am close to screaming. My
sphincter loosens and tightens, it loosens and tightens,
and every time it loosens he pushes another inch in.
Nothing, nothing can approach my feeling of joy as I
feel his balls right up against my asshole. He has got
it all the way in and has not grown soft. "I have a
surprise for you because I love you," he says. He takes
his cock out in one long, slow, inching movement that
leaves me sore but hungry for more.

F. and the blonde turn me over on my back on the
narrow sofa so that my head is lowered over the edge.
My Mexican lover dips his cock into a glass of white
wine to wash it, and F. tenderly cradles it with a white
linen napkin to wipe it dry and clean. He comes to
stand over me now, his legs astride my shoulders, his
cock pointing right at my mouth. Behind him somebody else has now come to stand between my parted
legs while the blonde puts more vaseline around and
into my asshole and F. kneels to put a finger into my
pussy and kiss me. When I am all wet the Mexican
—looking like an Aztec no more but now with eyes
filled with desire and love—puts his cock to my lips.
Behind him I can feel F. and the blonde spread and
lift my legs straight up into the air. The unknown

man's hands are on my ass, parting the cheeks, putting a thumb into the hole to test it. I can't see who it is. I feel a solid intrusion pressing me there and I raise my head as much as I can. I must know who this new man is. F. sees what I want to do and supports my head from behind even while the Mexican is presenting his cock to my mouth. I try to look past his shoulders, but the angle hides the second man's face. All I can see is an enormous shaft poised at my asshole. It glistens with power, thick and heavy, bulbous at the crown. It is at least eight inches long, but what worries me suddenly with fear of failure is that it is so much thicker than the Mexican cock that initiated my rear passage—a full two and a half inches in diameter! I have never taken a cock that fat before even in my pussy—how can I get it into my asshole? I grit my teeth and try to make a picture of it going in, slowly, slowly. I pretend it is my Mexican who is opening my secret little place behind. The picture in my mind helps relax my sphincter muscles. My desire grows and I am no longer afraid. I am determined to show the Mexican and my giant anonymous asshole-fucker that if they are men enough to fuck me together, I am woman enough to take them both. The Mexican now has his cock in my mouth. F. and the blonde are each holding one of my legs straight up in the air, and the giant anonymous cock at my asshole is beginning to press deeper into me. Again I try to see who the man behind is, but the Mexican has desires of his own. He takes my head lovingly into his hands and pushes his cock deeper into my mouth, forcing me to concentrate on him, on the big, round mouthful that is pushing in, almost choking me with its massive, meaty weight, and all the while I can feel the full, slow, unrelenting pressure on my back-fucker's blunt intrusion continuing into my ass. He has already gone deeper than the Mexican reached. Stop! Stop! Wait! Wait, I'm tearing, more oil . . . But the Mexican's cock is now at the back of my throat, moving slowly forward to give me time to get used to it. My mouth is full of saliva, I keep swallowing, swallowing, it eases the passage, I have more cock in my mouth than I have ever had before, I can feel the hair that covers the Mexican's balls tickling my closed eyes! I've done it! And all the while there is a continuing sense of pressure in my ass, that thick shaft is widening the opening for itself, but the sphincter is reacting, it never felt anything like this before, it is closing. F. sees what is happening, she sees that the pain is beginning to outweigh the pleasure. She leans forward to finger my clit, rubbing it till it juices and throbs. That does it! With an inner heave as if I am having an expelling bowel movement, my asshole yawns open and the giant cock in the rear rushes right into the passage, filling me up tight from wall to wall for the entire eight inches! I get so excited my cunt opens too, and I squirt juice right into F.'s mouth, which is on my clit. I have never felt anything like this—my whole heart heaves with joy for the man in the back. He has shot past the sphincter with one mighty heave, I have his cock in my grip. He does not move for a minute or two because I am gripping his shaft so tightly. F. is excited by the sight of that giant cock rammed up to the balls in my asshole. She leans in again to hold my head tenderly against her breasts. My rectum is now adjusted to the huge stretch, I can take it, I feel relieved, excited, and I start coming as I've never come before, the Mexican's hard cock still in my mouth, my legs straight up in the air, propped against my asshole-fucker's shoulders, straddling his ears, while his giant rod continues the pressure ever deeper into me. One rolling spasm after another contracts my belly, my whole pussy is standing wide open, pushed upward and forward from the pressure of the huge cock in my ass. People are gasping at the sight, men have grabbed women and are trying to fuck them in the ass too while the excited women grind backward to imitate me by impaling themselves on the cocks being shoved into their assholes, but I cannot care what anyone else is doing. The Mexican's Aztec cock is in my mouth all the way up to my tonsils. My eyes are covered by his balls and he is stroking the cheeks of my face, crooning how good my mouth is, and my mouth is covered by the hair of his balls as he pushes and pushes deeper into my throat. F. and the blonde have taken out a double dildo, shaped like a horseshoe, and knobbed at both ends. They hold each other close by the ass while shoving the knobs at each end of the dildo up their cunts. They ride up and back, seesawing back and forth. When one pushes her cunt forward, it drives the fat knob at the other end of the dildo farther up the second one's pussy. The nipples of their breasts brush each other, and they are watching me, jumping up and down with their own excitement and mine while the double dildo holds them belly to belly, snatch to snatch. My Mexican's cock has begun to jerk wildly in my mouth, and his semen flows like a river, running down my throat. I swallow and swallow it all. He stands over me, almost faint, weak at the knees, smiling at me and saying how much he loves me. But the heavy cock in my ass has grown even bigger because of the excitement! It is digging deeper and deeper. F. realizes that my legs must be feeling the strain of being extended up in the air so long. She bends them at the knees, bringing them back down toward my breasts. This spreads my rectum open even more, and I can feel the last inches of hard, thick cock rush up my ass. It is so big and in so deep that when I press on my belly I can feel the shaft in there! But this last feeling of my bowels opening for him against the head of his cock is too much for my rear-fucker, and he lets loose with a series of pushes and comes and comes, flooding my asshole and pouring out past my sphincter, gushing down the cheeks of my ass and wetting the sofa under me. I feel ten, twenty, thirty expansions and contractions of his cock inside my ass, he spurts and spurts and spurts more semen into me, and then his prick deflates with a soft whoosh of air and slips out. I open my eyes. The Mexican man is smiling at me very tenderly, F. and the blonde are smiling too, each one supporting my tired head and letting it lie against her soft breasts, the audience is applauding me, and as I have already guessed, it was Z. who was behind me, Z. who had that thick, powerful cock, it was Z. whom I took more deeply

into my body than any man I have ever known, it
was Z. who had never been my lover before, it is Z.
who is beside me now, looking young and black-
haired again, holding me in his arms, kissing me on
the mouth, telling me no woman had ever made him
feel like this. "I have always loved you," he says. "I
will never leave you again."

28

July Days, August Nights
(Continued)

"You are all here because of booze. The medical indications are you continue to drink long after
it has stopped being fun, after it has begun to damage
your marriage, your career, and is destroying your
body. You order another drink while praying to God
to help you stop. You have another drink when you
leave your boss's office after he tells you the next time
you'll be fired. You run out of the house after a
drunken fight, with your spouse threatening divorce,
and you have one to forget your sorrows. You wake
up puking the next morning, God knows where and
with whom, and the first thing you do is push another
snort of booze down your cringing gut, hoping enough
will stay down so that the nausea will stop. I've done
it myself.

"How many of you are on both booze and pills?"

Most of the people in the room raised their hands.

"Welcome," the doctor said. "You are the wave of
the future, the cross-addicts. Most of you were started
by your friendly pusher, your family doctor. You went
to see him because you were worried about your drinking, and he said you were drinking because you were
nervous and he gave you pills to calm you down, so
you took the pills but continued to drink anyway, and

now you're here. How many of you are just plain drunks, no pills?"

About ten people in the room raised their hands.

"Greetings," the doctor said. "The news I bring is that you are yesterday's people. We don't get too many whisky-only, old-fashioned drunks in here any more. But I have a special place in my heart for you. I used to be one myself.

"All of you are here because you have a disease, a medical condition, like pneumonia or diabetes. The symptom of the diabetic is his body cannot handle sugar. The symptom of the alcoholic is the whisky glass in his hand.

"There are people in this room who won medals for bravery in Vietnam. There are other men and women here who would be able to stay silent if they had atom-bomb secrets and they were tortured. A lot of you could pick up a white-hot bar of iron if you had to, or could run into a burning building to rescue your wife or child. So don't think that if you can't stop drinking, it has anything to do with lack of will power or courage. Will power and courage are false issues.

"Being unable to stop drinking has nothing to do with determination or intelligence. Anybody who has ever seen the cunning and determination of a drunk who wakes up without a penny, sick and shaking on a Sunday in a dry town, will quickly learn there is no-body on earth with more crafty tricks or will power than a drunk who needs a drink. I don't care what the odds are, he will have a glass in his hand before sun-down. Nobody can tell me a drunk doesn't have as much will power as anybody in the world. But that's a false issue too.

"Now, I want to make a little test. Close your eyes and listen to this. Try to imagine yourself in the situation I'm about to describe: *You will never have another drink again for the rest of your life!* No beer, no wine, no gin, no Scotch. Never another drop."

The speaker paused.

"If there is anybody in this room who heard these words without feeling a twinge of fear in his belly, stand up."

Nobody moved.

"Congratulations. Baby, you've arrived. You never have to wonder again 'Am I a heavy social drinker or am I an alcoholic?' You've passed the test. You know. You are a drunk. Alcoholism is a fatal disease for which there is no cure. But like certain forms of cancer, it is possible for some people to win lifelong remission of their symptoms. The only way you will ever know you are a success is on the day you die, when you are surrounded by your family and people you love and not naked, screaming and drunk in the streets and gutters of New York. Not drinking has milestones and anniversaries, but it never ends.

"For about two out of three of you listening to me— thirty-five or forty of the fifty-three people in this room —sobriety is your future. The remaining fifteen or so will go back to drinking when you leave the Institute. The news I have for you is this: the statistical probability is that two of you will be dead within a year. Maybe a fast suicide like pills, a gun or auto accident while drunk. Maybe you will take a couple more years to do it, and the course of your fatal disease will run slightly slower. But you will still overdose on booze— enough to explode your heart, drown your brain or jam your liver. Of the remaining dozen who go back to drinking, six of you will be dead within five years. Same reasons. Statistics.

"Booze is passive. It doesn't call you up on the phone, it doesn't invite you to parties, it doesn't jump into your glass in a bar, it doesn't force itself down your throat. Booze can wait. Booze doesn't lose patience, go stale or bored. It waits. It sits on the shelf, it sits in the bottle, it waits. Its day will come. It doesn't care what you swear today. Tomorrow is another day. Next year is another year. It doesn't get impatient, angry or tired. It doesn't go away. It never grows old. It waits.

"For the majority of you who choose to remain here for therapy at Brinkley Smithers it will wait in vain. I can promise you lifelong remission, not of your disease but of your symptoms. You will never hold a glass of gin in your hand again."

When the doctor stopped speaking, most of the people crowded around her to ask questions. Dr. Foreman and I stood up and walked out. We went over to the All Ireland Bar on Third Avenue.

"That's what I wanted you to hear," he said.

He was drunker than I.

29

Saturday-Morning Special

"A Spoken History."

I remember once on my eleventh birthday feeling very happy and sitting on a bench under a tree and saying to myself this is the best moment of my life and I will always remember it and how this tree looked, and if I am ever unhappy I will tell myself to remember this tree and I will feel better. I've forgotten how that tree looked but haven't forgotten what it feels to be that happy, and that is how I feel now, so I don't remember what number this tape should be, but it doesn't matter. It's Saturday afternoon, whatever I'm taking with me is packed, one suitcase is all I need; the less I have to remind me of California the better. I'm dictating this into the machine over a glass of wine, walking around the apartment, too keyed up to sit down, so glad to think I'll never see it again. Inez is out for an hour, and I'm waiting for her to come back so I can tell her and finish up here. I'm getting all this down before I drive over to Harry Maxwell's in La Jolla, and then it's the airport for me.

I left work at Speaking Volumes early yesterday, changed into shorts against the heat and got into the Jaguar. I was having my second beer at Hussong's Cantina about four thirty when the phone rang and they yelled out my name. Harry, from the pay phone in Mexico City. "This is your local Coca-Cola bottling works."

"You got the syrup?"

"Sweetest thing this side of heaven."

"See you soon."

I dropped off the pavement and onto the black-topped Carretera Numero Uno. At Ensenada I checked into El Presidente. Harry arrived. We had a drink and dinner together. He had snorted a line. He offered me some and himself to go with it.

"You nervous, Harry?" I'd never seen him use before.

"I'd be a freak if I weren't. Come on, have some. We can sleep it off together."

"No thanks."

"Why should I be an exception?"

"No meant yes until you said that."

We drove out to the tumbledown little civil airfield north of town about nine this morning. I hadn't slept well. I wanted this job to be over. I couldn't wait for it to be over. Felix had found a Weather guy somewhere called Goose. He had learned to fly in Vietnam. Goose had rented a Cessna 150 in Mexico City and was warming the engine.

"What kind of chute is that?" The shape was smaller than I was used to.

Harry started to say something but then looked away. Goose smiled. "Not to be nervous," he said. "We got you one of the new flat jobs. Those old war-surplus cheapos you been learning on, they wouldn't run far enough the kind of wind we got today."

"I don't like it."

"They go almost twenty miles an hour across the ground."

Harry smiles. "Got to be," he says. He likes saying it. He's in a nervous, bitchy mood. He has a carefully tied brown-paper package with him. He opens it and takes out a pair of stiff jeans, a heavy cotton sweatshirt and one of the standard big, floppy jump coveralls colored bright red, white and blue. I put it all on over the shorts. I had brought a helmet and boots with me.

"How high?"

"Seven, eight thousand feet maybe ought to do it," Goose says. "You want to use a static line, or you ready to enjoy yourself and pull your own rig?"

"I'll enjoy myself tonight. Rig the line. Who folded the chute?"

"Who do you think?" Harry says. He looks at me. He's still mad about last night. Or maybe about the whole last year.

"It'll be all right," Goose says. "You packed your own emergency, didn't you?"

"Yes."

"What's to worry?"

Harry is going to drive my Jaguar back. He walks over to the car. "See you in San Diego," he yells. He watches me get into the Cessna after Goose.

Up.

When I had returned to California from my dumb trip to New York, Blake drunkenly gone off to France, my show at the Korne Gallery a failure, nothing to do with my life and wondering why was I in California anyway, I had looked at the wall for two days and then phoned Felix. I said I wanted a job.

"I understand needing a job," Felix said, "but why work for me?"

"Why not start at the top?"

"You know what the job calls for?"

"Remember our days in Hoboken, Felix? I figured out a little more than just you and me."

He laughed.

"I wasn't as dumb as you thought."

"That's the one idea about you I never had," he said and added maybe he could use someone in San Diego. The phone went quiet a moment, and then he said OK, maybe we didn't like each other much any more, and maybe that would change if we worked together, maybe it wouldn't. "But I trust you, Clair."

The reading on the altimeter bolted onto the emergency chute on my chest says seven thousand feet, and we're climbing still. The Cessna motor is grinding like a coffee machine. I'm going to earn my money today. All my training jumps were made at two thousand eight hundred. Goose shouts not to worry, the higher the safer. I tell him he's not making the jump. When Goose levels out, the Cessna is pointed north, toward the border. He leans over and opens the door catch. The wind takes it immediately and it flies up and holds in place under the wing.

"Hurry up and get in the door," he yells. "We're less than two miles this side. I don't want the radar to pick us up for crossing." One last check on the static line.

I am sitting on the floor of the plane, my legs out the door. Tijuana is on my left, the blue Pacific beyond.

"OK?"

"OK."

He cuts the motor. In eerie silence I spread-eagle, brace, and exit the plane.

One thousand, two thousand, I've gotten into good aerodynamic position this time, no tumbling, three thousand—why don't I feel anything?—four thousand, *panic,* five thousand—SHOULD I PULL THE EMERGENCY?—six thousand and *CHECK FOR DEPLOYMENT!* I look up over my right shoulder. The big, flat, rectangular orange-and-blue canopy is floating up there like God's own smile, fully deployed, no Mae West bulges. These new chutes open so softly through the sleeve, I haven't felt it open at all behind the hammering of my heart. A mile or two away as I swing in the sky, another single-engine plane is dropping parachutists. The plane is too far to hear its engine. Tiny dots in the enormous sky, then canopies blossom out of nothing and silence—purple and white, red and yellow, more beautiful to me than any flower. Pulling the directional toggles until I can see where they are running to, I line up for a fast transverse to drop on their field right among them. Goose waggles his wings. Back to Mexico City to return the plane. I'm alone in the sky.

A thousand feet above the other parachutists, I'm running down on them. The breeze is good, my heart has gone back to normal, the canopy is open and filled, I'm singing out loud with nobody to hear me here on top of the world. Only when I'm close enough to the field to judge my lateral speed across ground can I see a cross breeze is making the chute slide too fast over the target. I'm afraid to work the toggles hard enough, *I don't know this kind of chute,* it's too fast for me. Heart-stopping fantasies of too much air spilling out. I overshoot the drop field by about a mile. A California State Highway Patrol car is waiting for me as I get to my feet.

"Bit more action than you expected, little lady?" the cop says with a smile.

I am gathering up the lines and fabric in bunches in my arms. Funny how childhood grips at these moments. What I want to do more than anything else is turn to him with tears in my eyes and ask him to let me go.

"Not too experienced a jumper, are you?" he says.

"This is only my fourth jump. I got overconfident and tried a new chute."

"I used to do a little diving myself. Before I got married. The wife doesn't like it. These new rigs travel something like hang gliders, don't they?"

"I borrowed it from a friend for a test. It's too fast for me."

He smiles. "Yes," he says, "seeing where you come down, I suppose we can say that. You mind telling me where you jumped from?"

I nod to where we can see four more parachutes opening in the sky. "The Saturday Skydivers' Club, over near Point Pacific Cape."

"You live near here?"

"I have an apartment in San Diego."

"Been living there long?"

"Almost two years."

"Employed there?"

"Yes."

"You got some ID?"

I showed him a check-cashing card with my photo on it from Speaking Volumes, Inc.

"Looks fine, little lady. Sorry to inconvenience you. Who did you say piloted the plane you jumped from?"

I told him the name Harry had given me and the number of the Saturday Skydivers' field.

"Come sit in the car with me until I radio through on that. Won't take but a minute." He spoke to the police dispatcher, and the man signed off. When he came back on again he said he had phoned the field. Yes, the man whose name I had given was a parachute taxi pilot there, and he confirmed I'd jumped with him but had been carried too far by the wind. The dispatcher finished with a physical description furnished by the taxi pilot, including the red, white and blue jump coverall.

The highway patroller looked at me. "Checks out OK," he said. "Checks out fine."

He took off his dark glasses. "Now, little lady, you mind coming into the station with me? A lot of cocaine coming over the border these days in little planes. We got a right fine police matron there, it won't take but a minute to search you, and you can be on your way. Be pleased to give you a ride back to the field, back home, anywhere you say."

"Harry?"

"Right."

"I think we'll have to let my membership in the Saturday Skydivers drop. I got questioned by the highway patrol."

"And?"

"And they said they heard people were smuggling cocaine over the border in light planes."

"What will people think of next. I take it you're home?"

"Yes."

"See you as usual?"

"Make it sooner."

"Anything up?"

"I've changed my plans."

"Give me an hour or two?"

"I'll be there."

I had not told him it was my last run.

For two years now I've been wondering how I felt about Blake, wondering what I'd say if I ever saw him again. A week ago, as if in a dream, I heard him on the phone from France asking me to take him back. He said he's stopped drinking and wanted me. He said he loved me. I heard myself answer in the same dream, all doubt gone at the sound of his voice, all the certainty of life in my own. I said I wanted him. Rosie, I'm so excited, this is like one of those picture postcards you send on your last day in Bermuda to a friend when it doesn't matter what you say because you know you'll beat the card home. I'll listen to it later. When I phoned Felix five days ago to tell him I was going back to Blake I didn't expect him to take the news easily. I tried to soften it by telling him I'd go through with this last job. But I wasn't prepared for how hard and furiously he took it anyway. Goddamn it, did I know what I was doing? Did I know how much money I was walking out on? How could I do this to him? How did I know Blake had stopped drinking? Fucking drunks always say they've stopped. "You'll get your head on his shoulder in the sack one night and you'll tell your story of the years you were away from him. Women always do." I couldn't trust Blake. *I must not tell him anything*. Drunks always blabbed when they drank. I realized Felix would miss me, miss the money I brought in. What got him most was that I was going back to Blake.

He must have heard the strange note in his voice himself. He always prided himself on never being jealous. He laughed and then, handsomely, let it all go. "OK, but if anything ever happens to Blake, you have your job back."

"What could happen to him?"

"I don't mean to Blake. I mean, between the two of you. Maybe it won't work out." A pause, another laugh. "Oh, hell, I'm just mad because I'm going to miss you. If he's stopped drinking, you'll be on top of the world. When's he arriving in New York?"

"Wednesday night."

"I'll be out of town. I'll drop in on the old bastard Saturday morning when I get back. I'm going to tell him, if he ever takes as much as one drop again I'll slit his nose. It'll be OK, Clair. It'll be fine. Just make this last jump and bring the Mexican Coca-Cola with you when you come on Monday. We'll shake hands and kiss goodbye. With all my love."

I said yes then, I'd wait and make the carry to New York on Monday; but Blake was still in France, he wasn't yet real. Now I know he is in New York, I can *feel* him in our old apartment waiting for me. I called Felix again a half hour ago to tell him I've just made the jump but I've changed my mind, I'm leaving today. But Felix wasn't home. Maxwell can bring the Coca-Cola east himself when he's finished rebottling it. My time in California is over. I never belonged here. Blake is waiting. Felix will understand when he sees me. Just as I did not understand my single days in the Village until they were over and I was married, and didn't understand my marriage to Blake until it was over too, I am only now coming to see what this period of my life has meant. My years in New York before marriage were only an extension of old high-school dances, the time I was married to Blake was only playing house, this last period of my life has been the exploration of sex that marriage should have been.

I go through my life one stage late, but these two years on my own have been the ritual in the wood. They've given me my chance to catch up with myself. A new woman is waiting to be born, and I'm eager to see who she is. And yet, what I have learned is what I already knew as a virgin on the train from De Haviland when I first saw the skyscrapers of New York rising in front of me across the flat Jersey swamps and plains: sex for its own sake is a dead end. My mother knew it, and I suppose she heard it from her mother too. It is something every woman must learn for herself. Our journey is to turn the banal into the real. This tape ends because Mrs. Nicholas Blake, childhood over, married at last, is going home.

30
Chemistry

Dear Frank:
I am sending this to your home address because
(1) if the N.Y.P.D. is anything like the San Diego
P.D. maybe you don't want everything sent out in the
open on the official Telex for everybody to read including members of your own department when it comes
to dope, and (2) I don't want to have to put this down
official and get subpoenaed later by a defense lawyer
wasn't I on a witch-hunting for evidence against his
client. The trials in California are never about did the
alleged perpetrator do it or not but is the evidence he
did it admissible or not.

A few days ago we got a call from the Royal Canadian Mounties in Toronto about a part-time revolutionist and full-time hophead ecology freak on the
F.B.I. list named Lester Fellows a.k.a. Goose. He was
the victim of a homicide that city, party or parties
unknown. The Mounties did not believe robbery for
cash was the motive as the victim had $3700 in cash
in his pocket when he was found dead in his hotel
room, or maybe the perpetrators were rushed. Victim
had a Rolls Royce in the hotel garage, the dealer's
sticker on the bumper said Sunset Pacific Import Motors, San Diego. Further check with Sunset Motors here
developed victim had paid cash for the car. Information further developed by the Mounties was the victim
must have been ripped off for drugs, there was a heavy
line of cocaine crystals from the closet to the door of
the hotel room and out. The bag must have ripped.
Where you come in is the piece Fellows was carrying
when found D.O.A. It was unfired, leading to the belief he was killed by someone he knew. I got a feeling

258

and phoned Toronto for a ballistics report and checked it against a recent homicide this city I Telexed you about, Harry Maxwell, in response to your request to develop information the Pottinger homicide your city. Our investigation of the Maxwell case developed he was a doper too. Positive identification of the revolver Goose was carrying at the time of death with the bullet killed Maxwell. The way it figures to me is Goose was an associate or customer of Maxwell and got rich by ripping him off for whatever he had stashed, it must have been plenty, and now an associate unknown has found Goose and taken it back. Further evidence has been developed Maxwell was in the process of refining more cocaine when killed but what Goose found was enough for him not to want to wait. The Goose homicide was not a professional job, one bullet in the stomach another in the chest. The bullets were not well placed but they did the job anyway. A lot of this is not checked out yet but it is my feeling. I don't know if this connects with your New York homicide Clair Pottinger, who was a known associate of Maxwell, but it figures.

The reason Goose first connected in my mind with Maxwell is that Maxwell is carried on our list as a political activist revolutionist too and Goose's wallet contained an airplane pilot's license rated up to twin-engine capacity and I remember we found a parachute and jumping gear in the deceased Maxwell's closet. We sent it to forensic at the time, but San Diego is not N.Y., it is not a big dept. I guess they were looking for hair or fingerprints or dope sewed in the seams of the parachute, they didn't know what to look for so they just put it aside.

Enclosed is a Xerox from a guy in forensic who just made some new tests for me. I had him write it up because it is technical but his report is opening a lot of eyes around here. I hope it helps you. If you see a connection any of this with your Pottinger homicide please let me know, also if you have any information that ties suspect Lester Fellows to anyone else in the dope, our understanding is that he is originally from back east. Give my regards to your family and I hope you are well.

Sincerely yours,

Joe Dolan

P.S. You will remember that the deceased Maxwell was an industrial chemist.

San Diego Police Department
Forensic Laboratory
MEMO

Dear Joe:

For your friend's information, here is a recap on the method we discussed. It is too sophisticated for routine analysis to turn up, and I only knew what to do after a talk with Narcotics Enforcement in the Treasury Department.

If fabric is soaked in cocaine base dissolved in pure alcohol, and then allowed to dry in the sun, the drug is absorbed by the fabric and becomes almost impossible to detect. When item arrives at its destination the article of clothing is soaked again in acetone for about 15 minutes. The liquid is then carefully wrung out and allowed to evaporate off in a flat container, like a baking tin. The end result is marketable. This process not only conceals the drug but also refines the cocaine base into finished cocaine. For every 9 ounces of cocaine base you start with in Colombia or Peru, the process yields 3 ounces of high-quality cocaine, ready for sale in the USA.

The parachute, jeans and sweatshirt, plus the jump overalls you gave us tested out to 49 ounces, 95 percent pure. Current import price for this grade is close to $1500–$2000 an ounce. When it is suitably cut with procaine, speed, quinine, etc., and sold on the retail market, it can bring up to $5000 per ounce. Whoever muled this batch into the USA was a hell of a valuable employee, and whoever killed Maxwell, if he had waited for Maxwell to process the cocaine out of the jumping clothes, would have been a lot richer. But maybe he found enough already there to make it worth his while anyway. The cocaine I recovered in my tests is worth from $200 to a quarter of a million dollars on the street.

Hope this helps.

Tony

31

July Days, August Nights (Concluded)

I had drunk myself past drunk and was sober again.

I was sitting and thinking, but when I tried to focus I could not remember what I had been thinking about. I seemed to be on a park bench. It was early, quiet, a little after dawn. There was something comforting I was trying to think about but I couldn't remember what. I didn't know how long I had been sitting there, but there was something I would remember in a moment that was definitely OK. Last night had started at the Glue, I'd had a talk with Lou and Anatole about eating somewhere, we'd started to walk to McGruddy's. I couldn't remember if we'd arrived. I was sweating, cold sweat that made my shirt cling to my back, but the shakes weren't too bad and I didn't have a hangover. I had stopped having hangovers. If you keep enough alcohol in the bloodstream, you stay at a cer-

tain high level and the hangover never has a chance to
catch on. I must have gone out of sync again, because
when I tried to remember what I was thinking about I
was still on the park bench but the light was different.
I was in Washington Square Park. People on Fifth
Avenue were catching buses and taxis to go to work. I
remembered what it was that was OK. I had most of a
fifth of gin in a paper bag in a canvas carryall between
my feet. I could feel my feet cramped around the
canvas sack, so nobody had stolen it. I would have another drink in a second or two, and then maybe go get
shaved at the barber's or even make it to a Turkish
bath and really get straight. I would have another
drink in a second or two, and then I'd go do it. The
anticipation of reaching down to find the fat, almost
full bottle was like money in the bank. I'd have that
drink in a minute. I had plenty, I didn't have to rush
it. Meanwhile I went to the water fountain and had a
drink of cold water because I was sweating so much,
and washed my face with cold water against the cold
sweat that was still pouring out of every pore, dewing
the backs of my hands and making them itch. When I
came into sync again—was it a minute later, an hour?
I didn't know—I didn't know what I had been thinking
about. I hadn't had that drink, but I'd have it now. I
opened the canvas bag. There was the bottle of
Fleischmann's gin, just as I remembered, but alongside
it was a second I didn't remember buying. It wasn't
even opened yet, so I didn't have to think about stock-
ing up before night so I wouldn't wake in the middle of
the night and find I'd run dry. That was what it was
that I had been feeling was OK. I went to the phone
booth on the corner of MacDougal and West Fourth
Street and stepped inside. I had a drink from the bottle
in there where nobody could see. I corked it and put it
back in the canvas bag. I patted the second, unopened
bottle. I was rich.

Where does this certainty come from? Someone else
is living in my mind. A man I don't know.

I finished the first bottle and moved the canvas bag
more firmly between my two feet. The unopened bottle
was safely there, waiting for me.

book five

HELLO

—then Felix said he was leaving the country.

The redhead had gone to the Ladies while I was making the phone call, and when I got back Felix had his one glittering blue eye fixed on the blonde who had just come into the 55. He pulled his eye patch more firmly over the other and dragged the blonde's barstool closer to his own. "Another trap," he was saying to her, "is Water Looking. You make it up to Central Park lake a Sunday afternoon, you see all these hand-in-hand illicit couples, they're proving they Respect Each Other as Persons Too. The reason ain't clear, but the best way seems the presence of large bodies of water. But museums, art galleries, even nondubbed foreign movies with no plot—they can be used too. The whole thing is called—Jungians deny it exists—the Spiritual Activity Reflex. You know what it's a sign?"

"No," the girl said, laughing.

"Sexual guilt. And I'm *never* guilty! If you expect me to take you to the Modern Art Museum or for a long spiritual walk through the Cloisters tomorrow, it's all off. Tell me, who's your analyst?"

"How do you know I'm in psychoanalysis?"

"You're a very integrated person. It's a quality I admire very much. I'm thinking of entering analysis myself. What school does your doctor belong?"

"Freudian."

"I knew it! I didn't think you were being treated by some EST cockamamie, some orgone-therapy Reichist. What I meant, what branch of Freud?"

"He talks about Erik Erikson a lot."

"Do me a favor? I know your doctor wouldn't take me as a patient because of the intense relationship you and I are about to begin. But the next time you see him, ask him recommend a doctor for me? *The same school he is?* If I could only get the same results you are!"

"Why do you want to go into analysis? Do you have problems relating?"

"You think I'm a very cool guy, right? That I've got it all put together?"

"I think you're probably very shy and insecure. That you talk a lot to hide the silence inside." I asked Felix to pass the sugar from the hamburger-and-coffee counter.

"You ever meet anyone like her?" he said to me in admiring tones. "Two minutes and she reads me like a book."

"You're probably afraid of women," the blonde glided on. "Some ex-wife or girl friend must have hurt you very, very deeply. But if you go into analysis, you will find it's just infantile rage that your mother preferred your father to you."

Felix shook his head wonderingly at her; he silently watched me spoon sugar into my Pepsi. He finished his beer. "She *knows* me—you know that, Nick?" He turned to her again. "Would I have to put up a big macho front with you? It's so *boring* to have to play superman all the time."

"Vulnerability is the most attractive thing a man can show a woman," the blonde said.

"You never know when you're going to meet fate sitting on a barstool and looking like a movie star, do you?" Felix said.

The blonde glowed.

Mel Parigi and Matti Cosworth came in. Felix spoke to them a moment; when he turned back to the blonde he had lost his place. "Look at those great legs!" he exclaimed with sudden but absentminded exuberance, hoisting her skirt six inches up the thigh. "Couldn't you just live on those legs *for a week?*"

"Marvelous address," Mel said.

The blonde decided she had been mistaken about Felix after all. She got off the barstool and walked away in a huff. Felix shrugged. He watched me stir my Pepsi.

"You're like a junkie coming *down,* that sweet shit, man, you know that?"

I asked why he wanted the blonde to give him the name of her analyst. "You already been going five years to your own."

"A loser like her," he said, "any guy she starts up with, her doctor is already suspicious of him up front. Technically, it's called he's in *resistance.* It's not the girl who's blocked. The doctor is in negative transference. So you send him messages in code to give him support and ego strength. The girl tells him what you said nice about his school of therapy her next free association, and his resistance is worked through. His message comes back in code too: the next time you see her, she says why do we always have to go out to expensive restaurants, why doesn't she cook us dinner her place."

Matti didn't like this kind of talk about the gullibility of women. "You know the trouble with you, Felix?" she said. She'd once had a number with him herself. "You outsmart yourself. You drove that girl away."

Felix patted the blue sunglasses in his shirt pocket, behind which nestled the piece of paper on which the blonde had written her phone number two minutes before; as his redhead came out of the Ladies, he converted it to patting the chair beside him where he wanted her to sit. He smiled at Matti: "You can't win them all," he said to her, too low for the redhead to hear, "thank God." The redhead sat down. "Who was that blonde you were talking to?" she said suspiciously. Felix took another piece of paper out of his pocket and gave it to the redhead. She looked startled for a moment and then lowered her lashes on eyes that were even warmer than the blonde's. She smiled with satisfaction and put the paper into a pocket of her own. On a bar napkin Felix, who had a pretty

fair hand at drawing, had done her portrait, naked
and pregnant.

You'll have to ask him, I thought. Yes I will but
not yet. If you don't ask him and just tell yourself
you might be wrong and forget it, well—you know the
best way to forget, don't you. The phone call I'd made
had been to Lou. I had asked if Felix's old girl friend
Jennifer had ever been a hatcheck. No, he'd said.
She'd been an airline stewardess ever since she'd hit
New York. Why was I asking? Was I with Felix? Why
was Jennifer's job important? Did she figure in Clair's
death? What did I know?

I'd hung up.

Looking at Felix's familiar, easy smile now as he
whispered something into the redhead's ear, fear
touched me. Maybe I wouldn't be able to.

"Forget that sweet crapola," Felix was saying to me,
"and have a real drink."

Wanting to play with fire, and yet wanting to save
something from the flames, I swung immobile in dead
center. A drink. Just one drink and I could ask him.

"Not yet," I said.

I was afraid of the answer.

The Alcohol Services people in Roosevelt Hospital
had begun talking about me going into Brinkley Smithers for booze therapy while I was still in detox. I told
them I already knew about it from one of their great
walk-around advertisements, the city medical examiner, Dr. Foreman. They looked embarrassed but said
it would give me time to think and I'd come out a new
man. Twenty-eight days later, when he came out, the
new man knew what the old one had known all along.
Not to drink. What they hadn't told him was how
to do that. My Blue Cross had lapsed and I was
almost broke, but if they wanted me so badly, it was
their headache. My third week I went to the cashier's
window to arrange something. It had been taken care
of; the records showed Felix's name. I phoned, but
he was out of town. I called again the day I graduated
to thank him. He accused me of being sentimental. If

I wanted to thank him I would kindly see that his money wasn't wasted by staying off the sauce "even if I offer it to you myself." All of which did not stop him from getting me up that night about eleven, phoning from the corner. Could he come up? "I need my number," he said. *"Got* to have the number!"

He came loping in, muttering to himself, flashing past without breaking stride, peering into my face to see if I was sober, never apologizing once for not having come to visit while I was in Brinkley Smithers, our strange phone conversation about cigarettes and the Weathermen disappeared from consciousness. He was circling around the apartment, rummaging in corners as if hunting for something I had deliberately hidden from him. He caught my puzzled look.

"It's the hair," he said triumphantly. "I got it cut short and parted the other side while I was away." He took out a black eye patch and put it on. "This is the turning point of my days, Nick. I'm changing my life. I'm a new man."

"You going to put your eye out to celebrate?"

"In case there's trouble tonight," he said darkly, "I'll tell everybody it was my bad twin brother."

"I didn't know you had one."

"People call up the next day, I say, 'No, that wasn't me broke your window. That must be my bad twin. Is he back in town again? He ships out. He's a merchant marine, was he wearing an eye patch?' And I tell them how much trouble he's always causing me mistaken identity department whenever he's in town." He had some vodka in a pint in his pocket. He hit it and put it back.

"I don't remember you used to drink so much. Before I went away to France."

"I'm closing up Hoboken," he said. "Too much agro. The money people owe me! A guy in Toronto, you wouldn't believe what I had to go through to get him to pay me. I'm selling the trucks. A few days all my assets will be converted to cash. Meanwhile it's like swimming underwater, Nick. I'm gasping, Nick. I need the booze to keep me going."

"What are you going to do?"

"I'll think about that tomorrow. I got to have noise and hilarity tonight, Nick. *I want to forget.*" He'd sung the last words in his *La Bohème* voice.

"Couple more drinks, you'll forget the day after to-morrow too."

He laughed and shrugged. "I just come from that new saloon, Hondo. I guess we'll have to add it to the list. I spend so many hours now eight different bars, each one thinks it's the only place I go. You look tired, Nick."

"We can both use a night's sleep."

But his voice was accusing: "You gone *toys in the attic?* Right out of the drunk farm and already a Good Influence?" He was rummaging in the kitchen closet. He let out a sigh of pleasure. He had found the panty-hose mannequin legs he had brought with him to my welcome-home party and had never taken away again.

"My number!"

He had the mannequin in his arms and was danc-ing. He picked up a bottle of gin from the kitchen bar and drank from the neck. When he put it down it was at my elbow. "Remember Betty Anne?" he said. "The new one—Erica's friend?—the one I been going with lately?"

"Sure."

"It's over."

"Didn't last very long."

"A day or two ago I sat down and thought, What's wrong my life? Only two things. Liquor and women. Everything else I got under control."

"So you've given up women?"

"And booze."

"How about that little bit of joypopping you were doing?"

"Kicked that too." He had another drink and watched me sweeten a glass of Pepsi. "Tonight I'm tapering off. Giving up women was hard enough for one night. I'll give up drinking tomorrow. You not drinking yourself?"

"I'm afraid, Felix."

He looked at me. "So am I." Then he laughed. "I'm

thinking moving down to the Dutch Virgin Islands. Maybe buy a house in Curaçao, some place like that. Who needs all these American laws, business hassles, taxes? What I'm afraid, I'll get fat, turn into a sober citizen, a Republican votes for the death penalty and bitches about communism. Well—what the hell is wrong with that? You sleep at night."

I asked if it had been difficult to break up with Betty Anne.

It sobered him. "That's the one thing I never get good at. Goodbyes. There's no way it can ever be easy —breaking up. Every time you do it, the next time it's harder. It takes more out of you. That's why I like psychoanalysis. You lay it off on the doctor. I told her, 'Betty Anne, I love you. No other girl ever made me feel this way. But it's my therapist. He says this relationship is regressive at this stage of my analysis. He wants me to give it up, at least till I've worked through my current problems. He says I'm destructive for you.' So she hates him instead of me."

"Is that what he really said?"

"Might as well. It's always true."

"Was this tonight?"

"I left her crying. I cried myself."

He had another drink. "It was only a few hours ago —I decided I just *can't* go through these scenes again, Nick. I don't have what it takes any more. The next one I start with, I'm afraid I'll ask her marry me so I won't have to go through another goodbye."

The weather report had said rain. He had a raincoat with him. He picked it up. "So," he said, "no more women. After tomorrow, no more booze. Then day after, goodbye, Hoboken. A new life. I got a place picked out in Curaçao. I feel good, Nick. Relieved. But I couldn't sleep tonight. *Down.* You want any of this gin?"

"It's definite? You leaving the country?"

But his smile was fading. A kind of irritation was in his eye, restlessness. He lit up again when he picked up the mannequin legs once more. "Let us not brood, Nicholas, let us not waste our youth on vain regrets. *Let's go out!* The saloon don't close another four, five

hours. I'm going to lay this new number on them." He
pulled the eye patch down more firmly in place. "If we
meet anybody we know, you will introduce me as Jack
the Sailor, Felix's unfortunate brother."

"Give me time to get dressed."

"I'm revved up, man. I can't wait. Don't go back to
sleep *or I'll come back for you.* Meet me at the 55."
He did a few quick dance steps around the room with
the mannequin legs in his arms and took a last jolt of
gin from the bottle and ran out the door, his hair cut
short and parted on the wrong side, his Jack Arm-
strong Magic Disguise Kit eye patch pulled rakishly
over his eye, holding the long naked legs over his
shoulders like a boy with a baseball bat. The first time
I had seen Hamlet had been in Chicago. I was twelve
and had gone with my father. He had tried to explain
that the ghost of Hamlet's father was not meant to be
taken as real, that it was a manifestation of Hamlet's guilty conscience, but I had believed in that ghost
at twelve; perhaps I believed in it still. Felix was im-
probable, my thoughts were impossible, everything in
me said no, no, it's insane.

Felix was the ghost of myself. The price Peter Pan
had paid for eternal youth was sexlessness. For all his
phallic narcissism, Felix had never grown into sex
either. He reminded me of that self that had loved being my father's son. He was the self I was trying to put
away. Don't let it be him, I thought. Don't let it be
me.

Someone was shrieking from down the bar when I
arrived, a few people were laughing, all heads turned
that way. At first I didn't understand what was happening: some woman had her legs beautifully agleam
in nylon, up on the wood, rhinestone-heeled shoes
nestling among the shot glasses. From the angle at
which they pointed to the ceiling, her head had to be
down near the floor, the skirt tangled up in her neck-
lace. The crowd cut the rest off from my sight, but it
was Felix of course; the legs were his mannequin's. He
smiled at the attention he was getting. He knocked
back his drink in one take and offered to buy me one.

He turned to say something to the redhead. She was the best-looking of the three girls his number had brought over, and that was how he'd met her.

"Don't misunderstand," he was saying to her. "You're safe with me. I've given up women. We'll have a long, beautiful, platonic friendship. I see us living in the same apartment house, you in your place, me in mine, and when we have tea together, *it don't matter* if it's raining outside. You got any kids?"

"A four-year-old boy."

"I'll be the role model he needs," Felix said. He had not yet asked her name. "Every time I meet a kid I tell him, 'Listen, you sing me a song or tell me about arithmetic your school, I'll bang you on the nose.' I tell them I'm not interested how old they are, and if they try to give me a kiss I'll change the shape of their head. I teach them things: If people say to them 'My, how you've grown,' I tell them to look startled and say, 'My, Uncle Fred, how bald you've grown.' "

Felix sipped his drink and looked glum.

"What's the matter?" the redhead said, smiling.

"The trouble is, I tell that to kids, they love me. They follow me around. Pretty soon some poor deluded woman is trying to make a home for me. Why *are* you smiling like that?"

"You're terrible," said the redhead. She had creamy ecru skin and was six inches taller than Felix.

"Listen," he said, "this is my friend Nick. I just went to his house and registered my New Year's resolution. I'm giving up women and booze."

"It's not New Year's Eve," said the redhead.

"We'll have a tragic, romantic affair," Felix replied.

"Did you hurt your eye?"

"An accident at sea," Felix said. "Listen, don't smile like that."

"What's wrong with my smile?"

"It's the Mona Lisa smile. A mother inviting her prepuberty son into bed."

"Terrible, terrible, terrible," the redhead said and stood closer to Felix. She said she wanted to buy him a drink.

"No, no, no," Felix said. He wanted to go to Ira's

Glue House. "They haven't seen the number with the legs there yet." He buttoned the raincoat up over the legs to hide them. The redhead was holding his hand, and she came with us, leaving her two girl friends behind.

"Not a bad night after all," Felix said to me. We were waiting for a cab.

"No."

"You should have seen last night."

"You never told me your name," the redhead said to Felix.

"Call me Jack."

"I'm Heather."

"I'll call you Mona. Do you mind?"

"In honor of your terrible joke?"

"In honor of my mother. She was called Mona."

"You're awful."

"What happened last night?" I asked Felix.

His face brightened. "Yeah," he said. "OK, China-town, four A.M. The beautiful Miss Colbert and her poodle, Big Mary, the bongos, all nonstop." He turned to the redhead. "A funny thing's been happening to me lately. That's why I'm giving up women and drinking."

"You haven't given up anything at all."

"When the women left, I tottered out a last drink at Django's, the after-hours I like to go." Felix was speaking to me, but the redhead was listening too. "I don't know if I meet her there, I don't even know her name. The last five mornings a row, the next thing I know there's this chocolate arm shaking me awake nine the morning, this beautiful little spade chick is in bed with me. 'Say, honey,' she says, 'here's three aspi-rin and I need ten dollars the taxi home.'"

"You ever see her sober?"

"I don't even know where I find her drunk. I asked Django, but he says lately I always been leaving his place alone."

"What are you going to do about her?" the redhead asked. She didn't like the story.

"Before I came out tonight I already put ten dollars

under the other pillow my bed. Here's the taxi. Hop in."

When we got to the Glue, Ira had taken off his apron and was standing inside at the door letting people out but no new people in. He wanted to close up early. Felix pulled the eye patch more firmly in place and didn't break stride. He went to the glass and yelled so the people who had been turned away could hear: "Here she is, Ira. *We found your sister!* She's sorry she ran away." He was pointing at the redhead.

Ira hid his smile and opened the door a crack. We slipped inside. Felix walked a little awkwardly because of the legs hidden under his raincoat. The beautiful redhead smilingly maneuvered until she had him blocked from sight; when she got out of the way he was leaning forward and over a barstool, as if bent over and kissing a girl like Valentino. The mannequin legs were tucked under his armpit, sticking up in the air behind him, over everyone's head. It got a pretty good laugh from the crowd at the bar.

"What a number!" Felix said to the redhead and me. He had put the legs away. "I bought it from a guy went bankrupt selling extra-size panty hose in a gay boutique on Greenwich Avenue." He turned to Ira. "What about some action?"

"What'll it be?"

"Let's have some Lady Effingham's Eggs," said Felix.

Ira laughed. "Wait'll some night we're less crowded. Then give me a sandwich."

Ira lined up three shot glasses in a row. He rimmed the first with 90-proof Fleischmann's gin, 100-proof bottled-in-bond bourbon in the second, 168-proof black Jamaica rum in the third. Felix drank them all in a row easy as walking on water.

Some out-of-town apple salesman was at Felix's elbow. He had been drawn by the number with the legs and was staring admiringly as Felix yelled to Ira for "some of that hot Chinese mustard for a chaser." The salesman was in the middle of a story about hating New York, he couldn't wait to get out, away from the muggers and the smog. "I wouldn't trade a shovel of dirt from home in Canalookaga County for all the stuck-up, frigid women in New York."

Anatole Fugelman was in the Glue with his blowup map of the Village. He was busy taking phone calls, moving pins here and there, telling new people who wanted to get on the map that they had better get a few seasons' practice bush-league drinking where they lived in Queens and Scarsdale first. "Felix," Anatole said, "you drink three more like that and live, I'll pay for it."

Felix told Ira to do it again. Ira poured three more.

"Death before dishonor," Felix said and did it again. *"And,"* he said, "turn the juke up louder."

The intellectuals and chess players took offense. "Ain't no juke here, man."

"Let's get out of here, Nick. They *don't hear it.*" Felix turned to the apple knocker. "Listen, I think New York is a great place for you to visit, but I'm shit glad you don't live here." He nuzzled the redhead's ear.

"You drink too much," she said.

"That's your *first,*" Felix said. *"Let's go!"*

"Where to?" the redhead said.

"McGruddy's. They ain't seen the number there yet."

Heather looked disappointed. She took her mirror out and pouted into it. "Why did that strange man call you Felix?"

"He mistook me for my square twin brother works for IBM."

We were waiting for a taxi on the corner. The redhead was still lost in her mirror.

"You want to take her on for me?" Felix jerked his head in the girl's direction.

"Take her on?"

"Don't let me go home with her the end the night. I'm not kidding, Nick. No more women."

"In the five minutes in the 55 when she went to pee, you were already coming on with that blonde. Can't you control yourself?"

"Put a glass of gin in your hand, can you?"

A taxi stopped about ten feet from us. The passenger inside was counting his change. Before we could

get to the door the driver flicked on his Off Duty sign.
The man inside was Lou.

He was beginning about Felix's eye patch and the
mannequin legs, but Felix gave him a wink and a look
at the redhead. Lou changed the subject. "I been looking for you two. I knew I'd find you one of these
places." The taxi meter said nine dollars and change.
He'd been looking hard.

He talked as if he and I hadn't spoken on the phone
about Felix earlier in the night. "Nick, what are you
up to? Your first day out, you're cruising the saloons."

"Where else you go meet your friends?"

"You sober, Nick?"

"Yes."

"So far," Felix said.

"So far," I said.

"Don't joke," Lou said.

Felix was arguing with the driver about taking us
as fares. He said he had lost his eye in Vietnam and
now he was always getting a bum's brush-off in the
States. The man insisted he wanted to go home.

"Listen," Felix said. "Attitude like that, you'd better quit show biz and get a straight job."

He turned to us. "We'll walk," he said. "I got *no
use* to wait." He led the way, war hero's patch on one
eye, the mannequin's legs over his shoulder. "Yeah,
yeah, yeah . . ." he was saying. "What a night!"

Lou and I tagged along behind.

"You remember I asked you once about somebody
named Johnson?" Lou said too low for Felix to hear.

"Some friend of Clair's? I never met him."

"Maybe it was a her."

"Nobody I know."

"Maybe it wasn't a friend of Clair's. You know any
Johnson yourself?"

"No."

"Think a minute."

"This official? I been wondering why you show up
wherever I go, Lou."

"I'm off the case."

"Why?"

He evaded my eye a moment. He licked his lips. "Just think. You know any Johnson?"

"There's a typist I use in L.A. for TV scripts when I work out there."

"If she knew anything about Clair, would she tell you?"

"I haven't seen her two years. L.A. papers don't pick up on every New York homicide. What makes you think Rosie even heard about Clair?"

"If she knew something, would she maybe tell the police?"

"Who wants to get involved with the police?"

I stopped walking. "What's some typist in L.A. got to do with Clair?" My hand was on his arm.

"Toomis doesn't talk to me about the case any more."

We were going along West Tenth Street, past Julius's toward Greenwich Avenue, past Casey's, past the Ninth Circle. Felix and the redhead were in front. She had a kind of low-slung-assed creamy glide. She didn't straighten her knees. She put each high-heeled shoe out before the rear knee had straightened; then she had to thrust her hips forward an extra distance to carry the weight over her foot. It meant nothing, she wasn't conscious of it; an orthopedic surgeon would frown or weep. It spoke to me.

"You know what's wrong with people always talking about love?" Felix was saying as if in counterpoint to thoughts of my own. He was still carrying the manne-quin legs over his shoulder like a bat, Lou and I trail-ing along behind. "Only *unloved* people think love is that interesting. Unloved people the ones made up the whole romantic tradition. *They* write the poems, the songs, *they* made up the literature. Who else got the time? Everybody else is home in bed. They *believe* love is magic, difficult to find, fleeting, overwhelming. And they make so much noise, they con the rest of us into going along with them. They made love a socially acceptable neurosis. Listen, love is like money. It's only important if you don't have it. You got it, you

wonder what all the fuss was about, why it isn't as
satisfying as it was cracked up to be." He maneuvered
awkwardly to get his hand into his raincoat pocket
without dropping the legs. He pulled out his pint of
vodka and hastily used it to flag a lonely cab that
turned a corner and came cruising by. The man said
he didn't want to take drunks. Felix gave him ten
and we jumped in. "I choose excitement over love and
happiness any day," Felix said nestling back against
the seat cushions. "I always know when I'm excited.
Happiness—I only know I been happy when it's over."
He uncorked the vodka and passed the bottle to Lou.
Lou had some and passed it on to the redhead. He
didn't offer it to me. She paused, the bottle at her lips.

"If that murderous drink they poured you in the
Glue House was a sandwich," she said to Felix,
"what is the one they refused to make for you—Lady
Effingham's Eggs?"

"If you don't know, ask somebody else. I don't want
to be the pusher turns you onto that."

Lou and I got out first when we got to McGruddy's.
The redhead stayed behind, whispering to Felix. "No,"
he said angrily. "I don't *want* to go home. I got a number going. Tomorrow ten different guys will be imitat-
ing me and it'll be no good."

"You getting out or not?" the driver said to him. "I
don't want to hang around all night, Jack."

Felix smiled at the redhead. "See? I told you that
was my name." He got out of the cab.

"Why aren't you home?" Lou said to me too low
for Felix to hear. "Why are you with Felix? You remember something?"

"No."

Heather had not yet gotten out of the cab. Felix
leaned back in to extend his arm to her. She just hud-
dled farther in her corner, very beautiful in the darkness. Felix straightened and closed the door.

"Good night," he said to her through the window.
"I may not know what I like. You are a work of art."

He gave the driver a ten-dollar bill. "Take madam
wherever she wants to go," he said.

The taxi drove off. Felix stood beside Lou and me

in the street a moment more, neatly buttoning up his raincoat to hide the mannequin legs. He surveyed the crowd in McGruddy's through the plate-glass window. "You know," he said, "the doctors tell us that Don Juan's list, it wasn't a list of victories but of defeats. And I suppose they're right. But I don't care how superb the girl is, a couple of weeks, a month or two, three . . . maybe it can last a year. But soon, soon, there's got to be a new gland activator comes along and disturbs your peace of mind.

"There's a kick in that illegal stuff you don't find home in your safe warm bed. You may find something else there, something I'm prepared to grant you may prefer in the long run. But you only live minute to minute, not in the long run. *Right now*. And the delights of the false ego, fleeting and harmful as they may be, are sweet."

He began to go in. I took him by the arm. A taxi had come around the corner, the driver softly tooting his horn to catch our attention. Smiling with pleasure at the surprise on our faces, the redhead was inside. She had merely circled the block.

Felix sighed. He went forward to open the door for her. "I find my pursuit of pleasure is *relentless*," he said and kissed the girl as she came into his arms.

Lou and I stood in a corner watching Felix doing his number with the legs. When he got his shout of laughter, Heather threw her arms around him. Lou sent them up a round of drinks. Felix brought his glass up to his eye patch in salute and thanks to Lou, and sent us two back.

"You going to drink that?" Lou said to me.

"What's the difference? Tonight. Tomorrow night. I already stopped four times in three months."

"What you got against staying sober?"

"It doesn't end."

"You had anything since you came out of the hospital?"

"No."

"Then bitch all you want." He finished one of the

two drinks Felix had sent over and drank mine too. I ordered Pepsi, and Lou watched me put sugar in. I asked why he was off the case.

"I told Toomis I asked Clair to move in with me."

"An affair?"

"It was more than that. To me, anyway. While you were in France."

"Did you love her?"

"I told you."

"Tell me again."

"Yes."

It helped.

Lou leaned closer to me. "You know something, don't you?"

Silence.

"That feeling you were one of them?" Lou said. "Was Felix the other guy?"

"The medical examiner said maybe the second one was a woman."

"Was it a woman?"

"Is that what the cops think?"

"Toomis doesn't say what he thinks. You think it was a woman?"

"No."

"You were there? *You know?*"

"I know Clair." Did I?

"But you remembered something? Where does Jennifer come into it?"

"I don't know."

"Was Felix the second man?"

"I know Clair." Did I?

"What the hell are you drinking Pepsi with sugar in it, for Christ's sake?"

"My father used to drink it when he went on the wagon."

I showed him two Hershey bars in my pocket, a trick they'd told us about at Brinkley Smithers. "You go off the booze, your little-kid tastes come back." I said I'd gained five pounds just that night.

"And twenty years," Lou said. "Do you know you're staring at him?"

"Who?"

"At Felix. You know something about him. About him and Jennifer?"

Silence.

"Was she the woman? *Was Jennifer the second one there?*"

Silence.

"Nick," Lou said, "I'm sorry."

"Sorry?"

"About Clair. About me and her. About what happened to her."

"We don't have to say anything about that again. Don't be sorry. But don't tell me any more."

A flash of anger in my belly. I decided not to have a drink.

Felix ran up to us. He had a new drink for Lou. "You two look like a morgue." He threw me a cigar. "Here, you're not going to drink something, then smoke. Don't keep watching me. *Smoke!*"

I lit up and looked away.

"Not yet."

"Oh, Jack . . ."

We walked aimlessly through the Village in the dark. I had lived on some of these streets, slept in others; buildings where I had visited, sat, waited, eaten, drunk, danced, made friends, made enemies, made love. Yesterdays. Barrow Street. Great Jones Street. Charles Street. Bleecker Street. Thompson Street. Minetta Lane. MacDougal Alley. Horatio Street. Who had I to stay sober for? I didn't like myself enough to stay sober for me. But as I watched the redhead walk along with Felix, the secret life of the body asserted itself. "Hello," a sudden erection said, "remember me?" It was the only part of me that felt alive. Face him with it, I thought. Ask him. At least you'll find out if you're wrong. But I thought: not yet.

When I'd first arrived in the Village, old-timers liked to say it wasn't what it used to be. Now, in my own turn, it wasn't what it used to be for me either. Five years from now, ten, my replacements would be saying the same thing to their replacements. The Village remained. In the warm September drizzle we circled and crisscrossed familiar streets, making the old Grand Tour I'd made with Felix and Lou—how many times? Maria's and the Riviera. Casey's. The Bistro. Original Louie's. Papa Leo's. When the doors closed at four A.M. we were in the old White Horse, where Felix's phone number was written on the Ladies' Room wall. Then we just walked west in the rain, Felix's coat draped over Heather, the mannequin legs hoisted on his shoulder like a rifle. Darkness was fading into predawn. We were getting wetter. It didn't seem to matter.

Under the West Side elevated highway a big white Holland America cruise ship was coming up the stream —glittering, self-contained, relentless, silent. A wet breeze chilled us. We turned. I stumbled over a body: a poor putrid drunk, passed out cold, his face dirty and bloodied, his clothes torn, one shoe missing, a gash on his forehead matted by scurfy hair.

There were pieces of chalk on the street beside him, blue pieces and white. He still held a piece of blue in his grimy hand, an empty bottle of California muscatel at his feet.

Lou leaned over him professionally. He was still breathing.

Sucking on his wine and driven by who knows what boozy demons to wander so far from his usual Bowery haunts, huddling for shelter beneath the elevated highway and looking for a dry place to wield his chalks, the drunk had finally drawn a giant valentine in the gutter.

Curlicued with both chalk colors, beribboned and belaced with both the blue and the white, elaborated, worked with enormous goofy love, fear and devotion, the heart drawn in the street at our feet was too carefully done, too strangely passionate, too filled with some meaning unknown perhaps even to that soaked brain for us to understand. Lou read the words aloud the bum had written, words drawn in letters almost two feet high, blue and white words buried in the center of the heart, words that said:

Mary

Mother of God

MERCY

"Let's go home," Felix said.

"And not see the day in?" I said.

Felix pretended outrage. "Get that one!" he said. "Nine Pepsi-Colas and a pound of sugar and he's high. You want to tip the band to play till noon?" He snorted and drank from the pint in his pocket. "No place open," he said.

"Django's."

He looked at me. Then he kissed the redhead. "Let's go," he said. "One last drink, I'll do my number for the smart breakfast crowd, and then we'll go home." The redhead hunched her shoulders dispiritedly but took his arm.

"Why?" Lou whispered to me.

"Felix is leaving town."

"He told you?"

"Yes."

"He tell you anything else?"

"No."

"But you know something?"

"I know I can't live like this."

Django was a pusher busted once too often. He had found a safer way to make a living, turning his cold-water flat on Gansevoort Street into an after-hours bar.

He now made his living in four hours a day—from four A.M., when the liquor license law said the bars had to close, till eight A.M., when the first cut-rate booze chains like the White Rose and Shamrock Houses legally opened for the day. I knew that law well.

Two rooms, one painted tropical pink, the other electric blue. A ham and a turkey sat on the bar, which was an old wooden door taken from a wrecked building. Free lunch, but the drinks were three bucks apiece. Music was from a kitchen radio, there were some white kitchen chairs scattered around. A drunk was sleeping it off on a broken-spring Castro Convertible bed near the window. Two elegant gays off an unsuccessful night at the Sailor's Snug on West Street were at the bar drinking green crème de menthe frappés. Two truckers from the Washington Street produce market had just come in from work and were drinking with them. A fly buzzed in a puddle of stale beer on the bar. Felix had done his number with the legs, but it was not the hour, it was not the place, this was not the audience. Nobody laughed. Felix glumly put the legs beside him on the bar and ordered an Irish coffee. Sunlight was peeping around Django's pulled-down window blinds and the all-night music station had turned into John Gambling announcing a list of commuter trains that were running late. Lou was half dozing over a Scotch and water. The redhead was asleep, her head on her crossed arms on the bar. I was sick of Pepsi and had a glass of ice water in front of me.

Felix took out his sky-blue sunglasses and put them on over his eye patch, against the dawn. "That's it," he said. He began shaking the redhead awake. "Just put her in a taxi, I'll be home safe." He was talking over his shoulder, using Django's carving knife to make himself a turkey sandwich.

"Nobody to drink with, man," he said. "Party's over."

"Felix?"

"Sure."

"That hatcheck?"

"Gottcha." Reaching for the bread.

"The one you told me about. When they found
Clair, and I got home the next morning from the police
station?"

He smiled briefly, as if beginning to remember,
but the redhead had come alive. She was licking his
ear, holding his hand, giving him the inside of her
thigh. She thought he was going home with her.

The gays were singing together with the radio.

"The one in the summer heat," I said over the noise.
"Her name was Jennifer?"

"Good old Jennifer." It was said without much
animation, his flicker of interest dying, social notes
from here and there. He drew breath to say something more over the bite of sandwich he had just
taken; the redhead had her mouth plastered on his.
He gave me a look and a helpless shrug of the shoulder.

"You said she was married when you knew her.
That was a couple of years ago?"

I was shouting over the radio and the singing gays.

Felix used two hands to take the redhead's mouth
away from his own. "Married to an airline pilot."

The redhead took the sandwich from his hand and
put it down. She began to tug him toward the door.

Off to one side, Lou was shaking his head at me:
No. "Jennifer was never married two years ago," he
whispered. "She only got married just now."

I moved. Lou was holding a fistful of my shirt.

"What if he says it was you?"

His voice was too low for Felix to hear.

"What if he says you were the second man?"

It was out in the open. He had named my fear.

I had been afraid of it for over a month and had
drunk my way into Roosevelt Hospital to forget it.
Maybe I'd been afraid of it longer than that, as far
back as the night I'd stormed out of the apartment to
get away from my quarrel with Clair and later drank
my way to France instead of flying to California to
find her again. I was afraid of murder.

I thought of the drunk passed out in the rain under
the elevated highway. I had been afraid of him for a
long time too.

"Felix, come on back and I'll buy us a last drink for the road." I was standing at the bar. I picked up a glass.

"To the women we have loved and lost," I said.

"Those are the best kind," Felix said.

33

A Long Night (Concluded)

Toomis stopped the tape recorder.

"So he started again?"

"A double martini, heavy on the vermouth."

"Seven o'fucking clock in the morning?"

"Not the first time in his life."

"Jesus," said Toomis. "You're still a little high yourself, right?"

"I was off duty."

"We'll get a more formal statement later you're sober."

Toomis started the tape recorder again: "Go."

"The next thing Felix is ordering one for himself, Nick is ordering two, the redhead is sulking at the door, but Felix and Nick are buying and drinking up and back, so she makes it over to stand near Felix again. The two of them pay her no attention. They're yelling for Django to bring new drinks before the old ones are finished. I don't know how Felix does it, he must of been speeding, Nick hasn't had a drink all night, Felix has been hitting it pretty hard, but there he is, right up there with Nick, double for double. He likes it. I can see he likes it that Nick's drinking again. You know how Nick is, a mild kind of guy? The booze is hitting him ugly. He's beginning to get nasty, and Felix likes that too. 'Why are you so slow,

Django?' he yells. 'Just leave the bottle here.' By this
time the redhead decides the hell with it, she has a
drink herself, she turns the radio to WRVR, the gays
are dancing with the truckers, and now everybody's
flying. Django is opening more gin bottles. Felix is
buying for everybody, he wants to keep Nick drinking,
there's a lot of dancing, smoking, yelling, *the radio is
loud*. Felix is writing a list of phone numbers for the
redhead to go to the phone to invite them to the party,
he's lighting cigars, stubbing out the old ones in the
white turkey meat free lunch, lighting new ones. 'Felix,' Nick says, 'when you knew Jennifer——?' 'What?'
Felix is yelling. He makes a face like he can't hear
Nick over the radio. 'Let's have another, Django,'
Felix says, but he starts to tell the redhead that
maybe it's time to go home, after all. The redhead is
overjoyed, she's kissing Felix. 'Make it the last one,
Django,' Felix yells, 'and make it a champagne cocktail for the lady.' He puts his mouth close to Nick's
ear. 'Jennifer,' he says, 'that's not something I want
talk about *in front of*,' he says, and moves his eyes
to the redhead, meaning he doesn't want to make her
jealous. 'Just call me tomorrow, Nick.' But the redhead
is steaming. She's heard enough. 'Who is this Jennifer?' she asks Felix. 'Who is this woman this drunk is
talking about? Why is he making trouble? Jack, you
tell him you're coming home with me now, him and
his Jennifer can go fuck themselves.' Felix sighs. 'You
heard the lady,' he says to Nick, 'we'll talk about it
tomorrow,' but Nick isn't listening. He's brooding.
He's got a strange, black look on his face. The gays
have turned the radio on loud as it can go. There's a
new set of doubles on the bar. Felix takes one and
drinks it. He takes the bottle off the bar and puts it
into his hip pocket. He picks up the panty-hose legs
and props them over his shoulder like a club again.
'And Django,' he yells over the noise, 'a quart of
Beefeater to go.' The redhead is overjoyed. She begins to believe the message. 'Then we're going home?'
she says. 'We can take the phone off the hook, we'll
stay in bed for days and days and days . . .' Felix
doesn't answer. He picks up one martini from the bar,

he's got the bottle of Beefeater in his hand, another in his pocket. 'What's the matter, Felix?' Django yells. 'You got all the booze you need, all the woman you can handle, why do you look so sad?'

"Felix drinks the martini, picks up another from the bar and pulls the ready-to-go redhead tighter to his side. 'Django,' he says, 'I dread the good times ahead!' "

Lou paused and swallowed two aspirin.

"Jesus," Toomis said. "What happens next?"

"Next was silence. Nick's pulled the radio cord out of the wall."

Lou coughed. "Give me a glass of water, will you, Frank? One the aspirin went down the wrong way."

Toomis watched while Lou finished the water and then switched on the tape recorder again.

"Felix is halfway back to the door by now," Lou said, "the redhead on his arm, those crazy plastic legs over his shoulder. Nick runs after him. He's yelling, he's red in the face, he's drunk, he's swaying on his feet, he's ugly and yelling. 'You had to tell me, didn't you? You had to drink so much you could forget it, but the next morning you still had to come and let me know. You and the hatcheck in the summer heat. Your sad story. *You were laughing at me!*' Felix gives him a look, he doesn't know what Nick is talking about, Felix is still heading for the door, now he's walking faster. 'You sent me the postcard,' Nick yells, coming after him. 'Jennifer never was a hatcheck! Jennifer was never married when you said she was! The only hatcheck you knew was Clair. You killed her!'

"The redhead screams. She's falling to the floor, Felix's dropped her. With the same motion he's swinging from the heels, the legs in his hand like a club, he's swinging like a baseball bat, and he takes Nick right on the side of the head before I can get up there to grab him. Nick goes over, he's knocked back against Django's wall, falling over the kitchen chairs, tripping the gays—and they're screaming—pulling Django's radio down off the table with him. Felix is after him like a bullet, he's got the carving knife from the free lunch in his hand. Nick is slumped back, on the floor. He's dazed, bleeding from the head. Felix has the knife, he's trying to put it in Nick's hand, he's bending Nick's fingers around the handle, he's shoving his own head out, offering Nick his neck. He's pleading with Nick, he's crying like a woman, tears all down his face. 'Cut me!' he's screaming at Nick. 'Cut me, you bastard, just stick it in my heart and get it over with. Cut me, I'll feel better! *But don't talk to me!* Don't say a word to me or I'll kill you!' "

"And?" Toomis said.

"Nick just closes his eyes. He doesn't want to look at Felix. He turns his face to the wall. By that time I'm up there, I've got the cuffs out, I've got them on Felix. Nick can't look at him. He's got his head turned away."

Toomis looked across the office to where Blake was lying on the sofa, a bandage on his head.

"You want anything? A cup of coffee?"

"Start with a glass of gin," Blake said.

Toomis grunted and opened a desk drawer. He took out a pint of bourbon. He poured two fingers for Blake. He poured two fingers for himself.

"You?" he said to Lou.

"Couldn't touch it."

Toomis gave Blake a glass and raised his own. He looked over the rim at Blake. "You don't have it, do you?" he said. "I wouldn't of needed his invitation. I'd of cut his heart out."

He put the bottle away.

A uniformed policeman came into the room.

"Dr. Robertiello is here."

"OK," Toomis said. "Give him a chair somewhere and tell him I'll be with him."

The policeman went out.

"I'll want a formal statement from you a little while," he said to Lou. He turned to Blake. "You too. First I want to talk to the son of a bitch."

"Want me to come with you?" Lou said.

"You're not on the case. That's reason one."

"What's reason two?"

"We still don't know who's the second man."

34

Hello

"It was Blake," Toomis said.

He poured himself a glass of water from the little plastic pitcher on the table. He drank with one eye on Felix and didn't offer him any.

"Maybe the last people at the party left the door open. What I think is you glommed a key off him while he's drinking. You come back from Hoboken, you go in. The apartment is dark. What you want is the dope you think she ripped off from you. You listen from behind the screen the door of the bedroom. You want to hear her laughing at you, telling him how she played you for a dummy. What you hear is them fucking. She's got her arms and legs around him. The one woman in the world you can't have. It's hypnotic, watching two people fuck, right? It gives you a feeling of power, they don't know you're watching. You want your dope, they're not talking about dope, but you can't go away. Your hot cock won't let you. You want her to say something, anything, some hint she ripped you off, and then you can bust in and face her with it, right there while she's in bed with him. But all the time you're getting horny. You begin to imagine taking her away from him. You want him to know about that time you used to secretly fuck her yourself. You know how it burns to be jealous. You want to fuck her right in front of him, and walk out on her. You want to laugh at her when she asks you to stay. You're so mad you don't know you want to fuck her or kill her. She's saying in the dark how much she's glad to be back with him, that she'll never leave him again, to fuck her harder, that he's the only man in the world for her. She yells that she's coming, she yells that she loves him, she screams and giggles. But her voice stops.

"Right on top of her, while he's still in her, the goddamn drunk passes out. You listen. She's crying. She's hurt. Here's your chance. You come out from behind the screen. You pretend you just came into the apartment. A crying woman is your meat. You just have to hold her, tell her you love her. You'll prove you're a better man than the dumb drunk she's married to. You'll get her back for as long as you want, and score him off too. But she surprises. You thought she'd be soft, easy, that she'd take the shoulder you offer to cry on. Instead the bitch is angry when she sees you. She's mad at him, but the goddamn cunt takes it out on you. You ask where the cocaine is, but she just laughs. She says she doesn't have your junk, she knows you started Blake drinking again, she's glad somebody did a number on you for once. You don't believe her. Your blood runs hot. Your blood runs cold. Even with him passed out in her bed, she wants him more than she does you. You try to choke what you want out of her. You go too far. She's dead."

"Poetry," Felix said.

"I'll tell you what we got," Toomis said heavily, "then we'll see who's talking poetry."

The rain of the night before had been followed by a mass of cool Canadian air. Afternoon sunlight fell on the alley cats and garbage cans outside the precinct house on West Twenty-second Street. Motes of dust floated in a bar of sunshine that came in through the steel-screened window; Felix and Toomis were in the same bare little room in which Blake had been questioned six months before. Toomis stood up and walked to the window and drew on his cigar. He had left his service revolver outside the interrogation room but the empty holster bulged on his heavy-boned hip.

Toomis came back. He sat down on the hard

wooden table on the side of Felix's chair. "Clair mules
the stuff in," he said. "We got that. What we also got
is Maxwell; he does the chemical shit, the refining,
the cutting. They live in San Diego because it's right
there on the border to Mexico. You put the snort on
sale the streets of New York. Not enough to bother the
heavy traders, enough to make yourself all the money
you want. The Saturday she's killed, Clair brings in a
consignment. We know about the parachute—maybe
she's also got twenty different ways to run it in, it
doesn't matter. It's her last carry. Maxwell is going to
process it over the weekend, add it to the stash he's already holding for you. On Monday Clair is going to
bring the whole business east. Her last run.

"Saturday night you phone California from Blake's
party—we got the phone company records—see if everything is all right. You find out Maxwell is killed,
the dope gone. You phone Clair's apartment in San
Diego. Her roommate says Clair took off suddenly. It
looks like she's doing a number on you. You don't
know yet this Goose is the one done the job. Don't
look surprised. We know about him. You call your
answering service. There was a call for you from Clair
but she leaves no message. But now you got a little
hope. Maybe she wanted to tell you she beat it out of
San Diego because she's heard about Maxwell, she's
heading east with the stash. Maybe she's suddenly got
the hots for her husband and she's going to surprise
him by turning up early. What I think, she's no
dummy. He swore he was off the sauce, but before
she moves in with him again for good she wants to
know that he is. She wants to arrive before he expects
her, to make sure, to surprise him to find out if he's
sober. Anyway you figure it, you're hoping she's heading for Hoboken with your stash before she goes home.
That she'll make the drop there first. You leave the
party. Lou comes with you. That's easy. You have a
quick drink together, you duck out on him and make
it to Jersey. No Clair. No delivery. You go back to the
apartment. She's there. You get too rough and do the
job on her. You make it back to Hoboken, fix up
the alibi with the broad over there and then stop by to
see Blake. You tell him you're sorry. You say you're

there as a friend just heard the bad news. What you're there for is find out if the cops told him anything that might have your name in it. You son of a bitch."

Felix crossed his leg over one knee and tapped his fingers on the ankle. "Is that all you've got?"

"Plus what you yelled out in Django's. I take that as a confession. So will a jury."

"You sure?"

"You want to try it in a court of law, Felix?"

"Do you, Sergeant?"

Felix took off his blue sunglasses. One lens had been cracked in the scuffle at Django's. He passed his hand through his white-streaked hair, still parted on the wrong side.

"Why do you wear them, the glasses smashed like that?" Toomis said.

"They're prescription."

Felix put the glasses back on.

"It isn't enough to hold me, Sergeant," Felix said.

"We got a warrant. We searched your place in Hoboken. We find the no-tax cigarettes there. We can hold you on that."

"Cigarettes?" Felix said. "You want to play for cigarettes, Sergeant?"

Toomis kicked the chair out from beneath Felix. He walked away while Felix got off the floor. Toomis stood looking out the window. "Don't pull my prick," Toomis said.

He came closer to Felix. "Next we got," he said, "we got the girl you claim to spend the night with in Hoboken. I wouldn't depend on her I was you."

Felix smiled. "OK, so I didn't stay in Hoboken," he said. "I don't have to prove where I was, Sergeant. You have to prove I went back to the apartment. Fifty people saw me leave. With a police officer at that. Nobody saw me come back."

"We got your saliva on the bite mark the deceased's tit."

"You got *somebody's* saliva. Maybe you even got a blood type off the saliva. I'm Type A. Twenty different guys at that party must have been Type A, Sergeant."

"You been getting ready? Reading forensic books, you son of a bitch?"

"You don't have me placed in the bedroom at the time of death, Sergeant."

"Don't call me 'Sergeant' so much like it's a joke."

"You got a temper, you know that, Sergeant? What's your blood type, by the way?"

Toomis took an angry step to the other side of the room. When he came back he had the Manhattan telephone directory in his hands. He showed it to Felix.

"You know what that is?"

"What?"

"It's soft, it don't leave no marks, that's what." Toomis hit Felix above the ear with the heavy book. Felix fell sprawling to the floor again. Toomis leaned over and took off Felix's blue glasses. "You think this is some Greenwich Village literary tea party a lot of fag smart talk about Ernest Hemingway?" He dropped Felix's glasses to the floor and stepped on them, splintering the lenses into pebble glass. "I told you. Don't pull my prick."

Toomis went to the door and yelled. When a uniformed policeman replied, he gave him Felix's smashed glasses.

"These got lost last night when he was fighting in the after-hours place," he said. "I figure they stay lost."

The cop smiled and took the glasses from Toomis. He went away.

Toomis closed the door and looked down at Felix. "The Canadian cops got a chambermaid that Toronto hotel. She says she saw a guy with an eye patch in the hall when Goose was killed. She says she can identify the eye-patch guy. One piece of physical evidence we find on you is an eye patch. I just been on the phone to the cops in Toronto, figuring out who got the better case. You better figure it out too, Felix. You want it here in New York or up there in Canada?"

Felix was silent a moment. He got up and looked at himself in the mirror set into one wall of the little interrogation room. He turned to Toomis: "You're talking about a deal." His voice was flat.

"You're the one doing the talking."

Felix smiled and went back to the mirror. He stood a little to one side of it and looked along and into it at an acute angle. "You know, Sergeant," he said, "you stand just right, you let the sunshine hit the mirror just right, you can see in the next room. Wouldn't it be surprising they can see and hear in here too?"

Toomis pushed a button concealed on the interrogator's underside of the wooden table.

"Harris?"

An amplified voice came into the room from a concealed speaker. "Yeah, sarge?"

"Leave us alone. Shut off the mike."

"Right."

Felix continued to stand at an angle in front of the mirror a few moments more. "OK," he said. He sat down.

"You don't have enough on me for murder," he said. "You need a deal."

"Keep talking."

"You're hoping, but you don't have it yet. My semen wasn't found in her. I didn't wake up in bed with her. Her jealous husband did. Give that to a lawyer like Bennet Williams, Melvin Belli. If they can't put a reasonable doubt in the minds of a jury, Sergeant, I'll be surprised. That's what you're afraid of. You try me on murder, I got a good chance to walk out free, forever."

Toomis did not reply. He poured himself a second glass of water. Felix swiveled in his chair to follow the detective's movements across the room. He leaned forward. His voice took on confidential tones. "The main thing," he said, "is you want me off the streets, right?"

"The main thing I want is you fucking dopers dead!" Toomis said. "Meanwhile I'll take what I can get."

"Then I'll plead," Felix. "If I can cop." He sat back.

Toomis stopped moving. "You want your lawyer here?"

"We come to a bargain, we can get the lawyer in later."

"What do you plead to?"

"To I hired Sam, the black guy tried to knock off

Blake. I'll feed you the guy carried the shotgun, too."

"What motive?"

Felix shrugged. "Strictly business. Clair was a valuable employee. Maybe I thought if she had no husband to go back to, she'd stay on the job."

"You weren't jealous?"

"I was never jealous of a broad in my life!"

Toomis smiled. "I like that," he said. "First emotion you show. I told you I figured you for jealous. And when Sam can't do the job, you go do it yourself. First thing Blake's back in town, you go over there Saturday morning and throw a party keep him drunk for three days till Clair gets back. You didn't want to let her go, but it wasn't strictly business, Felix. All the women in love with you, it figures you got to be stuck on her. The one can't see you."

"Have it your way." Felix shrugged. He was calm again.

"That's my way," Toomis said. "I like it." He sat down. "Tell me," he said, "why you suddenly want to plead to Sam? Death in the course of a felony is a tough rap. It don't matter the wrong guy got it. You're talking about murder one."

"That's not what I plead," said Felix.

"What do you plead? The dope?"

"You search my apartment? OK, then you find nothing's there. Nothing's ever *been* there. You already told me you went through my place in Hoboken. So you know the big surprise you find there is only a heavy-duty industrial vacuum cleaner. I don't plead to the dope. New York law is too heavy on dope. You don't have enough on me to bargain me into copping on dope."

Toomis lit a new cigar and went to stand at the window. "The way you read it, it's a Mexican standoff?"

"It's not a standoff," Felix said. "Ten to one if you take me to court on Clair, I walk out. Ten to one isn't good enough. I don't want to take a chance on a hysterical law-and-order jury. You never know what they're going to do in a sex case. Ten to one isn't good enough if I'm betting twenty years of my life. You let me take a soft rap. Time off for good behavior, a parole? I can do it. I'm not taking a chance on a long sentence. You tell the D.A. to indict me for conspiracy to commit. That's all. I plead guilty. No trial. No jury, no fuss, no muss. I get a sentence. You're happy. I'm off the street."

"Not fucking long enough!" Toomis said.

"Long enough for me."

Felix waited for a moment. Toomis said nothing. Felix waited. Then he silently released his breath and asked for a cigarette. Toomis threw him one and took out a match. Felix blew smoke out of his lungs. "If you don't want it," he said, "then I want my lawyer. I don't say anything more until I make my phone call."

Toomis walked out of the room.

When he came back the stub of his cigar was bitterly clamped between his teeth. He mashed it out. "You sign a waiver you didn't ask for your lawyer to be here when we had this talk?"

"If we have a deal, sure."

Toomis yelled out the door. A form was brought in.

Felix looked at the paper carefully. It took him a long time to read it.

"It's not a goddamn confession," Toomis said. "You don't have to read every word."

"You didn't mash up my glasses," Felix said, "it would read faster." He signed at the bottom of the page.

Toomis picked it up and put it away.

"Now," he said, "I'll tell you what we really got."

"I thought we had a deal," Felix shouted.

"My turn to pull your prick," Toomis said and took the black-and-brown leather mask out of his pocket and jammed it down over the water pitcher as if it were a head. The heavy zipper over the mouth was open—an ugly, crumpled smile. The strapped eyes were blind.

Felix lunged out of his chair, clawing at the briefcase in which Toomis had put his signed waiver. Toomis was eight inches taller than Felix. He weighed one hundred pounds more. He knocked Felix back onto the floor with a backhand slap to the Adam's apple.

"Harris, bring him a glass of water before he chokes. And tell Dr. Robertiello to come in here."

Felix was back in the chair. Toomis was standing at the window, one foot hiked up on the ledge. Pinned to the wall on a corkboard was a blowup photograph that resembled the surface of the moon. A short, heavy man in glasses stood in front of it.

"So what?" Felix said.

"That's a photo the bite mark taken off the dead woman's tit," Toomis said. He pointed his cigar at the man in glasses. "This is Dr. Robertiello. He works with us. He's an orthodontist. The work he does for us, he specializes in forensic dentistry. Show him your mouth."

Felix clamped his lips shut.

Toomis was beside him in one stride. His hands clamped on Felix's jaw, applying pressure. Felix's mouth opened. Toomis held it open while Dr. Robertiello looked at Felix's teeth and compared them to the photo on the wall.

"It'd be better if we could make a cast," he said to Toomis, "and rephotograph."

"OK, we'll get a court order," the detective said. "What do you think meanwhile?"

The dentist looked again.

"My preliminary feeling is that it will stand up in court. I can't give a professional opinion yet. I reserve the right to change my mind when we can make more exact tests with a plaster cast."

"But right now," Toomis said, "your opinion is this man's bite matches the bite marks on the victim's breast in the photograph?"

"Yes."

Toomis smiled and let go of Felix's jaw. "That's fine, Doc. We'll leave it to him"—he jerked his head in Felix's direction—"to figure out himself if the plaster cast will corroborate your opinion. He's the expert on that."

The dentist left the room.

Toomis was smiling into Felix's face. "So," he said. "I got you in the dead woman's bedroom when she was

naked and undressed. Got you there close enough to
put your teeth in her. So close to the time of death, the
teeth marks don't have a chance to heal. She sees you
in the bedroom. The goddamned drunk is out cold.
She's cool. She's playing with you. 'Hello, Felix,' she
says, and opens her legs, 'you're next.' You hate her,
you hate yourself, but you've seen too much, you're too
hot to turn back. And she's ready for anything. She
hates men. You're the nearest one. 'Put this on,' she
says. It's the mask. She's making you a stud, a fucking
goddamned dildo, some anonymous cock for her revenge on him. She doesn't care who you are, she
doesn't even want to see your ugly face, *she wipes you
out.*

"She wants to use you to forget her memory of him
passing out while he's still in her, their first night together. You bite her before you kill her, Felix? Or you
bite her after? The jury's not going to give a shit about
any other evidence. Hoboken, Shmoboken, they're going to listen to no alibis. They'll look at the mask and
see you wearing it. What kind of pervert is he, they'll
be wondering. The answer is you bite her because
you're trying to heat yourself up. You bite her because
you hate her. You bite her on the tit, maybe you got
your finger in her cunt and a hand on her ass, but it's
no good. That's the reason we don't find your semen in
her. She was playing games with you, she was going to
do to you what you did with a hundred girls, she was
going to fuck you and forget you. She puts you in a
mask to make you her faceless sex toy. She softens
your cock. You strangle her because she had the
power, and you—*you're impotent!*"

"You know what's funny about human nature?" said
Toomis. "Everybody's got his little thing, and he thinks
it's the worst thing in the world. A guy would rather
tell you he murdered three nuns in cold blood than admit what he likes is to fuck rats in the ass with a cu-
cumber. I got suspicious as soon as he didn't ask for
his lawyer right away. I got more suspicious when he
signed the waiver. What's he hiding, what's he

holding back that would come out in a trial, in cross-examining? He didn't want any investigation, he don't want it to come out that she put the mask on him and it made his cock melt like ice cream. The great lover, he's impotent! He didn't want to talk about it. So he pleads to the dope."

"We should have made him on murder," Lou said.

The two men were in Toomis's office.

"Listen," Toomis said. "You know the average jail time served guys found guilty of murder one? Our own statistics? A little over five years, that's all. And that's for murder first degrees, blacks, Puerto Ricans, cop killers. I hate to think the average time a guy spends inside he's white, middle class, no previous convictions and he's got enough money hire a good lawyer. Shit, Lou, look. What hard evidence we got? The teeth marks. We got an expert? Felix can hire ten experts, they'll say the teeth marks prove the opposite. Experts always contradict. He pleads to the dope. It's good enough. This state, dope carries a longer sentence than murder."

"I don't like it," Lou said.

"He's cooperating," Toomis said. "What's not to like? He give us the number of a safe deposit in the Chase Manhattan. That's where he kept it. Under a funny name. God knows how many boxes money he's got stashed away other funny names, how much more cocaine. One is all we need."

Lou stood up.

"No hard feelings?" Toomis said. "I had to take you off the case till we knew."

"No hard feelings."

The two men shook hands. Lou began to leave the office.

"Why did he say in his postcard Clair was the one wore the mask?"

"Greenwich Village poetry," Toomis said.

35

Goodbye

Felix skipped the country to San Vesco, a Central American republic with no extradition treaty with the U.S.A.

"That's why he pleaded to the dope," Lou said, "and didn't listen to his lawyer wanted him to fight the **murder rap**. Dope isn't a capital crime. The judge gave him bail." He had dropped by the apartment to give me the news.

"You didn't fight it?"

"He said if we let him out, he'd set up the guy shotgunned the black pusher Sam. He was cooperating. He was giving us evidence on the dope against himself. We found a half key cocaine in the safe deposit box he sent us to."

"You talk to Felix yourself, Lou?"

"Toomis let me back in the investigation."

"I don't mean the interrogation."

He looked uneasy. He had a manila envelope with him and put it down on the table. He drummed his fingers nervously.

"Did you, Lou?"

"Yeah."

"About me and Clair?"

"Yeah."

"What'd he say?"

"Not much."

"I've got to know."

"You don't want to hear."

"I'll sleep better."

He suggested we go out. We walked west along Ninth Avenue. We waited in front of the Homestead at Fourteenth Street for the light to change. Lou bit his lip.

"Felix said you were the one wore the mask."

I couldn't reply.

"I'm sorry," Lou said. "You asked. I didn't want to tell you."

"It's all right."

I said that was not how Toomis had reconstructed it for me. It made Lou mad.

"Toomis is full of bullshit. Toomis wasn't there. Listen, Nick, it don't matter what Felix said. He hates you. He told me some crap to make himself look better. To make Clair look worse."

"Tell me."

"He said he came back to the apartment looking for Clair and the snort he thought she'd ripped off. He heard her talking to you in bed. He wanted to listen because he wanted to hear where she hid it. Maybe you were both ripping him off together. Then he looked up, the mirror over the dresser. All the time you and Clair were in the sack, all the time you were making love, she's talking to you, you're talking to her, *he says Clair knew he was there.* That's why she fucked you, goddamned stupid drunk or not. When he looked up in the mirror, she was smiling at him over your shoulder in the glass! She was playing it all for him, he says. To make him jealous. She was using you to get back at him because he hadn't left his wife for her. She wanted to use him to get back at you because you swore you had stopped drinking and you passed out on her the first night she was home. She invited him into bed, he says. She had done you in. He said she was going to get her revenge on him next. *She was in her glory!* Felix says. He says that was what he couldn't stand. Fuck you both, forget you both. Her last laugh, she was going to run out the next day with all the C. she'd brought east with her."

"Anything else?"

"He said he had no eyes to make it with her at all. All he wanted was his cocaine and to get the hell out of there."

"Why'd he tell you all this?"

"It wasn't evidence. We were alone."

"What about the teeth marks?"

"He said the dentist was mistaken. The teeth marks weren't his. It was only a preliminary opinion, Nick. It's possible Dr. Robertiello was wrong."

"Any chance he'll come back to the States?"

"With what we got on him? It's goodbye Felix."

The light had changed and we walked across the street. A car brushed Lou and he dropped his manila envelope. He picked it up and looked at me.

"What's in the envelope?"

"Something I don't know to give you or not."

"Why not?"

"Let me think a minute."

Silence.

I asked if the manila envelope had something to do with Felix. Lou asked me instead if I'd heard Clair's last show two years before, right after we'd split, had been a flop.

"She never wrote me."

"*Art News* put her down because they said they were tired her reworking her old stained-glass themes. They wanted her to do something new. You saw those photos the new paintings she was doing in California? Masked people—that's what the mask was all about. Masked people were going to be her new thing. She was going to begin a whole new life with you. She brought the mask with her to begin to paint again."

"You don't think it was some kind of sex prop?"

Bitterly: "The whole idea the mask was sex was just something in Toomis's crazy, religious-fanatic brain! He'd get a kick out of kinky stuff like that, so he figures everybody else would. Felix just played his game for him. There's no evidence anybody wore the mask the night she was killed, Nick. None. God-damned Toomis, goddamned sex maniac."

"How do you think it happened?"

"I think you passed out. Felix was there. He asked Clair to come back to him. She said she wanted to stay with you. That's what he couldn't stand. He could let her go but he didn't want anybody else to have her.

I don't believe she invited him into bed. Never. He
couldn't stand how much she loved you."

"Toomis said there was no evidence a struggle, no
skin or blood under Clair's fingernails."

"He caught her from behind—maybe she was leaning over you. Maybe she was crying." Lou licked his
lips and swore again at Toomis. "Felix wanted to show
her she couldn't walk out on him. Felix can't handle
No from women. Even you were drunk, you were the
one she wanted, not him. He wanted to touch her,
leave his mark on her. He killed her."

"They were Felix's teeth marks, weren't they,
Lou?"

"We'll never know for sure now there's not going to
be a trial."

I was looking at him. He did not look at me.

Silence.

"What are you thinking?" Lou asked in a gruff
voice. He had given me the manila envelope but asked
me not to open it till I got home.

I said it didn't matter if Toomis told the story, it
didn't matter if Felix told the story, it didn't even matter if Lou told it. "Everybody sees what happened different. One thing is always the same. I'm the second
man. Another man kills my wife, in my bed. I'm
passed out, too drunk to stop it."

"These things happen."

"You mad, Lou?"

"You knew she was coming back, Nick. You told
her you were off the booze. You shouldn't have been
so drunk, Nick. It's none of my business. I'm sorry.
That's how I feel."

"You feel enough to tell whatever else you're holding back?"

"Felix said she propped you up in bed, as a come-on
to him. I don't believe this part, Nick. He says she
pulled the mask over your face. He says she said to
him, 'Let the goddamned drunk watch, it's all he's
good for.' He says that's what got him. Maybe half
of him was mad at you for getting Clair away from
him. Another half, you were still his friend, he says.
He says he couldn't have made it with her even if

he'd wanted, not with that thing on your face, watching him. He says he got mad instead. He couldn't stand her laughing at him, making a joke of you. He tried to choke what he wanted out of her. Where the dope was. He was so mad he went too far."

Silence.

"I'm sorry I told you," Lou said.

"I asked."

"I should have said I didn't talk to him."

"Are you telling the truth, Lou?"

He stopped walking. He stood a moment on the sidewalk. He turned and began walking in the other direction.

I ran and caught him by the arm.

"I'm sorry," I said. We were standing in front of La Perla, the Puerto Rican dance hall where Tom had thrown his party for the crew of his picture when we'd come home from France. A sign said that La Cubana was singing there still.

"I'll buy you a drink," I said.

Julio was behind the bar. A sign scotch-taped to the mirror behind him said:

JULIO'S SPECIAL MARTINI
You drink the first.
The first drinks the second.
The third drinks you.
$1.50

Lou asked for bourbon. I told Julio I'd wait. There was a turning of heads, a little applause. La Cubana began to sing:

Corazón . . . corazón . . .

"We found Clair's suitcase," Lou said.

"Where?"

"Lost and Found, O'Hare Field, Chicago. It got put on the wrong plane when she changed flights."

"Anything in it?"

"Clothes. Nothing important."

"You got in touch with Rosie Johnson?"

"Xerox's of some tapes she typed for Clair are in the envelope I gave you."

"Tapes?"

"She was keeping some kind of diary, people she knew. Nothing criminal."

"Am I going to like reading it, Lou?"

"How much you want to know about your wife?"

"You had the diary long?"

"We only found Johnson a couple of days ago."

He asked if I knew what I was going to do.

"I'm thinking of leaving New York."

"Maybe you can find some work in California."

"I don't think so."

Some people got up to dance.

... que te amaba ...

sang La Cubana. Lou told Julio he was going to have another bourbon.

"You want a Pepsi?"

"Not yet."

"You know where you're going?"

"No."

The life of imminence is the life that never happens and I no longer wanted to mortgage today to buy the hope of living more intensely tomorrow. I wanted no more bittersweet beginnings, sweetly bitter endings, no more easy jokes, easy highs, easy sex, the low-stakes game of no commitment. Since Clair's death the nature of my loss had grown and become clear but the secret, symbiotic life that booze led within me had grown too. A lot of Freudianoid crap has been talked about drinking. The answer is you drink because you are lonely. Five ounces of gin blur the perception that you are detached, not from the people with whom you are drinking but from yourself; five more make you forget they are not your friends anyway: loyal only to fake and megalomaniacal cartoon images of themselves, drunks are not capable of friendship. Marooned somewhere at the barren, armed and armored center of the false ego, you wake the next morning, in one bed or another, more isolated than ever. The thought is inevitable: why look for others to drink with? I'll drink alone. And if later, why not now?

Like the nun who gives her life to God, like the mystic who fasts to lose the self, like the potlatch Indians of the Pacific Northwest who ritually burn their wealth to outshame their enemies, I knew the ascetic pleasures, the left-handed luxury of self-destruction. My father was dead but the drinking habit he had taught me as patiently and tenderly as he had taught me to swim, to play the piano and drive a car, as matter-of-factly as he had inculcated into me not taking the world's ideas of success or failure as matters of any more weight than its presidents, had survived his passage. I knew where I was. People who want to be polite or liberal or kind have agreed to call alcoholism a disease. It is not a disease; euphemisms only pave the way to the grave. It is worse than a disease— which is not your fault. It is an addiction—which is. You don't become addicted by kissing a beautiful stranger in a barroom. There are no Alcohol Marys carrying the Haig & Haig germ. An addiction is slow. It takes you years to cultivate it. Then it cultivates you. Like an alien presence in my blood, my father's addiction lived and flourished within me, a life contrary to my own, perverse, exuberant and deadly, unheeding as a cancer that proliferates every day, uncaring that with the body of the host on which it feeds, which it kills, it dies too. Alcohol obeyed its own rhythms and seasons inside me, the compulsion coming or going as it willed. I could no longer control its course. If I walked into a bar to kill an hour between planes, I might walk out at the end of fifty-nine minutes to catch the flight, or I might stay a week and wake up drunk in Madrid. The alcoholic split, the alcoholic's knowledge of his loss of power: the mind that says no, the hand that reaches for the drink. I had become unpredictable to myself.

La Cubana finished singing and walked past the sculptured fountain to her dressing room. The image of

the fountain that ran not water but wine had won Clair
for me once. It had lost her for me, too. Julio came to
stand in front of us, silently waiting for our order.

Clair's blue-in-blue eyes, so recently sealed in death,
were open again on me now—asking what? The drunk
doctors at Brinkley Smithers would say that to blame
myself would be merely self-pity, an excuse to drink
again; you had to let the past go. In any court of law
I could plead booze-diminished responsibility. No
matter: my crime was endless, but Clair had been
punished for it. Life has no meaning but it has mystery. Felix held no surprise but surprise itself: "I
drink so much to make people like you interesting,"
was his standard reply to stupid questions, and I understood his boredom as wearily as I understood my
own; but Clair was emblematic of all I would never
know. I would read the Xeroxes of her diary when I
got home, but how much can be said in words and
paper? The mysteries that illuminate our lives are the
ones we never solve.

Lou had another bourbon and Julio asked if I'd
made up my mind.

"Not yet."

And Selected from Sphere's General Fiction List

9½ WEEKS

Elizabeth McNeill

The TRUE love story that goes beyond The Story of O.

The first time we were in bed together he held my hands pinned down above my head. I liked it.
The second time he picked my scarf up off the floor, smiled and said, 'Would you let me blindfold you?'
The third time I heard my voice, disembodied above the bed, pleading with him to continue.
I WAS BEGINNING TO FALL IN LOVE . . .

Nine and a Half Weeks is the story of a love affair like no other; a crazy, obsessive relationship that burned through two lives like a branding iron through flesh. To read it is to undergo a truly disturbing — and erotic — experience. For this book is not fiction or fantasy, but fact. Mirrored in its extremes of passion and pain, we find ourselves.

'Elizabeth McNeill fixes her story with a laserlike regard, calmly incinerating irrelevant detail . . . Alarming but convincing'

Newsweek

AUTOBIOGRAPHY   0 7221 5790 8   95p

And Selected From Sphere's Fiction List

BEACH HOUSE

Stephen Lewis

A shoreline summer retreat smouldering with the dreams and needs of six very different men and women. Where, for that summer, they thought they could escape.

The place where Ken, the ultra-male executive who thought himself too strong for love, met Marion, the wild, free spirit running from the prison of her past. Where Lynda, the romantic dreamer, found the one man who could unlock her fantasies of full womanhood. Where Howard, the thrill-seeking advertising whizz-kid, found the ultimate sensation — at the ultimate price!

Kicks and kinks, sexual secrets, desire and death, bared in the blazing summer sun. A scorching novel of men and women who drove each other to the outermost limits of experience — and beyond.

GENERAL FICTION   0722155093   £1.10

A selection of Bestsellers from Sphere Books

Fiction

THE WOMEN'S ROOM	Marilyn French	£1.50p ☐
SINGLE	Harriet Frank	£1.10p ☐
DEATH OF AN EXPERT WITNESS	P. D. James	95p ☐
THE VILLAGE: THE FIRST SUMMER		
	Mary Fraser	£1.00 ☐
BLOOD OF THE BONDMASTER		
	Richard Tresillian	£1.25p ☐
NOW AND FOREVER	Danielle Steel	£1.10p ☐

Film and Television tie-ins

THE PASSAGE	Bruce Nicolaysen	95p ☐
INVASION OF THE BODY SNATCHERS		
	Jack Finney	85p ☐
THE EXPERIMENT	John Urling Clark	95p ☐
THE MUSIC MACHINE	Bill Stoddart	95p ☐
BUCK ROGERS IN THE 25TH CENTURY		
	Addison E. Steele	95p ☐
BUCK ROGERS 2: THAT MAN ON BETA		
	Addison E. Steele	95p ☐
DEATHSPORT	William Hughes	95p ☐

Non-Fiction

NINE AND A HALF WEEKS	Elizabeth McNeill	95p ☐
IN HIS IMAGE	David Rorvik	£1.00 ☐
THE MUSICIANS OF AUSCHWITZ	Fania Fenelon	95p ☐
THE GREAT GAME	Leopold Trepper	£1.50p ☐
THE SEXUAL CONNECTION	John Sparks	85p ☐

All Sphere books are available at your local bookshop or newsagent, or can be ordered direct from the publisher. Just tick the titles you want and fill in the form below.

Name ....

Address ....

....

Write to Sphere Books, Cash Sales Department, P.O. Box 11, Falmouth, Cornwall TR10 9EN

Please enclose cheque or postal order to the value of the cover price plus: UK: 22p for the first book plus 10p per copy for each additional book ordered to a maximum charge of 82p

OVERSEAS: 30p for the first book and 10p for each additional book BFPO & EIRE: 22p for the first book plus 10p per copy for the next 6 books, thereafter 4p per book

Sphere Books reserve the right to show new retail prices on covers which may differ from those previously advertised in the text or elsewhere, and to increase postal rates in accordance with the GPO.